R25135
27644

AIRCRAFT SYSTEMS & COMPONENTS

landing gear shock strut
• tapered metering pin (function)
de buster
types actuator balanced/unbalanced
rotory
type ✓ valve
selector valves (3/4 way) a4
all valves

176

$F = AP$

$F2 = F2$

$A_1 \times P_1 = A_2 \times P_2$

$V = AL$

$L_1 = L_2$

$\dfrac{V_1}{A_1} = \dfrac{V_2}{A_2}$

by D.F. Garrett

▌▌JEPPESEN
Sanderson Training Products

JS312685A

Table of Contents

PART 1

Aircraft Electrical Systems

Chapter I

Theory and Principles

A. Discovery of Electricity

One of the first recordings of electricity was by the Greek philosopher Thales in about 500 B.C. He mentioned the fact that when substances such as amber and jet were rubbed, they would attract such light objects as feathers and bits of straw. Later in the eighteenth century, it was discovered that there were two kinds of forces, or charges, caused by rubbing certain kinds of materials. Charges of the same kind would repel each other while opposite charges would attract.

In about the middle of the eighteenth century, the practical mind of Benjamin Franklin found a way to prove that lightning was a form of electricity. In his famous kite experiment, he flew a kite into a thunderstorm and found that sparks would jump to the ground from a metal key attached to the wet string. Franklin made a logical assumption that whatever it was that came down the string was flowing from a high level of energy to a lower level. And so he assigned the term "positive" to the high energy, and "negative" to the lower level. It was not known what actually came down the string, but he used a term associated with the flow of water, and said that it was "current" that flowed down the string, from a positive charge to the negative.

This assumption of Franklin's was accepted until the discovery of the electron in 1897, and many textbooks in use today still speak of current as being from positive to negative. Not until the discovery that it is actually electrons (negatively charged particles of electricity) that move through a circuit could we understand the true nature of electricity.

B. Electron Theory

1. Composition of Matter

Matter can be defined as anything that has mass and occupies space (i.e., everything we can see and feel is matter). It can exist in any one of three states: a solid, liquid, or gas. Matter is composed of molecules that, in turn, are composed of atoms. Matter may be either a compound or an element.

A compound is the chemical combination of two or more different elements/atoms or molecules. A molecule is the smallest particle into which a compound can be divided and still retain its identity.

An element is a single, uniform substance made up of like atoms that cannot be chemically subdivided to form a different substance.

a. The Atom

All of the material from which our universe is made is composed of atoms, the smallest particles of which can exist, either alone or in combination with other atoms. Each atom consists of a nucleus, made up, usually, of positively charged protons, and neutrons having no electrical charge but equal in weight to the protons. Surrounding this nucleus and traveling at incredible speed are electrons. Each weighs only about $\frac{1}{1845}$ as much as a proton and carries a negative charge.

The most simple atom is that of hydrogen, which consists of only one proton, and no neutrons in the nucleus. Spinning around the nucleus is a single electron.

All electrons are alike, as are protons and neutrons, but the number and arrangement of these elementary building blocks in the atom determine the material the atoms make up. For example, copper has a nucleus of 29 protons and 36 neutrons. Surrounding the nucleus and spinning in 4 rings, or "shells," are 29 electrons. This combination is an electrically balanced atom, as there are exactly the same number of positive charges, protons, as there are negative charges, electrons. The neutrons have no electrical charge.

We are familiar with the diagrams of atoms in our textbooks and training manuals, but these cannot

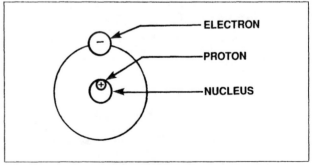

Figure 1-1. The simplest atom, hydrogen, has one electron spinning around the nucleus consisting of one proton. There are no neutrons in the nucleus.

possibly be drawn to scale. For example, to have the same *mass* as a proton, the electron would have to be about 1,845 times as large, and the distance between the electron and the nucleus would have to be about 100,000 times the diameter of the nucleus.

All matter contains energy, and energy in the atom causes electrons to spin around the nucleus. As they spin, centrifugal force tends to pull them away from the nucleus. But, there is an electrostatic field within the atom that produces a force that balances this centrifugal force and holds the electrons a specific distance from the nucleus.

The electrons spin around the nucleus in rings, or shells. When energy is added to an atom, such as is done when heated, the distance between the electrons and the nucleus is increased, and the bond, or force of attraction, between the nucleus and the electrons is decreased.

b. Ions

A positive electrical force outside the atom can attract electrons from the outer ring and leave the atom in an unbalanced condition. This unbalanced condition leaves the atom with an electrical charge. Charged atoms are called ions. For example, copper has one electron in its outer ring, and if a positive force is applied to the atom, this outer ring electron, which is negative, will be drawn from the atom and leave it with more protons than electrons. It then becomes a positive ion and will attract an electron from a nearby balanced atom. If an atom possesses an excess of electrons, it is said to be negatively charged and is called a negative ion. Electrons constantly move about within a material from one atom to another in a continuous but random fashion.

c. Free Electrons

The atomic structure of an element determines how well it can conduct an electrical current. Certain elements, mainly metals, are known as conductors because an electric current will flow through them easily. The atoms of these elements give up and receive electrons in the outer orbits with little difficulty. Electrons that move from atom to atom are known as free electrons.

There are often many free electrons drifting randomly among the atoms of any conductor. Only when free electrons move in the same general direction does an electrical current exist.

The number of electrons in the outermost orbit of an element's atoms determines if it is a conductor, semiconductor, or nonconductor (insulator). The outer orbit (shell) of an atom is known as the valence orbit. Atoms tend to completely fill their valence orbits with electrons. Atoms with fewer than half of their valence electrons tend to receive (accept) free electrons, whereas atoms with more than half their valence electrons tend to reject free electrons.

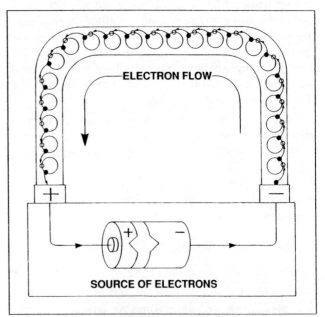

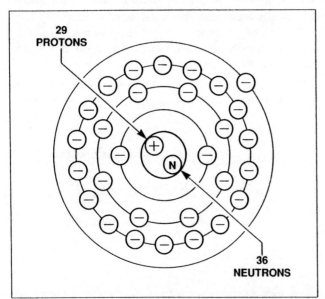

Figure 1-2. *The nucleus of a copper atom consists of positively charged protons and electrically neutral neutrons. Spinning around the nucleus are negatively charged electrons.*

Figure 1-3. *When an electron is attracted from the conductor by the positive charge of the source, it leaves a positive ion. This ion attracts an electron from an adjoining atom. This exchange continues through the conductor until an electron is furnished by the negative terminal of the source to replace the one that was taken by the positive terminal of the source.*

In general, atoms with less than four valence electrons are conductors; atoms with exactly four valence electrons are semiconductors; atoms with more than four valence electrons are nonconductors (insulators).

2. Electron Flow

What happens when a conductor made of copper is connected across a source of electrons? An electron is attracted from an atom by the positive terminal of the source, and it leaves the conductor. The atom which lost the electron has now become a positive ion and pulls an electron away from the next atom. This exchange continues until the electron that left the conductor is replaced by one from the negative terminal of the source.

Electron movement takes place within the conductor at about the speed of light; that is, about 186,000 miles per second. This is not saying that a single electron moves through the conductor from one end to the other at this speed, but because of

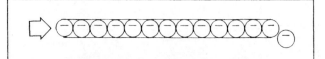

Figure 1-4. When one electron is forced into the conductor, it immediately forces an electron out of the opposite end of the conductor.

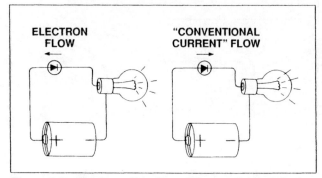

Figure 1-5. Electrons flow from the negative terminal of the source back to the positive terminal. Conventional current is said to travel from positive to negative.

the domino effect, an electron entering one end of the conductor will almost immediately force an electron out of the other end.

a. Effects of Electron Flow

We cannot see the movement of electrons within the conductor, but as they move they produce effects we can use. They cause a magnetic field to surround the conductor, and the greater the flow, the stronger the field. Also, as they are forced to flow, the opposition to their flow produces heat within the conductor.

b. Direction of Flow

The effects of electricity were observed long before electrons were known to exist. In explaining this, an incorrect assumption was made; electricity appeared to follow the rules of hydraulics in that pressure, flow, and opposition were present, and a definite relationship existed. Since the flow of electricity could not actually be observed, it was assumed that it flowed from a high level of energy to a lower level or, in electrical terms, from "positive" to "negative".

With greater knowledge of the atom, it became apparent that it was the electron with its *negative* charge that actually moved through the circuit, and electron flow was from the *negative* terminal of the source through the load, back to the *positive* terminal.

There are two ways to consider flow: electron flow, which is from negative to positive, and the flow of "conventional current", which, while technically incorrect, follows the arrows used on semiconductor symbols. We may use either method for tracing flow, but must be consistent. *In this text, we follow electron flow, from negative to positive, and use the terms electron flow and current interchangeably.* Where dealing with semiconductor devices and using their symbols, we may follow the flow of "conventional current" from positive to negative, because the arrows used in semiconductor symbols point in the direction of conventional current flow.

3. Units of Electrical Measurement

a. Quantity

The electron is such an extremely small particle of electricity that an enormous number are required to

CHARACTERISTIC	SYMBOL	UNIT	ABBREVIATION
Electrical Charge	Q	Coulomb	C
Potential Difference	E or V	Volt	V
Current	I	Ampere or Amp	A
Resistance	R	Ohm	Ω
Power	P	Watt	W

Figure 1-6. Summary of Electrical Characteristics and Corresponding Units.

have a measurable unit. The coulomb is the basic unit of electrical quantity and is equal to 6.28 billion, billion electrons, most generally written as 6.28×10^{18}. The symbol for quantity is Q.

b. Flow

When 1 coulomb flows past a point in 1 second, there is a flow of 1 ampere, or 1 amp. It is called current, and its symbol is I.

c. Opposition

The ohm is the standard unit of resistance, or opposition to current flow. It is the resistance through which a pressure of 1 volt can force a flow of 1 ampere. The symbol for resistance is R.

d. Pressure

The volt is the unit of electrical pressure and is the amount of pressure required to force 1 amp of flow through 1 ohm of resistance. There are a number of terms used to express electrical pressure. They are voltage, voltage drop, potential, potential difference, EMF, and IR drop and are often used interchangeably. The symbol for electrical pressure is E.

e. Power

The end result for practical electricity is power, and electrical power is expressed in watts. One watt is the amount of power dissipated when 1 amp of current flows under a pressure of 1 volt. The symbol for power is P.

C. Static Electricity

Electricity may be classified in two ways: current or static. In current electricity, the electrons move through a circuit and perform work, either by the magnetic field created by their movement, or by the heat generated when they are forced through a resistance. Static electricity, on the other hand, normally serves little useful purpose, and is more often a nuisance than a useful form of electrical energy.

1. Positive and Negative Charges

We cannot see electricity, but the effects are easy to observe.

A glass rod rubbed with a piece of wool or fur will pick up extra electrons, and become negatively charged. When held close to a pith ball which has a neutral charge, it will be attracted to the rod. As soon as the ball touches the rod, electrons will flow to the ball, give it a negative charge and be repelled by the rod.

A glass rod rubbed with a piece of silk will give up electrons to the silk, acquire a deficiency of electrons, and become positively charged. When held near one of the balls, it will attract the ball, and when in contact,

the ball will be repelled. This is the same thing that happens with the first ball, but with a difference. One of the balls is charged *negatively* and the other is charged *positively*. When they are brought close together, they will be attracted to each other.

This demonstration proves that there are two types of charges and that like charges repel, while unlike charges attract. The strength of the repelling and attracting force varies as the square of the distance between the two charges. For example, if the distance between the two balls is doubled, the force of attraction will be reduced to ¼. If they are moved three times as far apart, the force will be only ⅑ of the original. On the other hand, if they are moved closer together, the force of attraction or of *repulsion* will increase as the square of the separation. If the distance is decreased to ½, the force will be four times as great.

2. Electrostatic Fields

Lines of electrostatic force exist between charges. Lines leave one charged object (the one having the

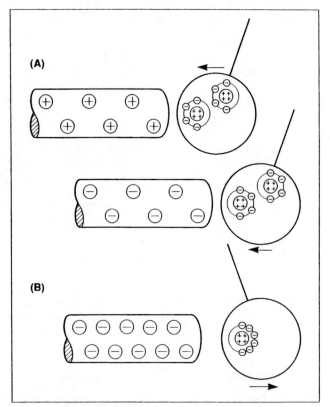

Figure 1-7.
  (A) An uncharged pith ball will be attracted to a rod that has either a positive or a negative charge.
  (B) Once the charged rod has contacted the ball, the ball will assume the same charge as the rod and it will be repelled by the rod.

positive charge) and enter the other (the one having the negative charge). If the charges are close together, the lines will link, and the two charges will form a neutral, or uncharged group. The lines of force from like charges repel each other and tend to push the charges apart. Electrostatic fields are also known as dielectric fields.

3. Distribution of Electrical Charges

When a body having a smooth or uniform surface is electrically charged, the charge will distribute evenly over the entire surface. If the surface is irregular in shape, the charge will concentrate at the points or areas having the sharpest curvature.

As the airplane flies through the air, friction causes a static charge to build up on the control surface. These surfaces are connected to the airframe structure by hinges which do not provide a particularly good conductive path, allowing the charge to build up in strength. Static discharges are attached to the control surface to dissipate this charge. They have sharp points on which the static charges concentrate and will discharge into the air before they can build up on the smooth surface sufficiently high to jump across the hinges and cause radio interference.

As a further aid in preventing radio interference, the control surface is bonded to the structure. A flexible metal braid is attached to both the control surface and the structure to act as a good conductor, so the charge can be dissipated as it forms.

D. Magnetism

1. Magnetic Characteristics

One of the most useful devices in the production and use of electricity is the magnet. By definition, a magnet is a body that has the property of attracting iron and producing magnetic fields external to itself.

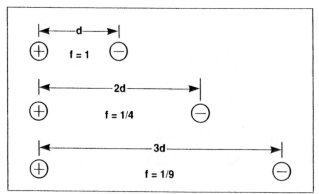

Figure 1-8. The force of repulsion or attraction decreases as the square of the distance between the charges.

The north-seeking end of a magnet is labeled "N", and the opposite south-seeking end is labeled "S". The labels refer to the direction sought by the pole of the magnet.

Lines of magnetic force (flux) are always complete loops that leave the magnet at right angles to its surface at the north pole. Since they are all polarized in the same direction, they repel each other and spread out. They draw closer together as they re-enter the magnet at the south pole at right

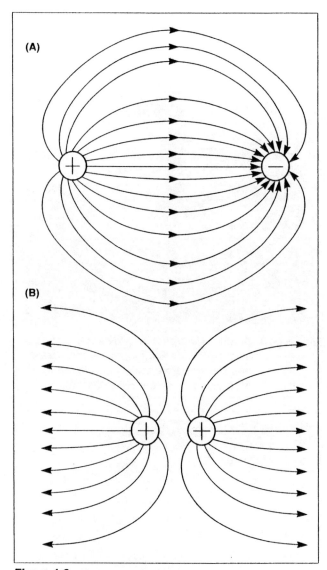

Figure 1-9.
    (A) Lines of force leave the charged body at right angles to its surface, and since they are polarized alike, spread apart. They enter the oppositely charged body at right angles to its surface.
    (B) Charged bodies reject lines of electrostatic force from other bodies having the same charge.

angles to its surface, and travel through the magnet to complete the loop.

The ends of the magnet where the lines of force leave and return are the poles, and are called the north- and south-seeking poles or, more commonly, north and south poles.

Unmagnetized iron contains an almost infinite number of magnetic fields oriented in such a random fashion that they cancel each other. If placed in a strong magnetic field, all of these little fields, or domains as they are called, would align themselves with the strong field, and the iron would become a magnet, having a north and south pole, and lines of magnetic flux.

Figure 1-10. Static dischargers provide sharp points from which static charges are dissipated into the air before they can build up to a high potential on the control surface.

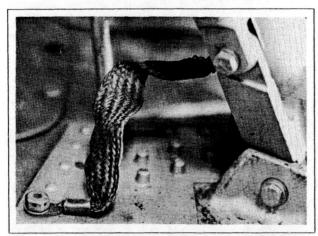

Figure 1-11. Bonding straps provide a low-resistance path between the control surface and the aircraft structure to prevent the buildup of a static charge on the control surface.

Soft iron has a very low retentivity, meaning that as soon as the magnetizing force is removed, the domains will lose their alignment, the fields will cancel each other, and the iron will no longer act as a magnet. Hard steel and some of the alloys of iron using aluminum, nickel, cobalt, and molybdenum have very high retentivities, and will retain the alignment of their domains long after the magnetizing force has been removed. Materials of this type are used for permanent magnets in aircraft magnetos, instruments, and radio speakers.

The number of lines of flux that loop through the magnet gives an indication of its strength. One line of flux is called 1 maxwell. Flux density is the number of lines of flux for a unit area and is measured in gausses, with 1 gauss representing a density of 1 maxwell per square centimeter.

Lines of flux always follow the path of least resistance as they travel from the north pole to the south. The measure of the ease with which lines of flux travel through a material or medium is measured in terms of permeability. Air is used as a reference and is given the permeability of 1. Flux can travel through iron much more easily than through air, since it has a permeability of 7,000, and some of the extremely efficient permanent magnet alloys have permeability values as high as 1,000,000.

Magnetism and lines of magnetic flux follow the same rules as charges of static electricity. Like poles repel each other, and the force of repulsion follows the inverse square law. This means that if the distance between the poles is doubled, the force of repulsion will be reduced to ¼. Unlike poles attract each other, and the force of attraction is squared as the distance is decreased. Halving the separation increases the force of attraction four times.

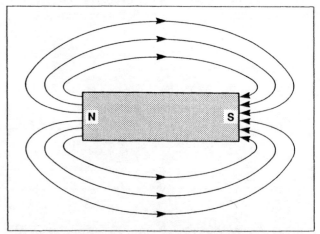

Figure 1-12. Lines of magnetic force form complete loops, leaving the magnet at its north pole and returning at its south pole.

E. Electromagnetism

Though the effects of magnetism had been observed for centuries, it was not until 1819 that the relationship between electricity and magnetism was discovered. The Danish physicist Hans Christian Oersted discovered that the needle of a small compass would be deflected if it was held near a wire carrying electric current. This deflection was caused by an invisible magnetic field surrounding the wire.

We can see the effect of this field if we sprinkle iron filings on a plate that surrounds a current-carrying conductor. The filings will arrange themselves in a series of concentric circles around the conductor.

By observing the effect of the field and applying the principles of electron flow, we can understand the principles of electromagnets.

Electrons are negative charges of electricity that can be forced to flow through a conductor. As they travel, they produce a magnetic field around the conductor. The greater the amount of flow, the stronger the magnetic field.

The left-hand rule gives the direction of lines of flux, and by knowing the direction, we can determine the polarity of electromagnets. If we grasp the conductor in our left hand with our thumb pointing in the direction of electron flow from negative to positive, our fingers will encircle the conductor in the direction of the lines of flux.

The magnetic field around the conductor does not serve a practical purpose because, while it has direction, it does not have poles and it is relatively weak. To increase its strength, and make it useful, we can wind the conductor into the form of a coil. When we do this, we concentrate the lines of flux and the coil attains the characteristics of a magnet.

In figure 1-17, the electrons flow into the coil from the right. As the conductor passes over the top of the

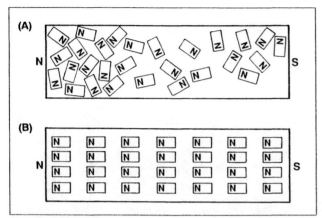

Figure 1-13.
- **(A)** *In an unmagnetized material, all of the individual magnetic fields, or domains, are arranged in a random fashion and cancel each other.*
- **(B)** *When the material is magnetized, all of the domains are aligned, and the material has a north and south pole, just like that of the individual domains.*

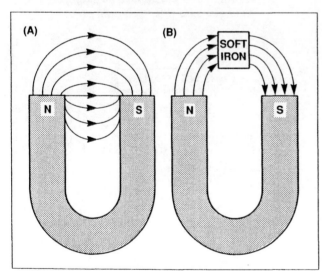

Figure 1-14.
- **(A)** *Lines of magnetic flux are assumed to leave the north pole of a magnet at right angles to its surface and travel to the south pole, where they enter at right angles to its surface.*
- **(B)** *The flux lines always seek the path of least resistance even traveling longer distances if they can travel through a material with a high permeability.*

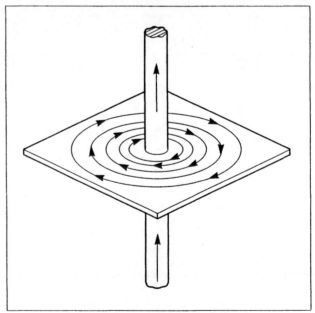

Figure 1-15. *Lines of magnetic force encircle a current-carrying conductor. These lines are relatively weak and have no polarity.*

coil, the electrons are flowing away from us. Below the coil, the electrons flow toward us. When electron flow is away from us, the lines encircle the conductor in a counterclockwise direction, and when they come toward us, the field circles the conductor clockwise.

The lines of flux around each turn aid, or reinforce, the flux around every other turn. The resultant field enters the coil from the left and leaves it from the right. When we use the same terminology used for permanent magnets, we find that in this electromagnet, the pole on the right is the north pole, since the lines of flux are leaving it, and the pole of the left where the lines enter is the south pole.

We can apply another left-hand rule — this one, the left-hand rule for coils. If we grasp a coil with our left hand in such a way that our fingers wrap around the coil in the direction of electron flow, our thumb will point to the north pole formed by the coil.

The strength of an electromagnet is determined by the number of turns in the coil and by the amount of current flowing through it. This strength (magnetomotive force) produced by the coil can be compared to electromotive force or electrical pressure of an electrical circuit.

We can further increase the strength of an electromagnet by concentrating the lines of flux. This is accomplished by using some highly permeable material, such as soft iron, for the core.

There are two types of electromagnets used in practical applications: those having fixed cores and those with movable cores. Fixed-core electromagnets

(called relays) are used in such devices as voltage regulators, where current proportional to the generator output voltage flows through the coil.

Movable-core electromagnets are called solenoids. A soft iron core is held out of the center of the coil by a spring. When current flows in the coil, a magnetic field will pass through the core and, in its effort

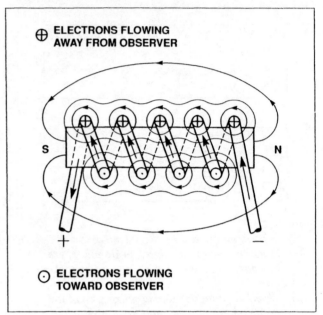

Figure 1-17. *By forming the conductor into a coil, the lines of flux can be concentrated, and the resulting coil will behave as a magnet and will have a north and a south pole.*

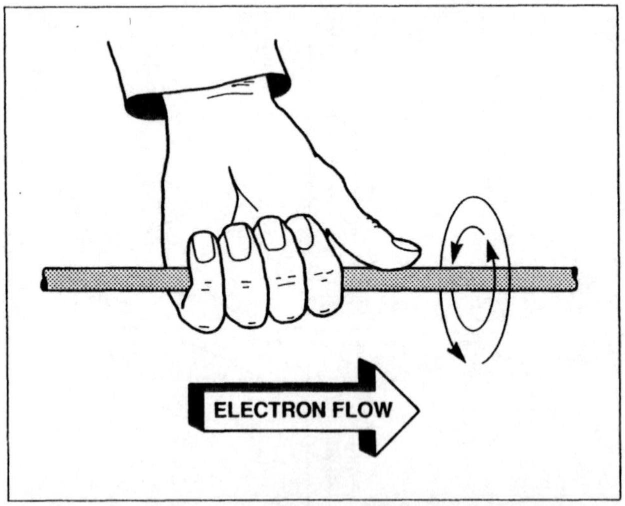

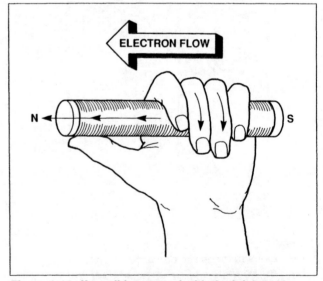

Figure 1-18. *If a coil is grasped with the left hand in such a way that the fingers encircle it in the same direction as the electron flow (from negative to positive), the thumb will point to the north pole of the electromagnet formed by the coil.*

Figure 1-16. *If a current-carrying conductor is grasped with the left hand, with the thumb pointing in the direction of electron flow (from negative to positive), the lines of force will encircle the conductor in the same direction as the fingers are pointing.*

to keep the loops of force as small as possible, pull the core into the center of the coil.

F. Sources of Electrical Energy

Within rather wide guidelines, energy may be converted from one form into another. The conversion of magnetic, mechanical, thermal, chemical, and light energy into electricity, and the exchange of electricity back into these other forms of energy are commonplace.

1. Magnetism

Lines of magnetic flux pass between the poles of a magnet. If a conductor is moved through these lines of flux, they transfer to the conductor and force electrons to flow through it. This is the principle of electromagnetic induction. Aircraft utilize generators

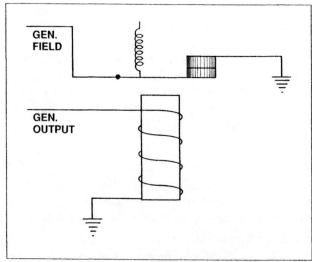

Figure 1-19. An electromagnetically operated switch with a fixed core is called a relay.

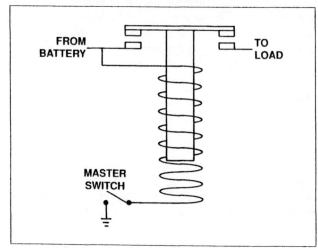

Figure 1-20. An electromagnetically operated switch with a movable core is called a solenoid.

or alternators to produce electricity based on this principle, as do atomic, hydroelectric, and fossil fueled powerplants.

The amount of electricity that is generated depends on the *rate* at which the lines of flux are cut, the number of conductors, and the strength of the maganetic field.

2. Chemical

In the chemical make-up of materials, there can exist an imbalance of electrons and protons. If a material having an excess of electrons is connected by a conductor to a material having a deficiency, electrons will be forced through the conductor.

For example, if a piece of aluminum and a piece of copper are immersed in a solution of hydrochloric acid and water, and the two pieces of metal are connected by a piece of wire, electrons will leave the aluminum and flow to the copper. The electrons which leave the aluminum are replaced by the negative chlorine ions from the acid. When the chlorine combines with the aluminum, it eats away part of the metal and forms a gray powdery material on the surface. Positive hydrogen ions will be attracted to the copper where they are neutralized by the electrons that came from the aluminum, and bubble to the surface as free hydrogen gas.

3. Thermal (Heat)

When certain combinations of wire, such as iron and constantan or chromel and alumel, are joined into a loop with two junctions, a thermocouple is formed. An electrical current will flow through the wires when there is a difference in the temperature of the two junctions. A cylinder head temperature measuring system has one junction held tight against the engine cylinder head by a spark plug (the hot junction), while the other junction is in the relatively constant temperature of the instrument panel (the cold junction).

4. Pressure

Crystalline material such as quartz has the characteristic that, when bent or deformed by a mechanical force, produces an excess of electrons on one surface, leaving the opposite surface with a deficiency. This is known as the piezoelectric effect and is commonly used in crystal microphones and phonograph pickups. In that this interchange between mechanical and electrical energy is reversible, it makes crystals useful for producing AC for radio transmitters. A piece of crystal has only one natural frequency at which it will vibrate, and if excited by pulses of electrical energy, will vibrate at this frequency. As it vibrates, it produces an alternating voltage having an accurate frequency.

5. Light

Light is a form of energy. When it strikes certain photoemissive materials, such as selenium, it imparts enough energy to the atoms that electrons are discharged from their bonds and are free to flow in a circuit and do work.

Switches may be controlled by light-sensitive devices to turn lights on at dark and off at dawn.

6. Friction

Although not a practical method of producing electricity for power, friction between two materials can produce static electricity. Many electrostatic-discharge-sensitive (ESDS) devices are used in electronics equipment aboard many aircraft.

G. Circuit Elements

All complete electrical circuits consist of a minimum of a source of electrical energy, a load device to use the electrical energy produced by the source, and conductors to connect the source to the load or loads in the circuit. These circuit elements do not comprise a practical electrical circuit, however. In order to make a circuit practical a control device, such as a switch, must be placed in the circuit to allow the loads to be easily and safely energized and de-energized. Some type of protection must be provided for the circuit wiring in the form of fuses or circuit breakers to stop current in the event of an overload or other circuit malfunction.

The source may be a battery, a generator, or other apparatus that converts some form of energy into electricity. The load may be anything that converts electrical energy into mechanical, heat, or light energy. Here, we are primarily concerned with the conductors used to join the source and the load, and components used to control the flow of current and protect the circuit.

1. Conductors

The purpose of a conductor is to provide a path for electron flow; from the source, through the load, and back to the source. It must do this with minimum of resistance, but other factors must also be taken into consideration, so the choice of a conductor is often a compromise.

Most aircraft electrical systems are of the single-wire type, meaning that the aircraft structure itself provides the path through which the current flows between the load to the source. Overall weight is reduced by using this type of system, but it is extremely important that a good connection capable of carrying all of the current be provided between the aircraft structure and the battery, generator, and all devices using the current.

The resistance of a conductor is affected by: its physical characteristics and its dimensions.

a. Physical Characteristics

(1) Resistivity

For most aircraft circuits, we use two types of conductors: copper and aluminum. Copper wire has only about ⅔ of the resistance of the equivalent gauge of aluminum wire, and is the one most generally used. But for applications requiring a large amount of current, aluminum wire is often used. Its resistivity is higher than that of copper, and a larger conductor is needed, but since aluminum weighs so much less than copper, aircraft weight can be reduced.

(2) Temperature

Most metals have what is known as a positive temperature coefficient of resistance. This means that the resistance of the material will increase as its temperature increases. This characteristic is used in some temperature measuring instruments where the resistance change in a piece of wire is used to measure temperature. For practical purposes, however, both copper and aluminum have such a small change in resistance with temperature over the temperature range encountered in flight that it is normally not considered.

b. Dimensions

(1) Length

For most common conductors, the resistance will vary directly with length. As length increases for a given specific conductor, its resistance will increase.

(2) Cross-sectional Area

The resistance of a conductor varies *inversely* with its cross-sectional area. Aircraft wire is measured by the American Wire Gauge (AWG) system, with the larger numbers representing the smaller wires. The smallest size wire normally used in aircraft wiring is the 22-gauge size which has a diameter of about 0.025". For carrying very large amounts of current, cables up to the 0000 size (pronounced "four aught" size) are used. These large cables have a diameter of about 0.52".

Since it is the area rather than the diameter of a conductor that determines its current-carrying capability and since almost all conductors are round rather than square, the circular mil measurement is used. A circular mil is the standard measurement of cross-sectional area, and is the area of a circle whose diameter is 1 mil, or ¹⁄₁,₀₀₀". To find the cross-sectional area of a conductor in circular mils, you need only square its diameter in mils. For example, if a round wire has a diameter of ⅛" (0.125" or 125 mils) it would have an area of 15,625 circular mils.

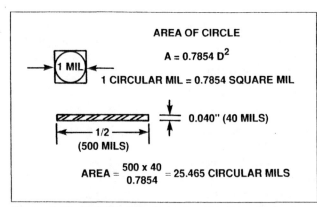

Figure 1-21. Relationship between circular mils and square mils.

c. Resistance of a Conductor

The resistance of a meterial varies directly as its length and inversely as its cross sectional area (temperature held constant).

(1) Resistance may be expressed as:

$$R = \frac{KL}{S}$$

where:

K - Resistivity of the material (constant)

L - Length of the material (feet)

S - Cross sectional area of the material (circular mils or mils)

COPPER ELECTRIC WIRE CURRENT-CARRYING CAPACITY				
Wire size Specification MIL-W-5086	Single wire in free air—maximum amperes	Wire in conduit or bundled—maximum amperes	Maximum resistance—ohms/1.000 feet (20 °C.)	Nominal conductor area—circular mills
AN-20	11	7.5	0.25	1,119
AN-18	16	10	6.44	1,779
AN-16	22	13	4.76	2,409
AN-14	32	17	2.99	3,830
AN-12	41	23	1.88	6,088
AN-10	55	33	1.10	10,443
AN-8	73	46	.70	16,864
AN-6	101	60	.436	26,813
AN-4	135	80	.274	42,613
AN-2	181	100	.179	66,832
AN-1	211	125	.146	81,807
AN-0	245	150	.114	104,118
AN-00	283	175	.090	133,665
AN-000	328	200	.072	167,332
AN-0000	380	225	.057	211,954

ALUMINUM ELECTRIC WIRE CURRENT-CARRYING CAPACITY				
Wire size— Specification MIL-W-7072	Single wire in free air—maximum amperes	Wire in conduit or bundled—maximum amperes	Maximum resistance—ohms/1.000 feet (20 °C.)	Nominal conductor area—circular mills
AL-6	83	50	0.641	28,280
AL-4	108	66	.427	42,420
AL-2	152	90	.268	67,872
AL-0	202	123	.169	107,464
AL-00	235	145	.133	138,168
AL-000	266	162	.109	168,872
AL-0000	303	190	.085	214,928

Figure 1-22. Characteristics of aircraft copper and aluminum wire.

NOTE: For an area given in mils the value must be squared.

2. Control Devices

a. Switches

(1) Toggle or Rocker Switches

Switches used to control the flow of electrons in most aircraft circuits are the enclosed toggle or rocker type. These switches are actuated by either moving the bat-shaped toggle or by pressing on one side of the rocker.

If the switch controls only one circuit and has only two connections and two positions (open and closed) it is called a single-pole, single-throw (SPST) switch. These may be used to control lights, either turning them ON or OFF.

Some switches are used to control more than one circuit and may be either the single- or double-throw type. The double-pole, single-throw (DPST) switch could be used to control both the battery and the generator circuit so they would both be turned ON and OFF at the same time. A double-pole, double-throw (DPDT) switch controls two circuits and has either two or three positions.

Both toggle and rocker switches may have one or both of their positions spring-loaded so they will return to the OFF position when your finger is removed.

(2) Wafer Switches

When a switch is used to select one of a number of conditions, a wafer switch is often used. These switches may have several wafers stacked on the same shaft, and each wafer may have as many as twenty positions. Wafer switches are seldom used for carrying large amounts of current and are most generally open with the wires soldered to the terminals on the wafers.

(3) Precision Switches

Limit switches, uplock and downlock switches, and many other applications require the switch to be actuated by mechanical movement of some mechanism. In these applications, it is usually important that the switch actuate when the mechanism reaches a *very definite and specific* position. These switches require an extremely small movement to actuate. Snap-acting switches of the type pioneered by Micro Switch, division of Honeywell, find a wide use in these applications. An extremely small movement of the plunger trips the spring so it will drive the contacts together. When the plunger is released, the spring snaps the contacts apart.

(4) Relays and Solenoids

It is often necessary to open or close a circuit carrying a large amount of current from a remote location and with a small switch. An example is the starter circuit for an aircraft engine. The starter motor requires a great deal of current and the cable between the battery and the starter must be as short as possible. But the starter switch must be located inside the cockpit and is often incorporated in the ignition switch.

A solenoid, or contactor, is used for this application. A small amount of current is used to energize an electromagnet which closes the contacts in the circuit carrying the large amount of current.

Figure 1-23. *Most of the switches found in modern aircraft are either of the toggle or the rocker type.*

Figure 1-24. *Wafer switches are used when it is necessary to select any of a large number of circuit conditions.*

If the electromagnet has a fixed core that attracts a movable armature, it is called a relay, but if the core is movable and is pulled into the hollow coil, it is called a solenoid.

3. Protective Devices

Protective devices are installed in electrical circuits to prevent damage caused by excessive current flow. Excessive current may be the result of overloading the circuit or a short circuit.

Figure 1-25. Precision switches snap open or closed with an extremely small amount of movement of the operating control.

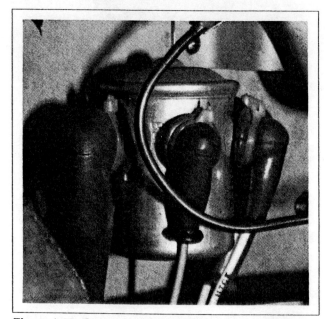

Figure 1-26. Starter solenoid switches control large amounts of current, but they are operated by a very small current that flows through the coil.

Overloading the circuit is the result of connecting loads that are too large for the wiring or of connecting too many smaller loads.

A direct short is when some part of the circuit in which full system voltage is present comes into direct contact with the return side of the circuit or ground. This establishes a path for current flow with little or no resistance, other than that of the conductors themselves. This will result in very large current flow, heating, and likely damage.

a. Fuses

A fusible link made of a low-melting-point alloy enclosed in a glass tube is used as a simple and reliable circuit protection device. The load current flows through the fuse, and if it becomes excessive, will melt the link and open the circuit. Some fuses are designed to withstand a momentary surge of current, but will melt if the current is sustained. These slow-blow fuses have a small spring attached to the link so when the sustained current softens the link, the spring will pull it apart and open the circuit.

b. Circuit Breakers

It is often inconvenient to replace a fuse in flight, so most aircraft circuits are protected by circuit breakers that will automatically open the circuit if the current becomes excessive, but may be reset by moving the operating control, which may be a toggle, a push-button, or a rocker. If the excess current was caused by a surge of voltage or by some isolated and nonrecurring problem, the circuit breaker will remain in and the circuit will operate normally. But

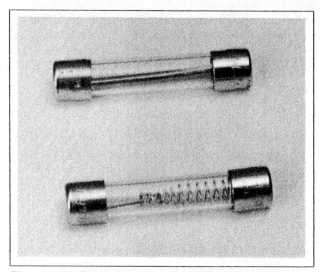

Figure 1-27. The heat caused by excess current melts the fusible link and opens the circuit. Slow-blow fuses will stand a momentary excess of current, but sustained overload will soften the link and the spring will pull apart.

if an actual fault such as a short circuit does exist, the breaker will trip again, and it should be left open.

Aircraft circuit breakers are of the trip-free type which means that they will open the circuit irrespective of the position of the operating control. With this type of breaker, it is impossible to hold the circuit closed if an actual fault exists.

There are two types of circuit breakers. Thermal breakers open the circuit when the excess current heats an element in the switch and snaps the contacts open. The other type is a magnetic breaker which uses the strength of the magnetic field caused by the current to open the contacts.

Automatic re-set circuit breakers that open a circuit when excess current flows but automatically close again after a cooling-off period are usually not used in aircraft circuits.

4. Resistors

It is often necessary in electrical circuits to control current flow by varying voltage, thus converting some of the electrical energy into heat. The resistors used may be classified as fixed or variable.

a. Fixed Resistors

(1) Composition

The great majority of resistors used to control small amounts of current are made of a mixture of carbon and an insulating material. The relative percentage of the two materials in the mix determines the amount of resistance a given amount of the material will have. Small amounts of material are used to dissipate small amounts of power and, for more power, more material is used. Composition resistors are normally available in sizes from 1/8 watt up to 2 watts. The larger the physical size of the resistor, the more power it will dissipate.

Most modern resistors are of the axial-lead type; that is, the leads come directly out of the ends of the resistor. The ohmic value of this type of resistor is indicated by 3 or 4 bands of color around one end.

The band nearest the end of the resistor is the first significant figure of the resistance, the second band represents the second figure, and the third band tells the number of zeros to add to the two numbers. For example, if the first band is green (5), the second is brown (1), and the third is yellow (0000), the resistor would have a resistance of 510,000 ohms.

(2) Wire-wound Resistors

When more power needs to be dissipated than can be handled by a composition resistor, special resistors made of resistance wire wound over hollow ceramic tubes are used. Some of these resistors are

tapped along the length of the wire to provide different values of resistance, and others have a portion of the wire left bare, so a metal band can be slid over the resistor allowing it to be set to any desired resistance. When the screw is tightened, the band will not move from the selected resistance.

b. Variable Resistors

When it is necessary to change the amount of resistance in a circuit, variable resistors may be used. These may be of either the composition or the wire-wound type. In the composition resistor, the mix is bonded to an insulating disk, and a wiper, or sliding contact, is rotated by the shaft to vary the amount of material between the two terminals. In that resistance varies with the length of the conductor, the farther the sliding contact is from the fixed contact, the greater will be the resistance.

Resistance wire may be wound around a form which is shaped so that the sliding contact will touch the wire at the edge of the form. As the contact is rotated, the length of wire between the terminals varies and the resistance changes.

Figure 1-28. Most circuit protection for modern aircraft is provided by circuit breakers than may be reset in flight.

Variable resistors having only two terminals, one at the end of the resistance material, and the other, the sliding contact, are called rheostats and are used to vary the amount of resistance in a circuit.

5. Circuit Considerations

All electrical circuits must contain three components: the source of electrical energy, a load device to use the energy, and conductors to connect the source and the load. Control devices such as switches and resistors and such protective devices as fuses or circuit breakers tailor the circuit to its purpose.

For a circuit to be complete (closed), there must be at least one continuous path from one of the terminals of the source, through the load and back to the other terminal. If there is any interruption (break) in this path, the circuit is said to *open* and there can be no flow of electrons. If, on the other hand, there is a path from one terminal of the source to the other without passing through the load the circuit is *shorted*; and not only is there no work being done, but the lack of resistance in the circuit will allow excessive current to flow. In this case, unless a protective device such as a fuse opens the circuit, the wiring, and even the source, are likely to be damaged.

H. Ohm's Law

1. Principle of Ohm's Law

A concentration of electrons will produce an electrical pressure that will force electrons to flow through

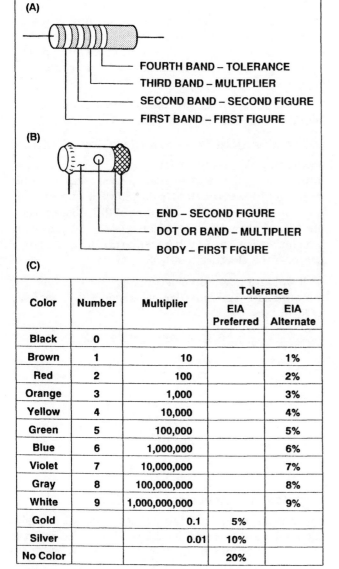

Figure 1-29.
- *(A) Color coding for axial-lead resistors.*
- *(B) Color coding for radial-lead resistors.*
- *(C) Resistor color-code values.*

(A)

FOURTH BAND – TOLERANCE
THIRD BAND – MULTIPLIER
SECOND BAND – SECOND FIGURE
FIRST BAND – FIRST FIGURE

(B)

END – SECOND FIGURE
DOT OR BAND – MULTIPLIER
BODY – FIRST FIGURE

(C)

Color	Number	Multiplier	Tolerance	
			EIA Preferred	EIA Alternate
Black	0			
Brown	1	10		1%
Red	2	100		2%
Orange	3	1,000		3%
Yellow	4	10,000		4%
Green	5	100,000		5%
Blue	6	1,000,000		6%
Violet	7	10,000,000		7%
Gray	8	100,000,000		8%
White	9	1,000,000,000		9%
Gold		0.1	5%	
Silver		0.01	10%	
No Color			20%	

Figure 1-30. Wire-wound resistors are used when there is a great deal of power that must be dissipated.

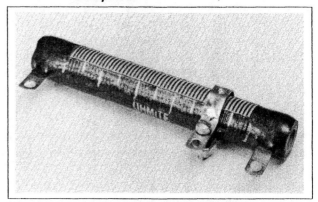

Figure 1-31. Wire-wound resistors may have a portion of the wire exposed and incorporate a movable tap.

Figure 1-32. Variable resistors allow the amount of resistance in a circuit to be changed by rotating the shaft.

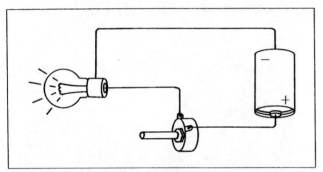

Figure 1-33. Rheostats are used to vary the amount of resistance in a circuit.

a circuit. By assigning values to the pressure, flow, and opposition, we can understand the relationship that exists between them, and can accurately predict what will happen in a circuit under any given set of conditions.

The German scientist George Simon Ohm proved the relationship between these values in 1826. Ohm's law is the basic statement which says, in effect, the current flowing in a circuit is directly proportional to the voltage (pressure) that causes it, and inversely proportional to the resistance (opposition). The units we use make this relationship easy to see — 1 volt of pressure will cause 1 ampere of current to flow in a circuit whose resistance is 1 ohm.

For ease of handling these terms in formulas voltage is represented by the letter E, current by the letter I, and resistance by the letter R. A statement of Ohm's law in the form of a formula is, therefore, $E = I \times R$. If we want to find the current, we use the formula $I = E/R$, and resistance may be found by the formula $R = E/I$.

Power in an electrical circuit is measured in watts, and 1 watt is the amount of power used in a circuit when 1 amp of current flows under a pressure of 1 volt.

The relationship between voltage, current, resistance, and power is such that any one value may be found when any two of the others are known. One easy way to find the correct formula is to use a series of divided circles representing the symbols in the formula. In figure 1-36, the voltage in the circuit is equal to the product of the current and the resistance; $E = I \times R$. The top half of the circle is equal to the bottom half. We also know that the current may be found by dividing the voltage by the resistance, $I = E/R$ and the resistance is equal to the voltage divided by the current, $R = E/I$.

The same relationship may be found between power, current, and voltage. We know that power is equal to voltage times current, $P = I \times E$. Figure 1-37 shows an easy way to find current by dividing power by voltage, $I = P/E$ and to find the voltage by dividing power by the current, $E = P/I$.

The other six relationships are just as easy to find when we use the circles of figures 1-38 and 1-39.

2. Mechanical Power in Electrical Circuits

Power is the time-rate of doing work. The mechanical unit of measurement is horsepower, which is the amount of power required to do 33,000 ft.-lbs. of work in 1 minute, or its equivalent of 550 ft.-lbs. of work in 1 second. A constant relates electrical power to mechanical power. Seven hundred and forty-six (746) watts is the electrical equivalent of 1 HP.

If we have a 24-volt electric hoist, we can find the amount of current needed to raise a 1,000-lb. load 6 ft. in 30 sec.

$$1,000 \times 6 = 6,000 \text{ ft.-lbs.}$$

$$\frac{6,000}{30} = 200 \text{ft.-lbs. per sec.}$$

$$\frac{200}{550} = 0.364 \text{HP}$$

$$746 \times 0.364 = 271.5 \text{ watts}$$

$$I = \qquad I = \frac{P}{E} = \frac{271.5}{24} = 11.31 \text{ amps}$$

3. Heat in Electrical Circuits

In circuits where mechanical work is not actually being done, power is still a very important consideration. For example, if a resistor in a light circuit drops the voltage from 12 volts to 3 volts for a light bulb that requires 150 milliamps, the resistance in ohms and the power in watts may be found that this resistor must dissipate.

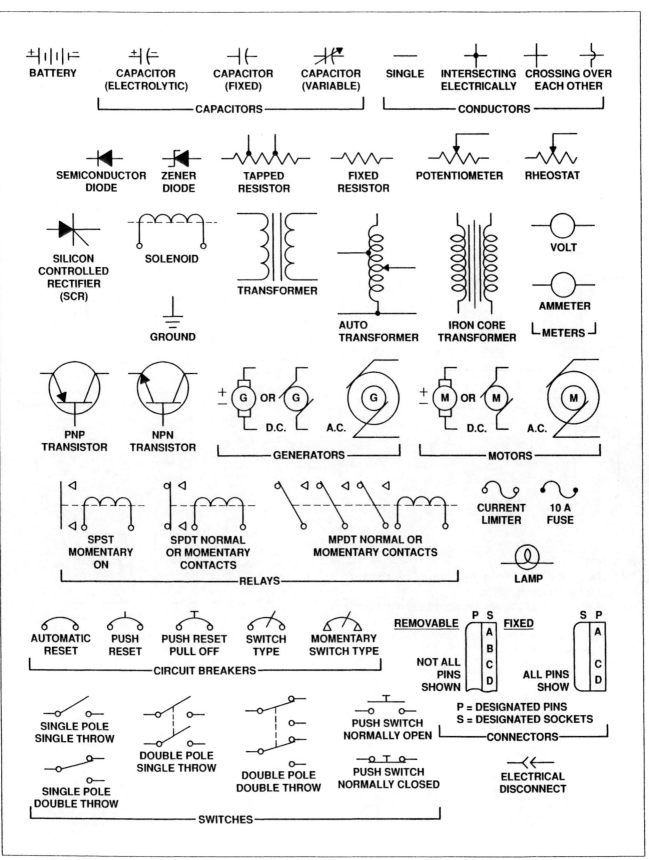

Figure 1-34. Electrical symbols.

19

To solve this problem, we must first find the voltage to be dropped:

$$E = 12 - 3 = 9 \text{ volts}$$

Find the resistance required:

$$R = E/I = 9/0.15 = 60 \text{ ohms}$$

Find the power dissipated in the resistor:

$$P = I^2 \times R = 0.15^2 \times 60 = 1.35 \text{ watts}$$

The resistor will only have to dissipate 1.35 watts, but for practical purposes, you will most probably use a 2-watt resistor.

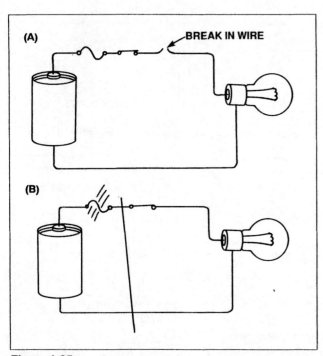

Figure 1-35.
(A) *An open circuit allows no current flow and the circuit cannot function.*
(B) *A short circuit causes excessive current flow and can damage the circuit components or wiring unless a protecting device such as a fuse opens the circuit.*

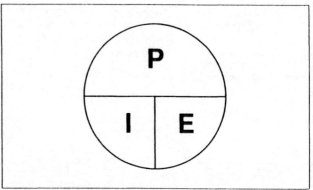

Figure 1-37. The relationship between power, current, and voltage.

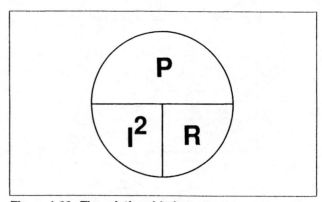

Figure 1-38. The relationship between power, current, and resistance.

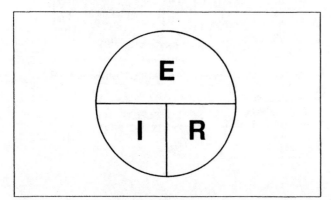

Figure 1-36. The relationship between voltage, current, and resistance.

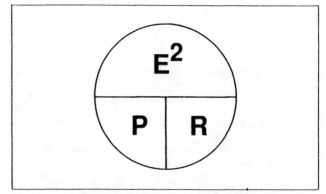

Figure 1-39. The relationship between voltage, power, and resistance.

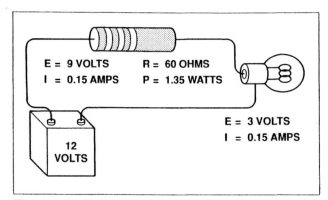

Figure 1-40. *Determining the characteristics of a resistor needed to drop voltage in a circuit.*

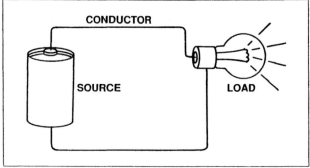

Figure 1-41. *All complete circuits must have a source of electrical energy, a load to use the energy, and conductors to join the source and the load.*

Chapter II

Direct Current

15-70% pers.. 20-25% budget

A. DC Terms and Values

1. Direct Current

Direct current (DC) is current which is nonvarying in nature, such as that obtained from a battery or filtered power supply. This type of current may be referred to as "pure DC", meaning that no alternating current, noise, etc., is present.

2. Pulsating DC

Pulsating DC is a current (or voltage) which varies from a zero reference level to a maximum or peak value, never dropping below the zero reference. Pulsating DC is produced by a rectifier in a power supply, and is filtered to remove the pulses or variations, thereby producing pure DC.

3. Average Value

The average value of DC is the average of the current or voltage excursion made by a pulsating DC waveform as it moves from zero to its maximum value. The average value is computed by multiplying the maximum value of the pulsating waveform by 0.637. Example: assume the maximum value for the waveform shown in figure 2-2 is 20 V. Multiplying 20 × 0.637 we obtain the average value of 12.74 V.

4. Polarity

The polarity of DC is expressed as being either positive or negative. Polarity is determined by establishing a reference point (usually ground) and measuring a voltage in reference to that point. For example, if we measure battery voltage, we measure from battery negative, which is connected to ground, to battery

positive and determine that battery voltage is +12 V. That is, the battery voltage has a value of 12 volts and has positive polarity with respect to ground.

B. Series DC Circuits

If there is only one path for electrons to flow, the circuit is called a series circuit. In figure 2-3 we have a typical circuit: a battery, lamp rheostat, switch, and fuse all in series (only one path for electron flow). If either the switch is open or the fuse is blown, the lamp cannot burn.

There are two laws developed by the German physicist Gustav Robert Kirchhoff that explain the behavior of voltage and current in electrical circuits. Kirchhoff's voltage law states that "the algebraic sum of the applied voltage and the voltage drop around any closed circuit is equal to zero". What this means is that the voltage dropped across the entire circuit must be exactly the same as that supplied by the source. In figure 2-4, we have an example of this. A 6-volt battery in series with a switch, 3 lamps, and a milliammeter. Each lamp is rated at 2 volts and requires 300 milliamps of current to burn at full brilliance. When the switch is closed, all of the lamps light up fully bright.

We can analyze the circuit and prove Kirchhoff's voltage law with a voltmeter that is capable of measuring up to 6 volts. With the positive lead at C, and the switch closed, it offers no resistance. According to Ohm's law ($E = I \times R$), if the resistance is zero the voltage will also be zero, and there will be no voltage reading across the switch. But when the switch is opened, there will be no current flowing in the

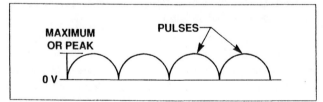

Figure 2-1. Pulsating DC waveform.

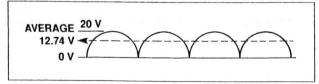

Figure 2-2. Average value of pulsating DC.

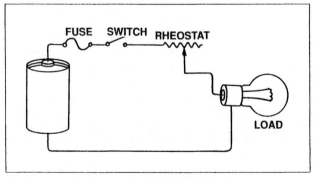

Figure 2-3. A rheostat in series with the load can drop part of the voltage and control the brightness of the light.

circuit, and there will be no voltage dropped by the lamps. The meter will read the full source voltage of 6 volts.

With the switch closed, the lamps burning, and the leads between D and E, the meter should read 2 volts indicating that the resistance of the lamp has dissipated enough power to drop this much voltage.

In measuring the voltage between points E and F, it should be 2 volts, as should the voltage between points F and G. The voltage between points D and G should be the same as between A and H, proving Kirchhoff's voltage law.

Ohm's law can also be applied to this circuit. Using a chart similar to that in figure 2-5, we can fill in the blanks. Since this is a series circuit with only one path for the electrons to flow, the current will be the same through each lamp as it is through the source. In this case, it is 300 milliamps.

The source voltage is 6 volts, and the voltage across each lamp is 2 volts. The sum of the voltage dropped across the lamps does, in fact, equal the source (applied voltage).

The resistance cannot be measured by an ohmmeter, because the resistance of a lamp is quite different when it is hot than when it is cold, so we find the resistance by Ohm's law.

$$R = E/I = 2/0.3 = 6.67 \text{ ohms}$$

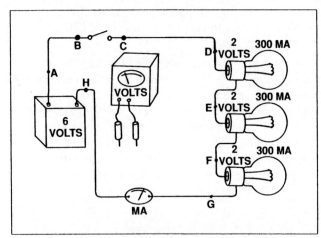

Figure 2-4. This series circuit operates according to Kirchhoff's voltage law.

Component	Voltage Volts	Current MA	Resistance Ohms	Power Watts
A	2	300	6.67	0.6
B	2	300	6.67	0.6
C	2	300	6.67	0.6
Source	6	300	20	1.8

Figure 2-5 Circuit conditions in a series circuit.

There are three lamps in series, so we have a total circuit resistance of 20 ohms. To prove this, apply Ohm's law to the source:

$$E = I \times R = 0.3 \times 20 = 6 \text{ volts}$$

This is our source of voltage.

The power dissipated by each lamp may be found by the formula:

$$P = I \times E = 0.3 \times 2 = 0.6 \text{ watt}$$

The three lamps will dissipate 1.8 watts, which is exactly the same as we find when we multiply by source voltage by the total current.

To briefly summarize the characteristics of a series circuit:

1. There is only one path for electrons to flow; from the source, through the load; back to the source.
2. The current is the same wherever it is measured in the circuit.
3. The sum of all the voltage drops equals the source voltage.
4. The total resistance of the circuit is the sum of the individual load resistances.
5. The total power dissipated in the circuit is the sum of the power dissipated in each of the individual load resistances.

C. Parallel DC Circuits

The most widely used circuit arrangement is the parallel circuit. A parallel circuit has two or more paths for electrons to flow. In a series circuit, if one of the lamps burns out, none of them burn, but in a parallel circuit, if a lamp burns out, it will have no effect on the others.

The behavior of a parallel circuit is explained in part by Kirchhoff's current law which states that "The algebraic sum of the currents at any junction of conductors is zero". This means that all of the current that arrives at any junction within the circuit must leave that junction.

In figure 2-6, we have a simple 3-lamp parallel circuit using the same components as in the previous series circuit, except that the source is 2 volts instead of 6. All of the current flows from the source then splits up, with some passing through each of the lamps. The amount that passes through each lamp is determined by its resistance.

There are three separate paths; from the source through the loads, and back to the source. Each route must obey Kirchhoff's voltage law. Since each path has only one load device, the total voltage dropped must equal the source voltage. Measurement may be made

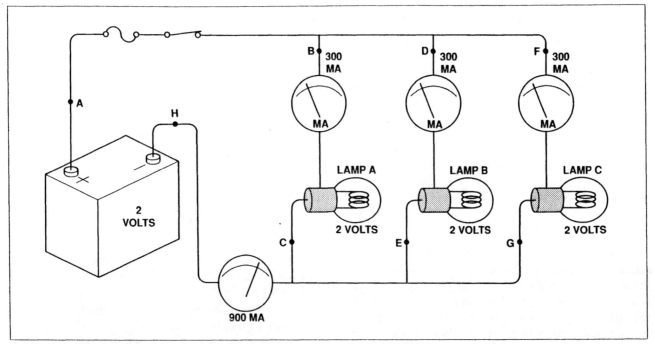

Figure 2-6. This parallel circuit operates according to Kirchhoff's current law.

with the voltmeter between A and H, B and C, D and E, F and G, and all will read 2 volts. From this we see that, in a parallel circuit, the voltage across each path is the same as the source voltage.

The current reading in each path indicates a 300 milliamp flow through each lamp, and a total current of 900 milliamps, verifying Kirchhoff's current law. The total current is the sum of the current flowing in each of the paths.

We can find the resistance of each lamp by Ohm's law:

$$R = E/I = 2/0.3 = 6.67 \text{ ohms}$$

The total resistance is 2.22 ohms. We can check by using Ohm's law on the source and find that:

$$R = E/I = 2/.9 = 2.22 \text{ ohms}$$

We can find the power at each lamp by using $P = I \times E$:

$$P = I \times E = 0.3 \times 2 = 0.6 \text{ watt.}$$

The total power is found by adding the power dissipated in each lamp.

To summarize the characteristics of a parallel circuit:

1. There is more than one path for electrons to flow; from the source, through each load, back to the source.
2. The voltage is the same across any of the paths/loads.
3. The total current is the sum of the current flowing through each of the individual paths/loads.
4. The total resistance of the circuit is less than the resistance of any of the paths/loads.
5. The total power dissipated in the circuit is the sum of the power dissipated in each of the individual load resistances.

1. Resistance in a Parallel Circuit

a. All Resistances with the Same Value

If the resistances are all the same in a parallel circuit, the total resistance is found by dividing the value of a single resistor by the total number of resistors:

$$R_T = R/n$$

R = resistance of one resistor

n = number of resistances

b. Two Unlike Resistances

If there are two unlike resistors in a parallel circuit, the total resistance may be found by dividing the product of the individual resistances by their sum:

$$R_T = \frac{R_1 \times R_2}{R_1 + R_2}$$

A 100-ohm resistor in parallel with one having a resistance of 200 ohms, will have a total resistance of 66.7 ohms, less than that of the smaller resistor (figure 2-8).

c. More Than Two Unlike Resistances

If there are more than two unlike resistors in parallel, the total resistance may be found by solving for the reciprocal of the sum of the reciprocals of the individual resistances:

$$R_T = \frac{1}{\frac{1}{R_1} + \frac{1}{R_2} + \frac{1}{R_3}}$$

A 12-ohm, 20-ohm, and 30-ohm resistor in parallel will have a total resistance of 6 ohms, less than the smallest of the three resistors(figure 2-9).

D. Complex DC Circuits

Combined circuits are more complex than individual series or parallel circuits. By carefully analyzing them, we can usually combine the series and parallel components, find equivalent values, then rearrange the entire circuit into a single equivalent resistance. By applying Ohm's law, we can then find all of the

Component	Voltage Volts	Current MA	Resistance Ohms	Power Watts
A	2	300	6.67	0.6
B	2	300	6.67	0.6
C	2	300	6.67	0.6
Source	2	900	2.22	1.8

Figure 2-7. Circuit relationships in a parallel circuit.

values we need. The arrangement in figure 2-10 is a typical exercise in circuit analysis.

The first step is to draw the circuit using the conventional symbols (figure 2-11). Since we know all of the resistance values, our next step is to find the equivalent resistance of each parallel combination. Starting with R_2 and R_3, we find their equivalent resistance to be 12 ohms (figure 2-12).

Our next step is to find the equivalent resistance of R_5, R_6, and R_7. This also happens to be 12 ohms (figure 2-13).

The next step is to combine $R_{5\text{-}6\text{-}7}$ with R_4. This gives us an equivalent series resistance of 24 ohms. (figure 3-14)

We now have a parallel combination of $R_{4\text{-}5\text{-}6\text{-}7}$ and $R_{2\text{-}3}$. The equivalent of these two combinations is 8 ohms (figure 2-15).

We now find the equivalent of the series combination of R_1 and $R_{2\text{-}3\text{-}4\text{-}5\text{-}6\text{-}7}$, which is 12 ohms (figure 2-16). This is equivalent resistance of the entire circuit.

With the equivalent resistance for the entire circuit, we can work the problem in its original form and find all of the missing values.

We start by finding the total current (figure 2-17).

$$I_T = E/R = 24/12 = 2 \text{ amps.}$$

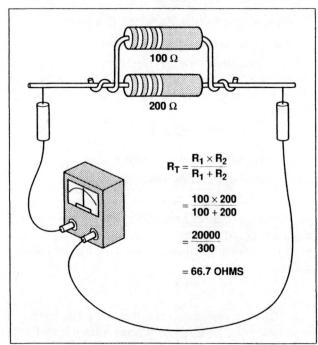

Figure 2-8. Finding the equivalent resistance of two unlike resistors in parallel.

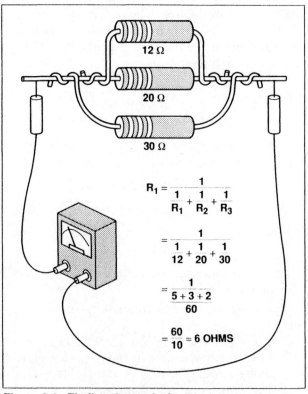

Figure 2-9. Finding the equivalent resistance of more than two unlike resistors in parallel.

26

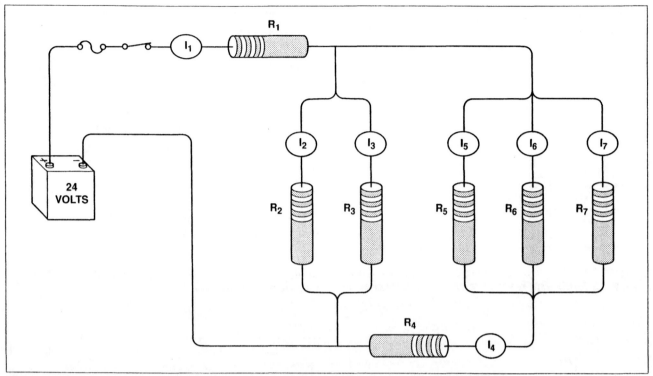

Figure 2-10. A complex circuit having both series and parallel combinations of resistance.

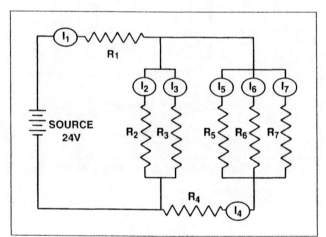

Figure 2-11. The complex circuit of figure 2-10 using conventional symbols.

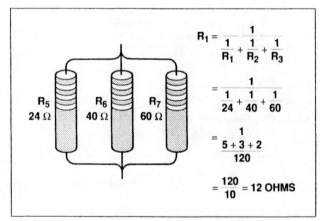

Figure 2-13. Equivalent resistance of R_5, R_6, and R_7.

$$R_1 = \cfrac{1}{\cfrac{1}{R_1} + \cfrac{1}{R_2} + \cfrac{1}{R_3}}$$

$$= \cfrac{1}{\cfrac{1}{24} + \cfrac{1}{40} + \cfrac{1}{60}}$$

$$= \cfrac{1}{\cfrac{5 + 3 + 2}{120}}$$

$$= \frac{120}{10} = 12 \text{ OHMS}$$

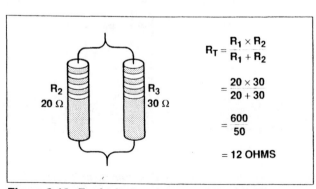

Figure 2-12. Equivalent resistance of R_2 and R_3.

$$R_T = \frac{R_1 \times R_2}{R_1 + R_2}$$

$$= \frac{20 \times 30}{20 + 30}$$

$$= \frac{600}{50}$$

$$= 12 \text{ OHMS}$$

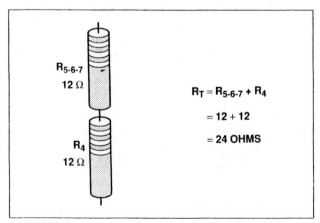

Figure 2-14. Equivalent resistance of $R_{5\text{-}6\text{-}7}$, and R_4.

$$R_T = R_{5\text{-}6\text{-}7} + R_4$$

$$= 12 + 12$$

$$= 24 \text{ OHMS}$$

All of the current flows through resistor R_1, which has a resistance of 4 ohms. The voltage dropped across it is 8 volts. When 8 volts is dropped across R_1, it leaves 16 volts across both the combinations R_{2-3} and $R_{4-5-6-7}$ (figure 2-18).

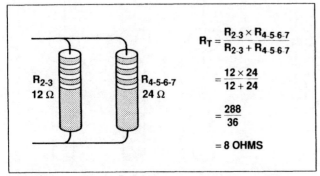

Figure 2-15. *Equivalent resistance of R_{2-3}, and $R_{4-5-6-7}$.*

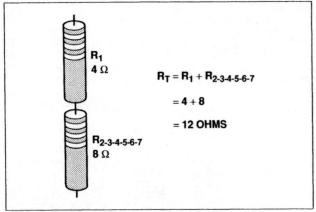

Figure 2-16. *Total equivalent resistance by adding R_1 to $R_{2-3-4-5-6-7}$.*

$$I_T = \frac{E}{R} = \frac{24}{12} = 2 \text{ AMPS}$$

Figure 2-17. *Total current flowing in the circuit.*

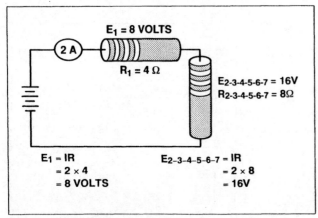

Figure 2-18. *Voltage dropped across R_1 and across $R_{2-3-4-5-6-7}$.*

The current through the first combination is 1.33 amps, and that through the second, 0.67 amp (figure 2-19).

The entire 0.67 amp flows through R_4, and the voltage drop across it is 8 volts. This same 0.67 amp flows through the combination R_{5-6-7}. Since its equivalent resistance is 12 ohms, there will also be 8 volts dropped across it (figure 2-20).

We can now find the current through resistors R_{5-6-7} (figure 2-21).

We can now find the current through R_2 and R_3 (figure 2-22).

We can find the power dissipated in each resistor by multiplying the current through each resistor by the voltage drop across each resistor (figure 2-23).

All of the values found by analyzing the complex circuit are in figure 2-24.

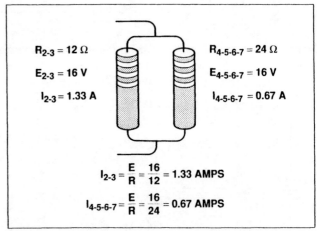

Figure 2-19. *Current flowing through R_{2-3}, and $R_{4-5-6-7}$.*

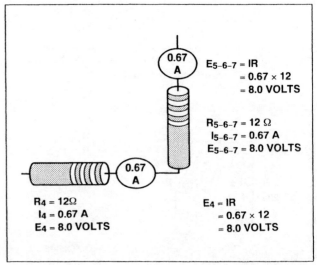

Figure 2-20. *Voltage dropped across R_4 and across R_{5-6-7}.*

28

We can check our analysis by verifying the following statements:

1. The total power is equal to the sum of the power dissipated in each of the resistors.

   48 watts = 48 watts.

2. The voltage drops across R_1, R_4, R_{2-3} and R_{5-6-7} must equal the source voltage.

24 volts = 24 volts.

3. Current through R_4 is the same as the sum of the current through R_5, R_6, and R_7.

   0.67 amp = 0.67 amp.

4. The current through R_1 is equal to the sum of the current through R_2, R_3, R_5, R_6, and R_7.

   2 amps = 2 amps.

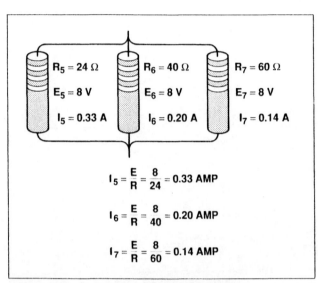

$$I_5 = \frac{E}{R} = \frac{8}{24} = 0.33 \text{ AMP}$$

$$I_6 = \frac{E}{R} = \frac{8}{40} = 0.20 \text{ AMP}$$

$$I_7 = \frac{E}{R} = \frac{8}{60} = 0.14 \text{ AMP}$$

Figure 2-21. Current through R_5, R_6, and R_7.

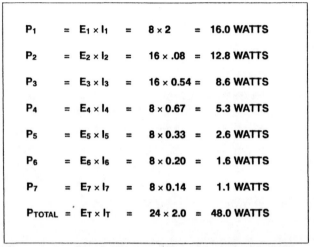

P_1	= $E_1 \times I_1$	=	8×2	= **16.0 WATTS**
P_2	= $E_2 \times I_2$	=	$16 \times .08$	= **12.8 WATTS**
P_3	= $E_3 \times I_3$	=	16×0.54	= **8.6 WATTS**
P_4	= $E_4 \times I_4$	=	8×0.67	= **5.3 WATTS**
P_5	= $E_5 \times I_5$	=	8×0.33	= **2.6 WATTS**
P_6	= $E_6 \times I_6$	=	8×0.20	= **1.6 WATTS**
P_7	= $E_7 \times I_7$	=	8×0.14	= **1.1 WATTS**
P_{TOTAL}	= $E_T \times I_T$	=	24×2.0	= **48.0 WATTS**

Figure 2-23. Power dissipated in each of the resistors.

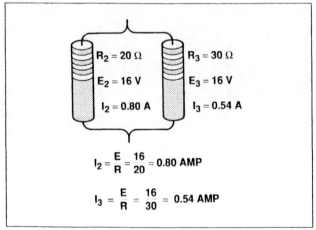

$$I_2 = \frac{E}{R} = \frac{16}{20} = 0.80 \text{ AMP}$$

$$I_3 = \frac{E}{R} = \frac{16}{30} = 0.54 \text{ AMP}$$

Figure 2-22. Current through R_2 and R_3.

Item	Voltage Volts	Resistance Ohms	Current Amps	Power Watts
R_1	8	4	2.00	16.0
R_2	16	20	0.80	12.8
R_3	16	30	0.54	8.6
R_4	8	12	0.67	5.3
R_5	8	24	0.33	2.6
R_6	8	40	0.20	1.6
R_7	8	60	0.14	1.1
Source	24	12	2.00	48.0

Figure 2-24. Circuit relationships in a complex circuit.

Chapter III

Alternating Current

The advantages offered by alternating current have resulted in it being adopted almost exclusively for commercial power systems. Even on a small scale, AC is used in medium and large aircraft systems for a number of applications.

A. Advantage of AC over DC

Alternating current, which continually changes its value and periodically reverses its direction of flow, has many advantages over direct current, in which the electrons flow in one direction only. AC is much easier to generate in the large quantities needed for homes, industries, and large transport aircraft.

More important, though, is the ease with which we can change the values of current and voltage to get the most effective use of electrical energy. For example, in homes and shops, most AC electricity has a pressure of about 115 volts, and with a kilowatt of power, almost 9 amps of current must flow. The current flowing in a conductor determines the amount of heat generated, and therefore the size of conductor needed. If we can get the same amount of power with less current, we can use smaller conductors which will reduce both cost and weight.

In order to use the smallest conductor possible for cross-country delivery of electrical power, the voltage carried in transmission lines is boosted to several thousand volts. For example, at 15,000 volts, only 0.067 amp is needed for 1 kilowatt of electrical power. Before the electricity is brought into homes or shops, it is transformed down to a usable value

of around 115 volts, so it will be safer and more convenient to handle. Between the generation of AC and its final use, the voltage and current may be changed many times. The transformers that do this are quite efficient and very little energy is lost.

B. Generation of AC

We have seen that there is a close relationship between magnetism and electricity. Any time electrons flow in a conductor, a magnetic field surrounds the conductor, and the strength of this field is determined by the amount of electron flow. When a magnetic field is moved across a conductor, electrons are forced to flow in it. The amount of this flow is determined by the rate at which the lines of magnetic flux are cut by the conductor. Increasing the number of lines of flux by making the magnet stronger, or increasing the speed of movement between the conductor and the magnet, will increase the amount of electron flow.

If a conductor, wound in the form of a coil, is attached to an electrical measuring instrument, and a permanent magnet moved back and forth through the coil, the meter will deflect from side to side. This indicates that the electrons flow in one direction when the magnet is moved into the coil, reverse, and flow in the opposite direction when the magnet is withdrawn. This is alternating current (AC).

AC is most commonly generated by a rotary generator in which a conductor, in the form of a coil, or coils, is rotated within a magnetic field. The changing value of the voltage, as the coil is rotated, starts at zero, rises to a peak, then drops back to zero. As the coil continues to rotate, the voltage increases in the opposite direction to a peak and then drops back to zero. There is one complete cycle of voltage change for each complete revolution of the coil.

The wave form of AC (voltage produced by a rotary generator) is called a sine wave. The voltage or current changes according to the sine of the angle through which the generator is rotated.

The sine of an angle is the relationship between the length of the hypotenuse of a right triangle to the length of the side opposite the angle. When the coil is in position A (figure 3-3), it does not cut any lines of flux as it moves, and no voltage is generated. This is the zero-degree angle.

Figure 3-1. Transformers are used to change the values of alternating current and voltage.

As the coil rotates through 45° (point B), it cuts some lines of flux, and the voltage generated is 0.707 times the peak voltage. As the coil continues to rotate, it reaches 90° (point C) where it cuts a maximum number of lines of flux, and here produces peak voltage. Further rotation decreases the number of lines of flux cut for each degree of rotation until, at point E, the coil is cutting no flux, and the output is again zero.

Rotation beyond this point brings the opposite side of the coil down through the flux near the south pole of the magnet, and the voltage increases in the opposite direction. The change in voltage is continuous and smooth, and its instantaneous value may be found by multiplying its peak value by the sine of the angle through which the generator has rotated since its zero-voltage position.

C. AC Terms and Values

1. Cycle

A cycle is one complete sequence of voltage or current change, from zero through a positive peak, back to zero, then through a negative peak, and back to zero where it can start over and repeat the cycle.

2. Alternation

An alternation is one half of an AC cycle in which the voltage or current rises from zero to a peak and back to zero.

3. Period

The time required for one cycle to occur is known as the period.

4. Frequency

The number of complete cycles per second is the frequency and is expressed in hertz. One hertz is one cycle per second. The frequency of the AC produced by a generator is determined by the number of pairs of magnetic poles in the generator and the speed in revolutions per minute of the rotating coils. Frequency may be found by the formula:

$$\text{Frequency (Hz)} = \frac{\text{Poles}}{2} \times \frac{\text{RPM}}{60}$$

The frequency of commercial alternating current in the U.S.A. is 60 Hz, while in some foreign countries it is 50 Hz. The AC used in most aircraft is 400 Hz.

5. Phase

In a DC circuit, a change in the voltage will cause an immediate change in the current, and so the voltage and current are said to be in phase.

In AC where the values are constantly changing, certain circuit components cause a phase shift between the voltage and the current. When some components cause the current to change before the voltage changes, the current is said to lead the voltage. When

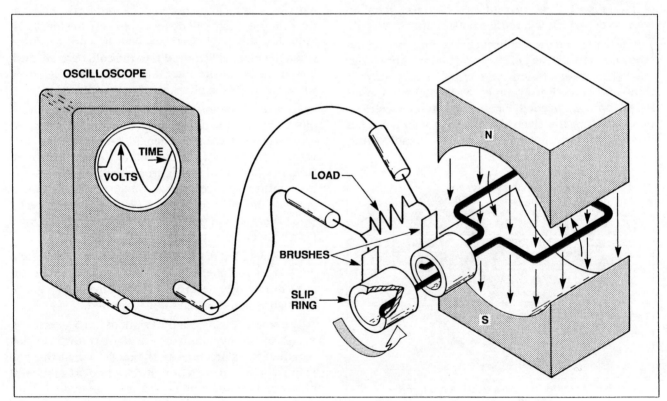

Figure 3-2. Alternating current is produced in a conductor when it is rotated within a magnetic field.

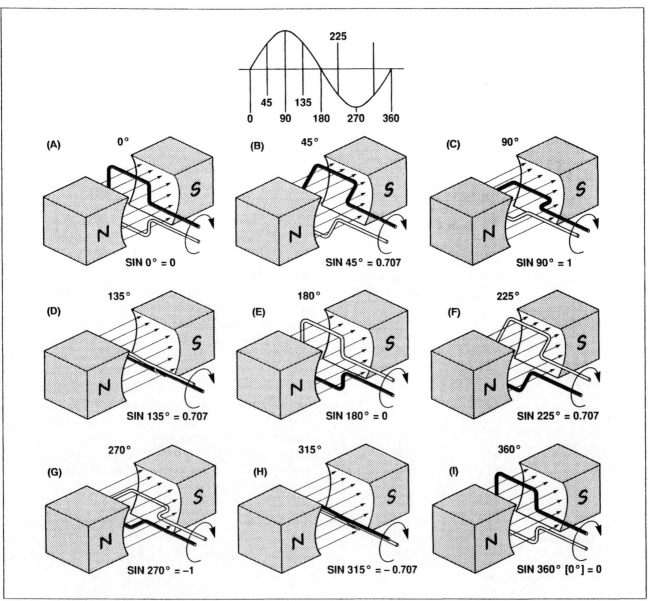

Figure 3-3. Production of sine wave AC.

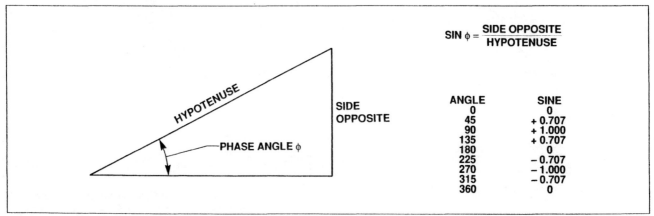

$$\text{SIN } \phi = \frac{\text{SIDE OPPOSITE}}{\text{HYPOTENUSE}}$$

ANGLE	SINE
0	0
45	+ 0.707
90	+ 1.000
135	+ 0.707
180	0
225	− 0.707
270	− 1.000
315	− 0.707
360	0

Figure 3-4. The sine of the phase angle is the ratio of the length of the side opposite the angle to the length of the hypotenuse.

other components cause the voltage to change before the current, the current is then said to lag the voltage.

6. Power

a. Apparent Power

In DC, electrical power is the product of the voltage and current and is measured in watts. In AC, the current is not necessarily in phase with the voltage; the product of the voltage and current is the apparent power and is expressed in volt-amps rather than in watts.

If the current is in phase with the voltage, we have the condition seen in figure 3-7. The power developed at any instant is the product of the voltage and the current, and as long as the voltage and the current are in phase, the power will be positive; that is, the generator is supplying power to the load. Remember, when multiplying signed numbers

having like signs, whether positive or negative, the product will be positive.

b. True Power

If the current and the voltage are not continually in phase; that is, if the current either leads or lags the voltage, there will be at least part of the cycle in which the voltage is positive while the current is negative. The product of unlike signed numbers is always negative and the power that is produced during this portion of the cycle is negative power; that is, the load will be forcing power back into the generator.

True power is expressed in watts and is the product of the voltage and only that portion of the current that is in phase with the voltage.

c. Power Factor

"Power factor" is a term used to indicate the amount of the current that is in phase with the voltage, and it may be found as the ratio between the true power and the apparent power. If the power factor is 0.5, only 50% of the current is in phase with the voltage. If all of the current is in phase with the voltage, as it is in a circuit having no opposition other than resistance, the power factor will be 1.0.

If the amount of phase shift between the voltage and the current is known, we can find the power factor, as it is the cosine of the phase angle. In a right triangle, the ratio of the length of the side adjacent the phase angle to the length of the hypotenuse is the cosine of the angle.

When the current and the voltage are in phase, or the phase angle is zero, the side adjacent the 0° angle and the hypotenuse are the same length, and so the

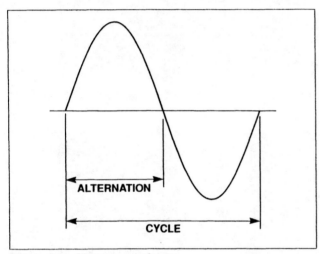

Figure 3-5. *Sine wave values.*

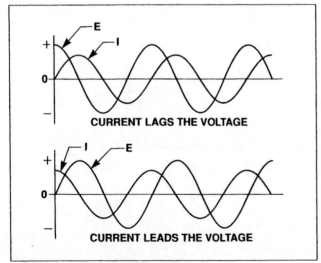

Figure 3-6. *Phase relationship between current and voltage in an AC circuit.*

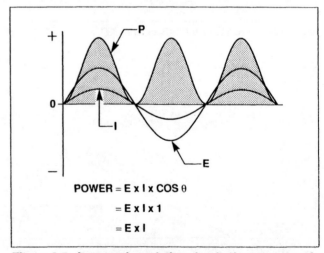

$$POWER = E \times I \times COS\ \theta$$
$$= E \times I \times 1$$
$$= E \times I$$

Figure 3-7. *In a purely resistive circuit, the current and the voltage are in phase (the phase angle is zero). The power is the product of the current and the voltage.*

34

ratio is 1.00. The real power is equal to the apparent power.

For a 45° phase angle, the length of the side adjacent (the true power) will be only 0.707 as long as the hypotenuse (the apparent power).

When the current and the voltage are 60° out of phase, the true power is only 0.50 as much as the apparent power. If the current and voltage are 90° out of phase, the adjacent side will have a length of zero, and the power factor will also be zero. There can be no real power produced in the circuit, even though voltage is present and current is flowing.

The true power in a circuit is found by multiplying the product of the voltage and the current by the power factor.

Power (watts) = E × I × power factor

Circuits that have inductive or capacitive reactance as the chief opposition to the current flow have very low power factors and low current flows. Very little true power is produced.

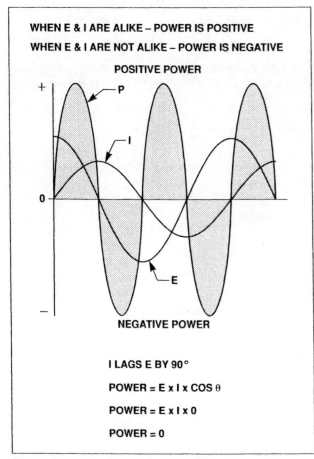

Figure 3-8. The negative power equals the positive power when the current and the voltage are 90° out of phase.

7. Sine Wave Values

a. Peak Value

This is the maximum value of voltage or current in either the positive or the negative direction.

b. Peak-to-peak Value

This is the maximum difference between the positive and the negative peak values of alternating voltage or current and is equal to two times the peak value.

c. Average Value

If all of the instantaneous values of current or voltage in one alternation or half-cycle of sine wave AC are averaged together, they will have a value of 0.637 times the peak value. The average value has very little practical use.

d. Effective Value

If we square all of the instantaneous values of voltage or current in one alternation and find the average of these squared values, then take the square root of this average, we will have the root-mean-square, or rms, value of the sine wave. This value is 0.707 of the peak value and is equal to the amount of direct current required to produce the same amount of heat the peak value of AC will produce.

We can see that 70.7 volts of DC will force enough current through a circuit to produce the same amount of heat as sine wave AC having a peak value

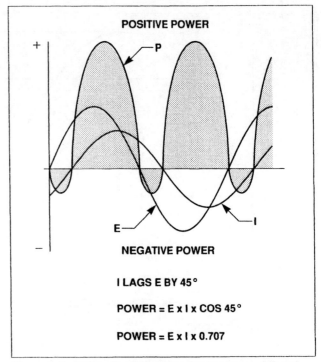

Figure 3-9. When the voltage and current are 45° out of phase, the true power is 0.707 times the apparent power.

35

of 100 volts. For this reason, the rms value of AC is called its effective value.

D. Inductance

When current flows in a conductor, a magnetic field surrounds it and the strength of the field is determined by the amount of current flow. The direction of the lines of flux around the conductor may be found by the left-hand rule for generators, which states that if the conductor is held in the left hand so that the thumb points in the direction of electron flow (from the negative to the positive terminal of the source), the fingers will encircle the conductor in the direction of the lines of flux.

As the amount of current flow changes, the magnetic field expands or contracts. As it does, the flux cuts across the conductor and induces a voltage into it. According to Lenz's law, the voltage that is induced into the conductor is of such a polarity that it opposes the change that caused it. For example, as the voltage begins to rise and the current increases, the expanding lines of flux cut across the conductor and induce a voltage into it that opposes, or slows the rise.

When the current flow in the conductor is constant, lines of flux surround it, and since there is no change in the amount of current, these lines do not cut across the conductor, and so there is no voltage induced. When the current decreases, the lines of flux cut across the conductor as they collapse, and induce a voltage that opposes the decrease.

When a conductor carries AC, both the amount and the direction of the current continually change, so an opposing voltage is constantly induced into the conductor. This induced voltage acts as an opposition to the flow of current.

1. Factors Affecting Inductance

Inductance opposes a change in current by the generation of a back voltage, and all conductors have the characteristic of inductance, since they all generate back voltage any time the current flowing in them changes.

The amount of inductance is increased by anything that concentrates the lines of flux or causes more of the flux to cut across the conductor. If the conductor is a coil, the lines of flux surrounding any one of the turns cut not only across the conductor itself, but also across each of its turns, and generates a greater induced current to oppose the source current.

If a soft iron core is inserted into the coil, it will further concentrate the lines of flux and cause a still higher induced current, which allows less source current to flow.

2. Mutual Inductance

When AC flows in a conductor, the changing lines of flux radiate out and cut across any other conductor

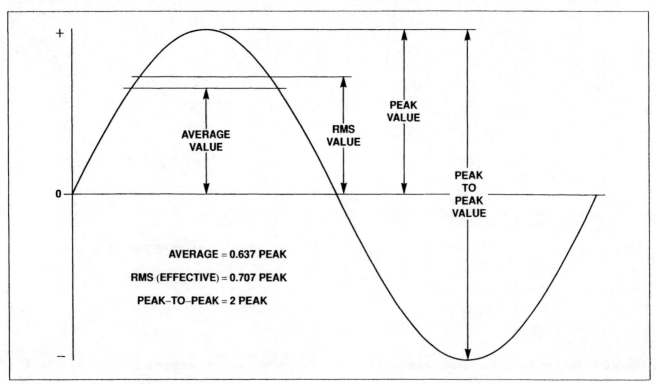

AVERAGE = 0.637 PEAK

RMS (EFFECTIVE) = 0.707 PEAK

PEAK–TO–PEAK = 2 PEAK

Figure 3-10. Values of sine wave AC.

that is nearby. As they cut across a conductor, they generate a voltage in it even though there is no electrical connection between the two. This voltage is said to be generated by electromagnetic induction (mutual inductance), the basis for transformer action, that is so important in AC as it allows the values of AC voltage and current to be changed.

Consider two coils of wire, a primary and a secondary, wound around a common core, but not connected electrically.

When an alternating current flows in the primary, a voltage will be induced into the secondary, and current will flow in it.

The amount of voltage generated in the secondary winding of a transformer is equal to the voltage in the primary, times the turns ratio between the primary and the secondary windings. For example, if there are 100 turns in the primary winding and 1,000 turns in the secondary, we have a turns ratio of 1:10, and if there are 115 volts across the primary, there will be 1,150 volts across the secondary. A transformer does not generate any power, so the

product of the voltage and the current in the secondary must be the same as that in the primary. Because of this, there must be a flow of 1 ampere in the primary winding to produce a flow of 100 milliamps in the secondary.

E. Capacitance

Electrical energy may be stored in the magnetic field which surrounds a conductor through which electrons are moving. It may also be stored in electrostatic fields caused by an accumulation of electrical charges that are not moving, but are static. The electromagnetic field strength is determined by the amount of current flowing in the conductor, but the strength of the electrostatic field is determined by the amount of pressure (voltage) on the static charges.

A capacitor, sometimes called a condenser, is a device that stores electrical energy in the electrostatic fields that exist between two conductors that are separated by an insulator (dielectric).

In figure 3-14, we have two flat metal plates arranged so they face each other, but are separated by an insulator. One of the plates is attached to the positive terminal of the power source and the other to the negative terminal. When the switch is closed, electrons will be drawn from the plate attached to the positive terminal and will flow to the plate attached to the negative. There can be no flow across the insulator, but the plates will become charged. If the voltmeter reading were taken across points C and D, it would be found to be exactly the same as that taken across points A and B. Current flow would be indicated by the ammeter during the time the plates are being charged, but when they become fully charged, no more current will flow.

1. Factors Affecting Capacitance

A capacitor is a device to store an electrical charge. The capacity is affected by three variables: the area of the plates, the separation between the plates, and the dielectric constant of the material between the plates.

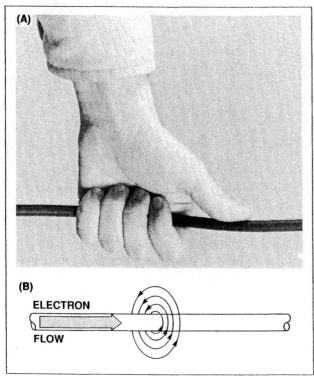

Figure 3-11.
   (A)   *When a conductor is grasped by the left hand with the thumb pointing in the direction of electron flow, from negative to positive, the fingers will encircle the conductor in the same direction as the lines of magnetic flux.*
   (B)   *The relationship between the direction of electron flow and the lines of magnetic flux.*

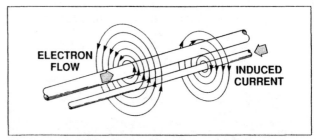

Figure 3-12. *Mutual induction causes a voltage to be induced into a conductor not electrically connected to the conductor through which the source current flows.*

The larger the plates, the more electrons can be stored. One very common type of capacitor has plates made of two long strips of metal foil separated by waxed paper and rolled into a tight cylinder. This construction provides the maximum plate area for its small physical size.

The distance the plates are apart determines the strength of the electrostatic field between them, and this affects the capacity. If the plates are widely separated, the field will be weak, and it will not pull very many electrons onto the negative plate. If, on the other hand, they are very close together, the attraction caused by the unlike charges will produce a very strong field in the dielectric; and many electrons will be held on the negative plate. The strength of the electrostatic field increases inversely as the separation between the plates. When the space between the plates is cut in half, the strength of the electrostatic field will double.

One problem with getting the plates too close together is the possibility of the field becoming so strong that electrons will be pulled across the insulator and actually flow to the positive plate. When this happens, in most capacitors, the dielectric will be damaged and a conductive path set up, shorting the capacitor and making it useless. For this reason, all capacitors are rated with regard to their working

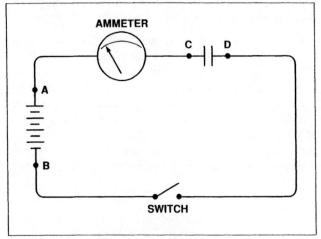

Figure 3-14. Current flows only when the capacitor is charging or discharging.

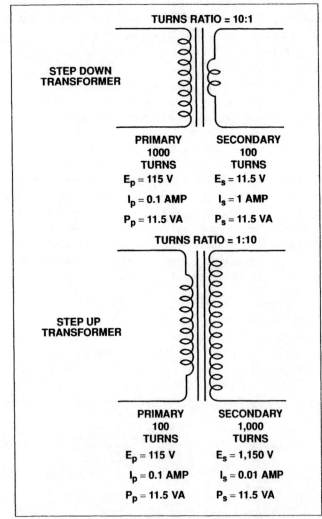

Figure 3-13. Voltage increases directly as the turns ratio between the primary and secondary windings or a transformer, while the current decreases in proportion to the turns ratio.

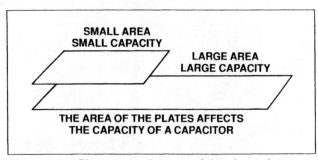

Figure 3-15. The greater the area of the plates the greater will be the capacity of the capacitor.

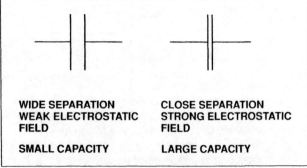

Figure 3-16. The closer the plates of the capacitor the greater will be the capacity.

voltage, which is a DC measurement indicating the strength of the dielectric.

The third factor which affects the capacity of a capacitor is the material of the dielectric. More specifically, it is the dielectric constant of the insulating material. Energy is stored not only in the stress across the dielectric, but by the distortion of the orbits of the electrons in the material of which the dielectric is made. Air is used as the reference for measuring the dielectric constant and it is given a value of 1. If glass, which has a dielectric constant of 8, is substituted for air as an insulator, the capacity will increase 8 times because of the energy stored in the distortion of the electron orbits within the glass.

F. Converting AC into DC

It is often necessary to convert AC into DC to power various circuits in the aircraft, and within electronics equipment. The conversion of AC to DC is accomplished by a circuit referred to as a rectifier. Rectifier circuits employ vacuum tube or solid-state diodes, which allow current flow in only one direction.

1. The Diode Rectifier

There have been a number of different types of rectifiers used to change AC into DC. All of these devices are simply electron check-valves that allow electrons to pass in one direction, but block them when they attempt to flow in the opposite direction.

a. The Vacuum Tube

Inside the glass envelope of a vacuum tube is an electrode called the cathode. When it is heated with a small electric heater, the electrons in its material loosen their bond and are attracted to the plate during the half-cycle of the AC when the plate is positive. During this half-cycle, the current can flow, but during the half-cycle when the plate is negative, the electrons are forced back to the cathode and no current flows.

This type of rectifier has been used for many years, but its large size and the need for an electric heater have caused it to be replaced by the more modern solid-state diode.

b. The Solid-state Diode

Solid-state electronics ushered in a revolution in communications, control, and in almost all aspects of electricity. One small piece of an insulating material such as germanium or silicon is "doped" with an element having an excess of electrons and is called an N material. Another piece of the same material is doped with an element having a deficiency of electrons, and this is called the P material. These two pieces are fused together and act as a check

valve. Electrons can easily pass from the N material to the P, but they cannot flow from the P to the N.

2. Half-wave Rectifier

A half-wave rectifier circuit uses a single diode in series with the voltage source (secondary of the transformer in figure 3-18) and the load. Electrons can flow only during the half-cycle when the cathode, represented by the bar across the arrowhead, is negative. The output waveform of this type of rectifier is $\frac{1}{2}$ of the AC wave, and because of this, it is a very inefficient type of circuit.

3. Full-wave Rectifier

In order to change both halves of the AC cycle into DC, we can use a transformer with a center-tapped secondary winding and two diodes.

To simplify tracing the flow through the solid-state diodes, we follow the flow of *conventional* current, which is from the positive side of the source, through the load to the negative side.

Conventional current, whose direction is opposite that of electron flow, follows the direction of the arrowheads in the diode symbols.

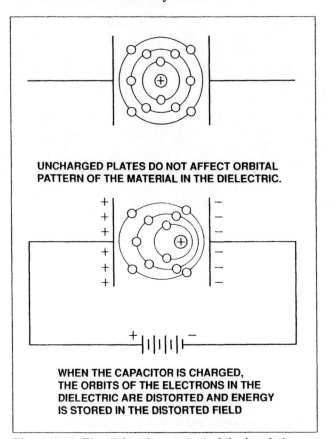

UNCHARGED PLATES DO NOT AFFECT ORBITAL PATTERN OF THE MATERIAL IN THE DIELECTRIC.

WHEN THE CAPACITOR IS CHARGED, THE ORBITS OF THE ELECTRONS IN THE DIELECTRIC ARE DISTORTED AND ENERGY IS STORED IN THE DISTORTED FIELD

Figure 3-17. The dielectric constant of the insulation between the plates of a capacitor determines its capacity. Energy is stored in the stress of the dielectric.

During the half-cycle, when the top of the secondary winding is positive, current flows through diode D_1, and passes through the load from the top to the bottom. This causes the top of the load to be positive. After leaving the load, the current flows into the secondary winding at the center tap which is negative during this half-cycle.

During the next half-cycle, the bottom of the secondary winding will be positive and the center tap

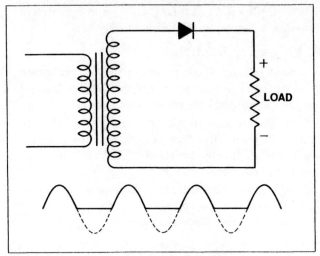

Figure 3-18. A semiconductor diode half-wave rectifier with its output waveform.

will be negative with respect to the bottom. Current will flow through diode D_2 and through the load resistor in the same direction it passed during the first half-cycle. The output waveform is pulsating direct current, whose frequency is twice that of the pulsating DC produced by a half-wave rectifier.

4. Bridge-type, Full-wave Rectifier

The 2-diode, full-wave rectifier requires a transformer that will give the desired output voltage across just ½ of the secondary winding. This is inefficient, and may be overcome by the bridge-type full-wave rectifier, in which we use the entire secondary winding and four diodes instead of two.

During the half-cycle when the top of the transformer secondary is positive, the current flows through diode D_1 and through the load resistor from the right to the left, then down through diode D_2 and back to the bottom of the secondary winding, which is negative. During the next half-cycle, the polarity of the secondary has reversed, and current flows through diode D_4, through the load in the same direction as before, up through diode D_3 to the top side of the transformer, which is negative. The output waveform is similar to that produced by the 2-diode full-wave rectifier, but the voltage is higher because the entire secondary winding is used.

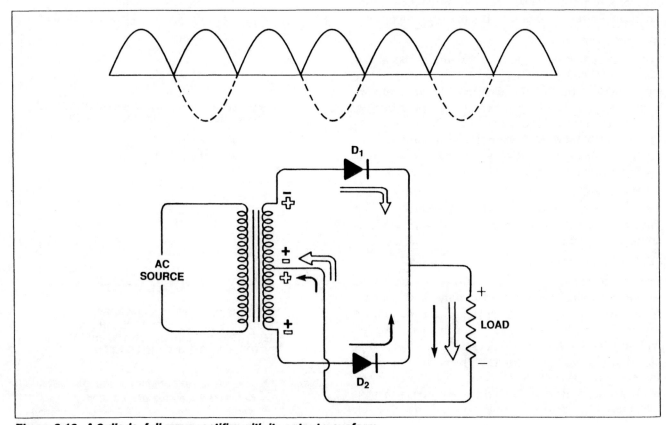

Figure 3-19. A 2-diode, full-wave rectifier with its output waveform.

40

5. Full-wave, 3-phase Rectifier

The most familiar 6-diode, 3-phase full-wave rectifier is the one found in the DC alternator, which has rapidly replaced the generator as a device for producing direct current electricity for our modern aircraft. This alternator uses a 3-phase stator and 6 silicon diodes.

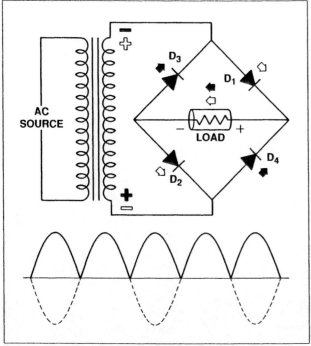

Figure 3-20. A 4-diode, bridge-type, full-wave rectifier with its output waveform.

To examine the current flow through the load resistor for one complete cycle of all three phases, we utilize conventional current, which is opposite electron flow, but follows the direction indicated by the arrowheads in the diode symbols.

In that portion of the cycle when the output end of phase A is positive, current leaves it and flows through diode D_1 down through the load, making its top end positive. After leaving the load, current flows through diode D_2 and coil C, whose output lead is negative.

As the alternator field rotates, it causes the output end of the coil B to become positive and the output of coil A to be negative. Current flows out of B, through diode D_3, the load, diode D_4, and back through coil A.

Continued rotation causes the output of coil C to be positive and B to be negative. The current leaves C, passes through diode D_5, the load, diode D_6 and back into coil B.

The output waveform of this rectifier gives a very steady direct current as the current from the three phases overlaps. There is never a time when the current drops to zero.

G. Changing DC to AC

Often, it is necessary to change DC to AC. For example, many aircraft require alternating current to power equipment such as flight instruments, navigation receivers, etc. During an emergency, when normal aircraft power is not available, power is taken from the battery to operate all electrical

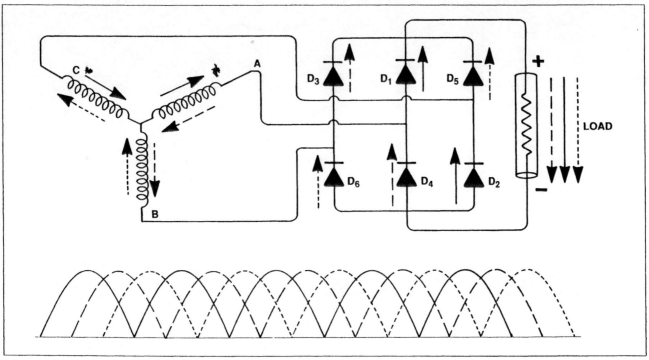

Figure 3-21. 3-phase, 6-diode, full-wave rectifier and its output waveform.

loads. Since batteries are capable of only storing DC, a means must be provided to change DC to AC.

The device used to change DC to AC is the inverter. Inverters may be either of two distinct types: the rotary inverter or the static inverter. Rotary inverters are essentially DC motors driving an AC generator. They are powered by a DC source and have AC as an output.

Static inverters are electronic devices containing a specialized circuit known as an oscillator. An oscillator is capable of changing DC to AC through electronics. Oscillators are used in conjunction with amplifiers to produce the correct value of AC from the DC input provided to it. The static inverter has replaced the rotary inverter in most applications, as it is much quieter and more efficient.

Chapter IV

Electrical Generators and Motors

A. DC Generators

Energy for the operation of most electrical equipment in an airplane depends upon the electrical energy supplied by a generator. A generator is any machine which converts mechanical energy into electrical energy by electromagnetic induction. Generators designed to produce alternating current are called AC generators; generators which produce direct current energy are called DC generators.

For airplanes equipped with DC electrical systems, the DC generator may be the regular source of electrical energy. One or more DC generators, driven by the engine(s), supply electrical energy for the operation of all units in the electrical system, as well as energy for charging the battery. Aircraft equipped with AC systems use electrical energy supplied by AC generators, also called alternators.

1. Theory of Operation

After the discovery that an electric current flowing through a conductor creates a magnetic field around the conductor, there was considerable scientific speculation about whether a magnetic field could create a current flow in a conductor. In 1831, English scientist Michael Faraday demonstrated this could be accomplished. This discovery is the basis for the operation of the generator.

When a conductor is moved through a magnetic field (figure 4-1) an electromotive force (emf) is induced in the conductor. The direction (polarity) of the induced emf is determined by the magnetic lines of force and the direction the conductor is moved through the magnetic field.

The left-hand rule for generators (not to be confused with the left-hand rule for coils) can be used to determine the direction of the induced emf (figure 4-2). The first finger of the left hand is pointed in the direction of the magnetic lines of force (north to south), the thumb is pointed in the direction of movement of the conductor through the magnetic field, and the second finger points in the direction of the induced emf. When two of these three factors are known, the third may be determined by the use of this rule.

When a loop conductor is rotated in a magnetic field (figure 4-3), a voltage is induced in each side of the loop. The two sides cut the magnetic field in opposite directions, and although the current flow is continuous, it moves in opposite directions with

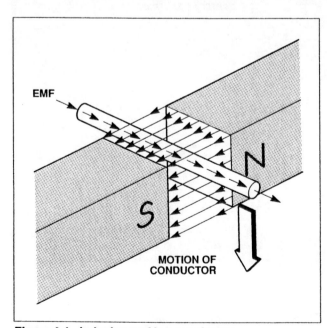

Figure 4-1. Inducing emf in a conductor.

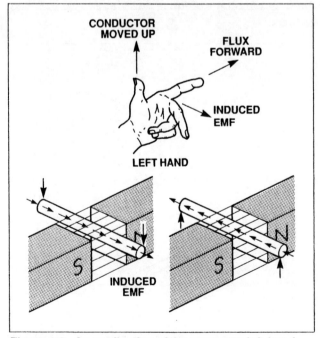

Figure 4-2. An application of the generator left-hand rule.

respect to the two sides of the loop. If sides A and B of the loop are rotated half a turn, so that the sides of the conductor have exchanged positions, the induced emf in each wire reverses its direction. This is because the wire formerly cutting the lines of force in an upward direction is now moving downward.

The value of an induced emf depends upon three factors:

1) The number of wires moving through the magnetic field.
2) The strength of the magnetic field.
3) The speed of rotation.

A simple generator is illustrated in figure 4-4, together with the components of an external generator circuit which collect and use the energy produced by the generator. The loop of wire (A and B of figure 4-4) is arranged to rotate in a magnetic field. When the plane of the loop of wire is parallel to the magnetic lines of force, the voltage induced in the loop causes a current to flow in the direction indicated by the arrows. The voltage induced at this position is maximum, since the wires are cutting the lines of force at right angles and thus are cutting more lines of force per second than in any other position relative to the magnetic field.

As the loop approaches the vertical position (figure 4-5), the induced voltage decreases because both sides of the loop (A and B) are approximately parallel to the lines of force and the rate of cutting is reduced. When the loop is vertical, no lines of force are cut since the wires are momentarily traveling parallel to the magnetic lines of force, and there is no induced voltage.

As the rotation of the loop continues, the lines of force cut increases until the loop has rotated an additional 90° to a horizontal plane. As shown in figure 4-6, the lines of force cut and the induced voltage once again are maximum. The direction of cutting, however, is in the opposite direction to that occurring in figure 4-5, so the direction (polarity) of the induced voltage is reversed.

As rotation of the loop continues, the lines of force being cut again decreases, and the induced voltage becomes zero at the position shown in figure 4-7,

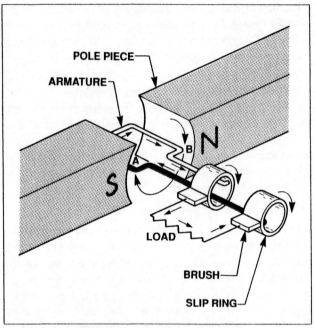

Figure 4-4. Inducing maximum voltage in an elementary generator.

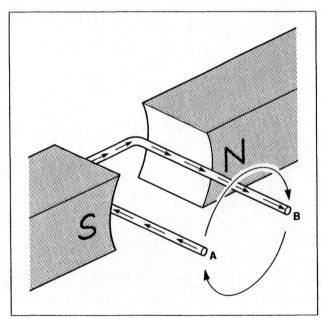

Figure 4-3. Voltage induced in a loop.

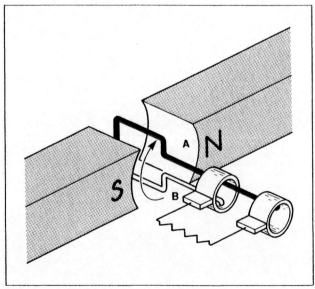

Figure 4-5. Inducing minimum voltage in an elementary generator.

since the wires A and B are again parallel to the magnetic lines of force.

If the voltage induced throughout the entire 360° of rotation is plotted, the curve shown in figure 4-8 results. The output of a loop rotating in a magnetic field is alternating current. By replacing the slip rings of the basic AC generator with two half-cylinders (called a commutator), a basic DC generator (figure 4-9) is obtained. In this illustration, the black side of the coil is connected to the black segment and the white side of the coil to the white segment. The segments are insulated from each other. The two stationary brushes are placed on opposite sides of the commutator and are mounted so that each brush contacts each segment of the commutator simultaneously as it revolves with the loop. The rotating part of a DC generator (coil and commutator) is called the armature.

Figure 4-10 illustrates the generation of a DC voltage using a commutator. The loop in position A is rotating clockwise, but no lines of force are cut by the coil and no emf is generated. The black brush is shown coming into contact with the black segment of the commutator, and the white brush is just coming into contact with the white segment.

In position B, the flux is being cut at a maximum rate and the induced emf is maximum. The black brush is contacting the black segment and the white brush is contacting the white segment. The deflection of the meter is toward the right, indicating the polarity of the output voltage.

At position C, the loop has completed 180° of rotation. Again, no flux lines are being cut and the output voltage is zero. The black brush at the 180° angle is contacting both black and white segments on one side of the commutator, and the white brush is contacting both segments on the other side of the commutator. After the loop rotates slightly past the

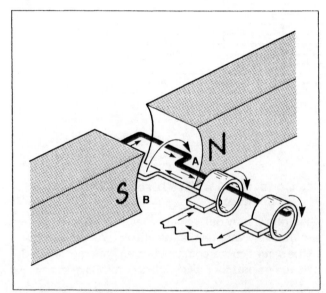

Figure 4-6. Inducing maximum voltage in the opposite direction.

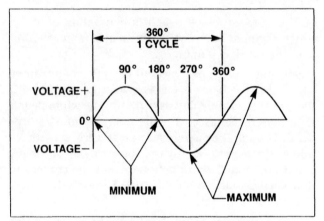

Figure 4-8. Output of an elementary generator.

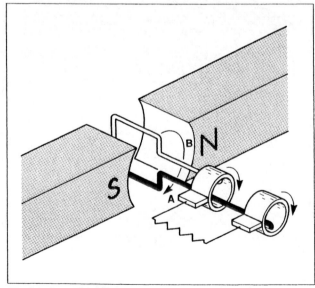

Figure 4-7. Inducing a minimum voltage in the opposite direction.

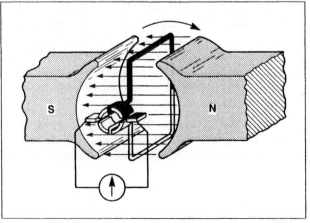

Figure 4-9. Basic DC generator.

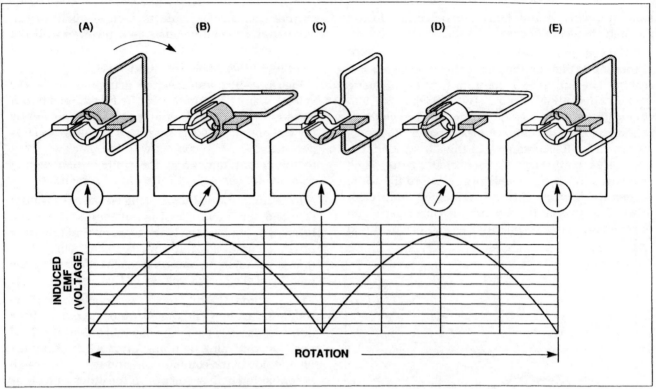

Figure 4-10. Operation of a basic DC generator.

180° point, the black brush is contacting only the white segment and the white brush is contacting only the black segment.

Because of this switching of commutator electrodes, the black brush is always in contact with the coil side moving downward, and the white brush is always in contact with the coil side moving upward. Though the current actually reverses its direction in the loop in exactly the same way as in the AC generator, commutator action causes the current to flow always in the same direction through the external circuit or meter.

The voltage generated by the basic DC generator varies from zero to its maximum twice for each revolution of the loop. This variation of DC voltage is called "ripple", and may be reduced by using two or more loops, or coils as shown in A of figure 4-11. As the number of loops is increased, the variation between maximum and minimum values of voltage is reduced, and the output voltage of the generator approaches a steady DC value.

The number of commutator segments is increased in direct proportion to the number of loops; that is, there are 2 segments for 1 loop, 4 segments for 2 loops, etc.

Increasing the number of loops does not increase the maximum value of the generated voltage, but increasing the number of turns in each loop will.

2. Construction Features of DC Generators

Generators may differ somewhat in design, since they are made by various manufacturers. All, however, are of the same general construction and operate similarly. The major parts, or assemblies of a DC generator are

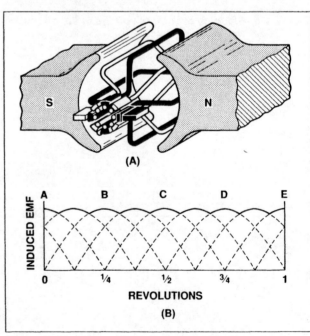

Figure 4-11. Increasing the number of coils reduces the ripple in the voltage.

46

a field frame, a rotating armature, and a brush assembly. The parts of a typical aircraft generator are shown in figure 4-12.

a. Field Frame

The field frame (also called the yoke) constitutes the foundation for the generator. The frame has two functions: It completes the magnetic circuit between the poles and acts as a mechanical support for the other parts of the generator. In A of figure 4-13, the frame for a 2-pole generator is shown in cross-section. A 4-pole generator frame is shown in B of the same figure.

In small generators, the frame is made of one piece of iron, but in larger generators, it is usually made of two parts bolted together. The frame, together with the pole pieces, forms the major part of the magnetic circuit. The field poles (pole shoes) (figure 4-13) are bolted to the inside of the frame and form a core on which the field coil windings are mounted. The poles are laminated to reduce eddy current losses and serve the same purpose as the iron core of an electromagnet; that is, they concentrate the lines of force produced by the field coils. The entire frame,

including the field poles, is made from high quality magnetic iron or sheet steel.

A practical DC generator uses electromagnets instead of permanent magnets. To produce a magnetic field of the necessary strength with permanent magnets would greatly increase the physical size of the generator.

The field coils are made of many turns of insulated wire and wound on a form which fits over the iron core of the pole shoe to which it is securely fastened (figure 4-14). The exciting current, which is used to produce the magnetic field and which flows through the field coils, is obtained from an external source or from the current generated by the unit itself. No electrical connection exists between the windings of the field coils and the pole pieces.

Most field coils are connected in such a manner that the poles show alternate polarity. Since there is always one north pole for each south pole, there must always be an even number of poles in any generator.

Note that the pole pieces (figure 4-13) project from the frame. Because air offers a great amount of

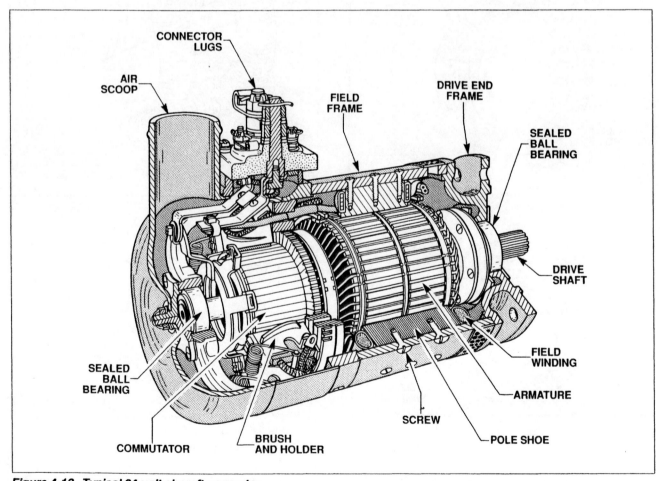

Figure 4-12. Typical 24-volt aircraft generator.

reluctance to the magnetic field, this design reduces the length of the air gap between the poles and the rotating armature and increases the efficiency of the generator. When the pole pieces are made to project (figure 4-13), they are called salient poles.

b. Armature

The armature assembly consists of armature coils wound on an iron core, a commutator, and associated mechanical parts. Mounted on a shaft which rotates in bearings located in the end frames of the generator, the armature rotates through the magnetic field produced by the field coils. The core of the armature acts as an iron conductor in the magnetic field and, for this reason, is laminated to prevent the circulation of eddy currents.

A drum-type armature (figure 4-15) has coils placed in slots in the core, but there is no electrical connection between the coils and core. The use of slots increases the mechanical safety of the armature. Usually, the coils are held in place in the slots by means of wooden

or fiber wedges. The coil ends are brought out to individual segments of the commutator.

c. Commutators

Figure 4-16 shows a cross-sectional view of a typical commutator. The commutator is located at the end of the armature and consists of wedge-shaped segments of hard-drawn copper, insulated from each other by thin sheets of mica. The segments are held in place by steel V-rings or clamping flanges fitted with bolts. Rings of mica insulate the segments from the flanges. The raised portion of each segment is called a riser, and the leads from the armature coils are soldered to the risers. When the segments have no risers, the leads are soldered to short slits in the ends of the segments.

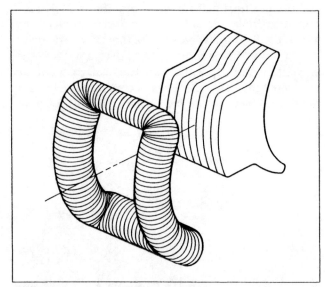

Figure 4-14. A field coil removed from a field shoe.

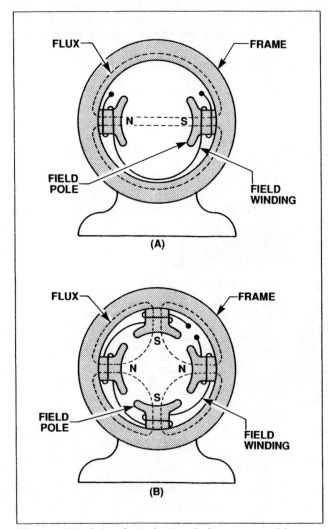

Figure 4-13. A 2-pole and a 4-pole frame assembly.

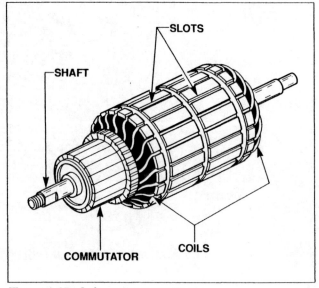

Figure 4-15. A drum-type armature.

One end of a coil attaches to one bar and the other end is soldered to the adjacent bar. Each coil laps over the preceding one. This method is called lap winding and is illustrated in figure 4-17.

The brushes ride on the surface of the commutator, forming the electrical contact between the armature coils and the external circuit. A flexible, braided-copper conductor, commonly called a pig-tail, connects each brush to the external circuit. The brushes, usually made of high-grade carbon and held in place by brush holders insulated from the frame, are free to slide up and down in their holders in order to follow any irregularities in the surface of the commutator. The brushes are usually adjustable so that the pressure of the brushes on the commutator can be varied

and the position of the brushes with respect to the segments can be adjusted.

The constant making and breaking of connections to the coils in which voltage is being induced necessitates the use of material for brushes which has a definite contact resistance. Also, this material must be such that the friction is low, to prevent excessive wear. The high-grade carbon used in the manufacture of brushes must be soft enough to prevent undue wear of the commutator and yet hard enough to provide reasonable brush life, and since the contact resistance of carbon is fairly high, the brush must be quite large to provide a large area of contact. The commutator surface is highly polished to reduce friction as much as possible. Oil or grease must never be used on a commutator, and extreme care must be used when cleaning it to avoid marring or scratching the surface.

3. Types of DC Generators

There are three types of DC generators: series-wound, shunt-wound, and shunt-series or compound-wound. The difference in type depends on the relationship of the field winding to the external circuit. Since the series-wound generator has such poor regulation, it is never employed as an airplane generator. Generators in airplanes have field windings which are connected either in shunt or in compound.

A summary of the characteristics of the various types of generators is shown graphically in figure 4-19.

a. Starter-generators

Most small turbine engines are equipped with starter-generators rather than separate starters and

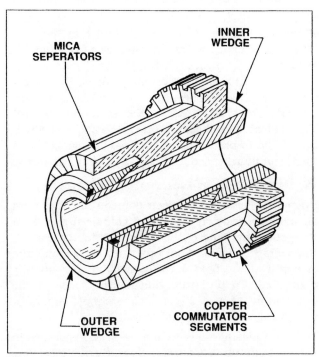

Figure 4-16. *Commutator with portion removed to show construction.*

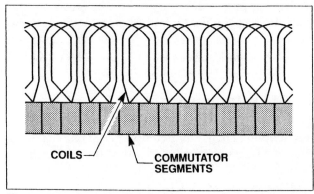

Figure 4-17. *Lap winding connects one end of two coils to each commutator segment and the ends of each coil to adjacent segments.*

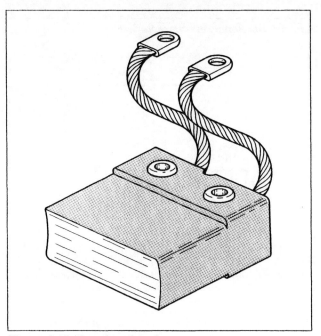

Figure 4-18. *A carbon brush.*

49

generators. This provides an appreciable weight saving, as both starters and generators are quite heavy and they are never used at the same time.

The armature of a starter-generator is splined to fit into a drive pad on the engine, rather than being connected through a clutch and drive jaws as starters are.

Starter-generators are equipped with two or three sets of field winding. The generator circuit consists of the armature, a series field around the interpoles and a shunt field for generator control. A series motor field is wound around the pole shoes inside the field frame.

For starting, current flows from the battery or external power unit through the series winding and the armature. As soon as the engine starts, the start

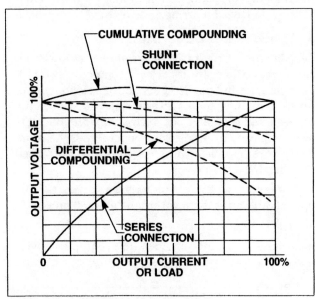

Figure 4-19. Generator characteristics.

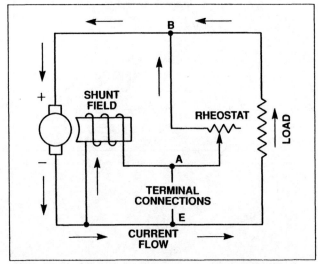

Figure 4-20. Regulation of generator voltage by field rheostat.

relay disconnects this winding and connects the generator circuit to the aircraft electrical system.

4. Generator Ratings

A generator is rated in power output. Since a generator is designed to operate at a specified voltage, the rating is usually given as the number of amperes the generator can safely supply at its rated voltage. Generator rating and performance data are stamped on the name plate attached to the generator.

The rotation of generators is termed either clockwise or counterclockwise, as viewed from the driven end. Usually, the direction of rotation is stamped on the data plate. If no direction is stamped on the data plate, the rotation may be marked by an arrow on the cover plate of the brush housing. It is important that a generator with the correct direction of rotation be used; otherwise the polarity will be reversed.

The speed of an aircraft engine varies from idle RPM to takeoff RPM; however, during the major portion of a flight, it is at a constant cruising speed. The generator drive is usually geared to revolve the generator between 1⅛ and 1½ times the engine crankshaft speed. Most aircraft generators have a speed at which they begin to produce their normal voltage. Termed the "coming-in" speed, it is usually about 1,500 RPM.

5. Regulation of Generator Voltage

Efficient operation of electrical equipment in an airplane depends on a constant voltage supply from the generator. Among the factors which determine the voltage output of a generator, only one, the strength of the field current, can be conveniently controlled. To illustrate this control refer to the diagram in figure 4-20 showing a simple generator with a rheostat in the field circuit.

If the rheostat is set to increase the resistance in the field circuit, less current flows through the field winding and the strength of the magnetic field in which the armature rotates decreases. Consequently, the output of the generator decreases. If the resistance in the field circuit is decreased with the rheostat, more current flows through the field windings, the magnetic field becomes stronger, and the generator produces a greater voltage.

B. DC Alternators

Two of the limitations of DC generators for aircraft installations are the limited number of pairs of poles that can be used, and the fact that the load current is produced in the rotating member and must be brought out of the generator through the brushes.

DC alternators solve these two problems, and since they produce 3-phase AC and convert it into

DC with built-in solid-state rectifiers, their output at low engine speed allows them to keep the battery charged even when the aircraft is required to operate on the ground with the engine idling as it must often do when waiting for clearance to takeoff.

1. DC Alternators

DC alternators do exactly the same thing as DC generators. They produce AC and convert it into DC before it leaves the device. The difference being that in an alternator, field current is taken into the rotor through brushes which ride on smooth slip rings. The AC load current is produced in the fixed windings of the stator, and after it is rectified by 6 solid-state diodes it is brought out of the alternator through solid connections.

a. The Rotor

The rotor of an alternator consists of a coil of wire wound on an iron spool between two heavy iron segments that have interlacing fingers around their periphery. Some rotors have four fingers and others have as many as eight. Each finger forms one pole of the rotating magnetic field.

The two ends of the coil pass through one of the segments and each end of the coil is attached to an insulated slip ring. The slip rings, segments, and coil spool are all pressed onto a hardened steel rotor shaft which is either splined or has a key slot machined in it. This shaft can be driven from an engine accessory pad or fitted with a pulley and belt driven from an engine drive. The slip-ring end of the shaft is supported in the housing with a needle bearing and the drive end with a ball bearing.

Two carbon brushes ride on the smooth slip rings to bring current into the field and carry it back out to the regulator.

b. The Stator

The stator coils in which the load current is produced are wound in slots around the inside periphery of the stator frame, which is made of thin laminations of soft iron. There are three sets of coils in the stator and these sets are joined into a Y-connection with one end of each set of windings brought out of the stator and attached to the rectifier.

With the stator wound in the 3-phase configuration, there is a peak of current produced in each set of windings every 120° of rotor rotation. The AC produced in the stator looks much like what we see in figure 4-24(A), and after it is rectified by the 3-phase, full-wave rectifier, the DC output is much like that in figure 4-24(B).

The large number of field poles and the equally large number of coils in the stator cause the alternator to put out its rated current at a low alternator RPM.

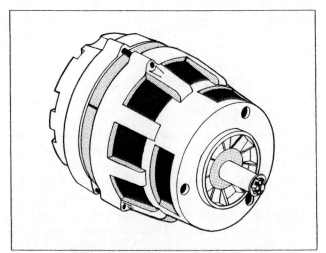

Figure 4-21. DC alternators are used in almost all of the modern aircraft that require a low or medium amount of electrical power.

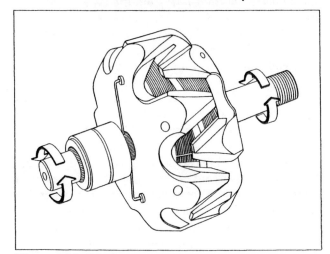

Figure 4-22. DC alternator rotor.

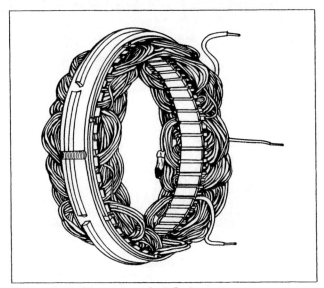

Figure 4-23. The stator of a DC alternator.

c. The Rectifier

The 3-phase, full wave rectifier is made up of 6 heavy-duty silicon diodes of which 3 are pressed into the slip-ring end frame, and the other 3 are pressed into a heat sink that is electrically insulated from the end frame.

In figure 4-25, we see the way this rectifier converts the 3-phase AC output of the stator into DC. Since we are dealing with solid-state devices whose symbols use arrowheads, it is easier to follow the action if we think in terms of conventional current that follows the direction in which the arrows point. This imaginary flow is from positive to negative.

At the instant the output terminal of winding A is positive with respect to the output end of winding C, current flows through diode 1 in the heat sink, through the load, and back through diode 2 that is pressed into the alternator end frame. From this diode, it flows back through winding C. As the rotor continues to turn, winding B becomes positive with respect to winding A and the current flows through diode 3, the load, and back through diode 4 and winding A. Next, C becomes positive with respect to B and current flows out through diode 5 and back through diode 6. In this way, the current flows through the load in the same direction all of the time. The terminal connected to the heat sink is the positive terminal of the alternator and the end frame into

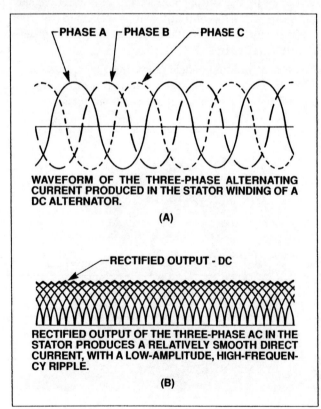

WAVEFORM OF THE THREE-PHASE ALTERNATING CURRENT PRODUCED IN THE STATOR WINDING OF A DC ALTERNATOR.

(A)

RECTIFIED OUTPUT OF THE THREE-PHASE AC IN THE STATOR PRODUCES A RELATIVELY SMOOTH DIRECT CURRENT, WITH A LOW-AMPLITUDE, HIGH-FREQUENCY RIPPLE.

(B)

Figure 4-24. Output of a DC alternator.

which the anodes of diodes 2, 4, and 6 are pressed becomes the negative terminal of the alternator.

2. Alternator Controls

The voltage produced by an alternator is controlled in exactly the same way it is controlled in a generator, by varying the field current. When the voltage rises above the desired value, the field current is decreased and when the voltage drops too low, the field current is increased.

This action may be accomplished in low-output alternators with vibrator-type controls which interrupt the field current by opening the contacts. A much more efficient means of voltage control has been devised which uses a transistor to control flow of field current.

The transistorized voltage regulator utilizes both vibrating points and transistors for voltage control. The vibrating points operate in exactly the same way they do in a normal vibrator-type voltage regulator, but instead of the field current flowing through the contacts, only the transistor base current flows through them. This is so small compared with the field current which flows through the emitter-collector portion of the transistor that there is no arcing at the contacts. A simplified schematic of this circuit is shown in figure 4-26.

The transistorized voltage regulator is a step in the right direction, but semiconductor devices may be used to replace all of the moving parts and a completely solid-state voltage regulator may be built. These units are very efficient, reliable, and generally have no serviceable components. If the unit is defective it will be removed and replaced with a new one.

Alternator control requirements are different from those of a generator for several reasons. An alternator uses solid-state diodes for its rectifier and since current cannot flow from the battery into the alternator, there is no need for a reverse-current cutout relay. The field of an alternator is excited from the system bus, whose voltage is limited either by the battery or by the voltage regulator, so there is no possibility of the alternator putting out enough current to burn itself out, as a generator with its self-excited field can do. Because of this, there is no need for a current limiter. There must be one control with an alternator, however, that is not needed with a generator, and that is some means of shutting off the flow of field current when the alternator is not producing power. This is not needed in a generator since its field is excited by its own output. An alternator uses either a field switch or a field relay.

Most modern aircraft alternator circuits employ some form of overvoltage protection to remove the

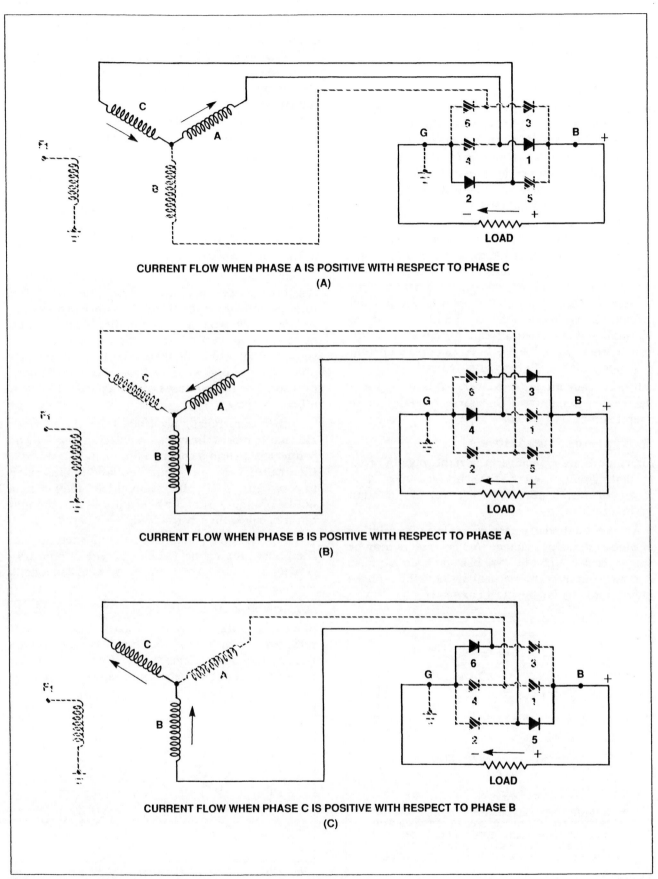

CURRENT FLOW WHEN PHASE A IS POSITIVE WITH RESPECT TO PHASE C

(A)

CURRENT FLOW WHEN PHASE B IS POSITIVE WITH RESPECT TO PHASE A

(B)

CURRENT FLOW WHEN PHASE C IS POSITIVE WITH RESPECT TO PHASE B

(C)

Figure 4-25. 3-phase, full-wave rectifier used in a DC alternator.

alternator from the bus if it should malfunction in such a way that its output voltage rises to a dangerous level.

C. Alternators

DC is normally used as the main electrical power for small aircraft, because it can be stored and the aircraft engines can be started using battery power. Large aircraft require ground service facilities and external power sources for starting, and can take advantage of the weight saving provided by using AC for their main electrical power.

AC has the advantage over direct current in that its voltage can be stepped up or down. If we need to carry current for a long distance, we can pass the AC through a step-up transformer to increase the voltage and decrease the current. The high voltage AC can be transmitted to the point it will be used through a relatively small conductor, and at its destination it is passed through a step-down transformer where its voltage is lowered and its current is stepped back up to the value we need.

It is an easy matter to convert AC into DC when we need direct current to charge batteries or to operate other DC systems.

1. Types of Alternators

Alternators are classified in several ways in order to distinguish properly the various types. One means of classification is by the type of excitation system used.

Another method of classification is by the number of phases of output voltage. AC generators may be single-phase, 2-phase, 3-phase, or even 6-phase and more. In aircraft electrical systems the 3-phase alternator is by far the most common.

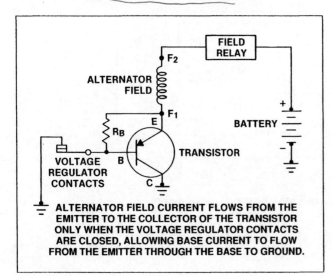

Figure 4-26. Transistorized voltage regulator.

Still another means of classification is by the type of stator and rotor used. There are two types: the revolving-armature type and the revolving-field type. The revolving-armature alternator is similar in construction to the DC generator, in that the armature rotates through a stationary magnetic field. The revolving-armature alternator is found only in alternators of low power rating and generally is not used.

a. 3-phase Alternator

A 3-phase or polyphase circuit is used in most aircraft alternators, instead of a single or 2-phase alternator. The 3-phase alternator has 3 single-phase windings spaced so that the voltage induced in each winding is 120° out of phase with the voltage in the other two windings.

A simplified schematic diagram, showing each of the three phases, is illustrated in figure 4-27. The rotor is omitted for simplicity. The waveforms of the voltage are shown to the right of the schematic. The three voltages are 120° apart and are similar to the voltages that would be generated by three single-phase alternators, whose voltages are out of phase by 120°. The three phases are independent of each other.

Rather than having six leads from the 3-phase alternator, one of the leads from each phase may be connected to form a common junction. The stator is then called Y- or star-connected, and is illustrated in A of figure 4-28. The common lead may or may not be brought out of the alternator. If it is brought out it is called the neutral lead.

A 3-phase stator can also be connected so that the phases are connected end-to-end as shown in B of figure 4-28. This arrangement is called a delta connection.

b. Brushless Alternators

Most of the AC generators used in the large jet-powered aircraft are of the brushless type and are usually air cooled. Since the brushless alternators have no current flow between brushes or slip rings,

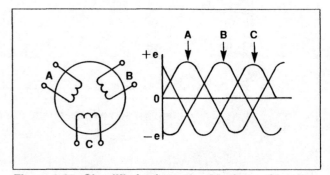

Figure 4-27. Simplified schematic of 3-phase alternator with output waveforms.

they are quite efficient at high altitudes where brush arcing could be a problem.

The exciter field current is brought into the alternator from the voltage regulator. Here it produces the magnetic field for the 3-phase exciter output. Permanent magnets furnish the magnetic flux to start the generator producing an output before field current flows. The voltage produced by these magnets is called residual voltage. The output from the exciter is rectified by 6 silicon diodes, and the resulting DC flows through the output field winding. The exciter output winding, the 6 diodes, and the output field winding are all mounted on the generator shaft and rotate as a unit. The 3-phase output stator windings are wound in slots in the laminated frame of the alternator housing, and their ends are connected in the form of a Y with the neutral and the 3-phase windings brought out to terminals on the outside of the housing. These alternators are usually designed to produce 120 volts between any of the phase terminals and the neutral terminal and 208 volts between any of the phase terminals.

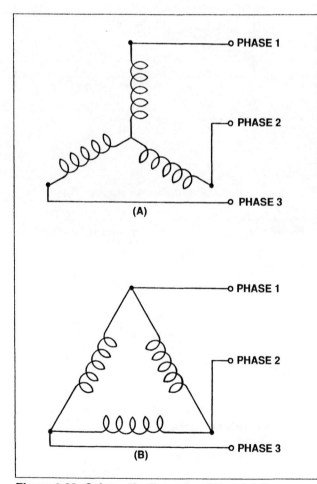

Figure 4-28. Schematic diagrams of Y and delta connections.

2. Alternator Ratings

The true power produced in an AC generator is the product of the voltage and that portion of the current that is in phase with the voltage and is expressed in watts or kilowatts. It is this power that determines the amount of useful work the electricity can do.

a. KVA

AC generators are rated, however, not in watts, but in volt-amps, which is a measure of the apparent power being produced by the generator. Because of the output of most large aircraft alternators, the ratings will generally be expressed in KVA (kilo-volt amperes). The reason for using this rating is that it is the heating effect of the current in the generator windings that limits generator output, and this current flows in the windings whether it is producing power or not.

b. Frequency

The frequency of the AC produced by an AC generator is determined by the number of poles and the speed of the rotor. The faster the speed, the higher the frequency will be; the lower the speed, the lower the frequency becomes. The more poles on the rotor, the higher the frequency will be for any given speed. The frequency of the alternator in cycles per second (Hz) is related to the number of poles and the speed, as expressed by the equation

$$F = \frac{P}{2} \times \frac{N}{60} = \frac{PN}{120}$$

where

P = the number of poles

N = the speed in RPM

For example, a 2-pole, 3,600 RPM alternator has a frequency of

$$\frac{2 \times 3,600}{120} = 60 \text{ cycles per second (Hz)}$$

Inductance is a characteristic of a conductor that produces a back voltage when current changes its rate of flow or direction. Since AC is constantly changing its rate and periodically changing direction, there is always a back voltage being produced. This back voltage causes an opposition to current flow that we call inductive reactance. The higher the frequency of AC, the greater this opposition will be. Commercial AC (house current) in the U.S. has a frequency of 60 Hz, but most aircraft systems use 400 Hz AC. At this higher frequency, the inductive reactance is high and current is low. Motors can produce their torque when wound with smaller wire and transformers can be made much smaller and lighter for use with this higher frequency.

To provide a constant frequency as the engine speed varies, many engine-driven aircraft AC generators are

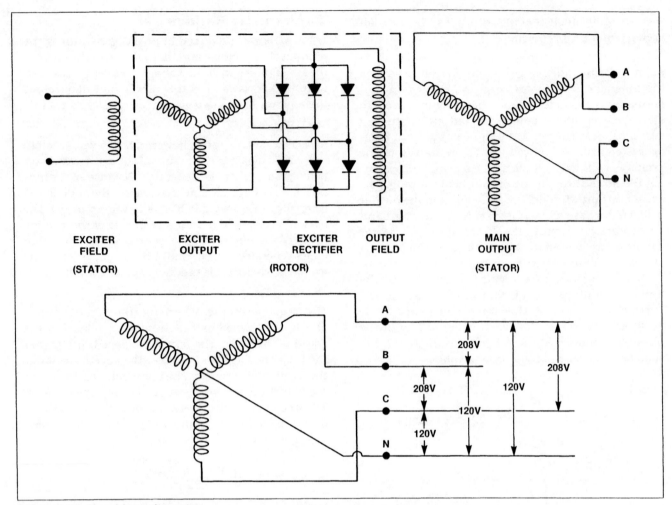

EXCITER   EXCITER   EXCITER   OUTPUT   MAIN
FIELD   OUTPUT   RECTIFIER   FIELD   OUTPUT

(STATOR)   (ROTOR)   (STATOR)

Figure 4-29. Brushless alternator.

connected to the engine through a hydrostatically operated constant speed drive unit (CSD).

These drive units normally consist of an axial-piston variable-displacement hydraulic pump driven by the engine, supplying fluid to an axial-piston hydraulic motor which drives the generator. The displacement of the pump is controlled by a governor which senses the rotational speed of the AC generator. This governor action holds the output speed of the generator constant and maintains the frequency of the AC at 400 Hz, plus or minus established tolerances.

Some of the modern jet aircraft produce their alternating current with a generator similar to the one we see in figure 4-31. This unit is called an Integrated Drive Generator (IDG), and it includes a constant speed drive unit in the housing with the generator.

D. DC Motors

Many devices in an airplane, from the starter to the automatic pilot, depend upon the mechanical energy furnished by DC motors. A DC motor is a rotating

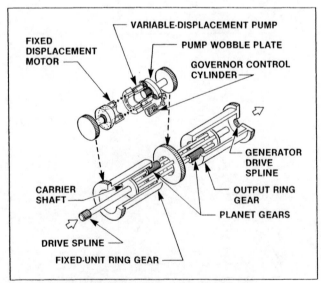

Figure 4-30. Constant-speed drive axial-gear differential used in the Sunstrand Integrated Drive Generator.

machine which transforms DC electrical energy into mechanical energy.

1. Motor Theory

Whenever a current-carrying wire is placed in the field of a magnet, a force acts on the wire. The force is not one of attraction or repulsion; however, it is at right angles to the wire and also at right angles to the magnetic field set up by the magnet.

The action of the force upon a current-carrying wire placed in a magnetic field is shown in figure 4-32. A wire is located between two permanent magnets. The lines of force in the magnetic field are from the north pole to the south pole. When no current flows (diagram A) no force is exerted on the wire. When current flows through the wire, a magnetic field is set up about it (diagram B). The direction of the field depends upon the direction of current flow. Current in one direction creates a clockwise field about the wire, and current in the other direction, a counter-clockwise field.

Since the current-carrying wire produces a magnetic field, a reaction occurs between the field about

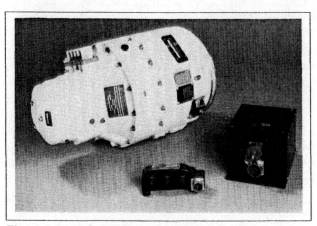

Figure 4-31. A Sunstrand Integrated Drive Generator with its control unit and a current transformer assembly.

the wire and the magnetic field between the magnets. When the current flows in a direction to create a counterclockwise magnetic field about the wire, this field and the field between the magnets add or reinforce at the bottom of the wire because the lines of force are in the same direction. At the top of the wire, they subtract or neutralize, since the top lines of force in the two fields are opposite in direction. Thus, the resulting field at the bottom is strong and the one at the top is weak. Consequently, the wire is pushed upward as shown in diagram C of figure 4-32. The wire is always pushed away from the side where the field is the strongest.

If current flow through the wire were reversed in direction, the two fields would add at the top and subtract at the bottom. Since a wire is always pushed away from the strong field, the wire would be pushed down.

a. Force between Parallel Conductors

Two wires carrying current in the vicinity of one another exert a force on each other because of their magnetic fields. An end view of two conductors is shown in figure 4-33. In A, electron flow in both conductors is toward the reader, and the magnetic fields are clockwise around the conductors. Between the wires, the fields cancel each other because the directions of the two fields oppose each other. The wires are forced in the direction of the weaker field, toward each other. This force is one of attraction.

In B, the electron flow in the two wires is in opposite directions. The magnetic fields are, therefore, clockwise in one and counterclockwise in the other, as shown. The fields reinforce each other between the wires, and the wires are forced in the direction of the weaker field, away from each other. This force is one of repulsion.

To summarize, conductors carrying current in the same direction tend to be drawn together; conductors carrying current in opposite directions tend to be repelled from each other.

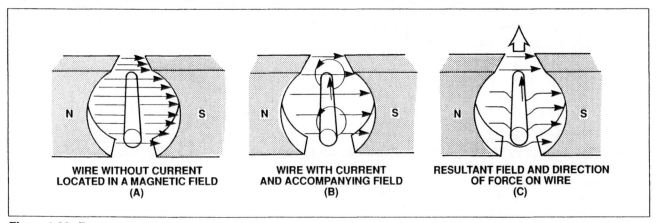

WIRE WITHOUT CURRENT
LOCATED IN A MAGNETIC FIELD
(A)

WIRE WITH CURRENT
AND ACCOMPANYING FIELD
(B)

RESULTANT FIELD AND DIRECTION
OF FORCE ON WIRE
(C)

Figure 4-32. Force on a current-carrying wire.

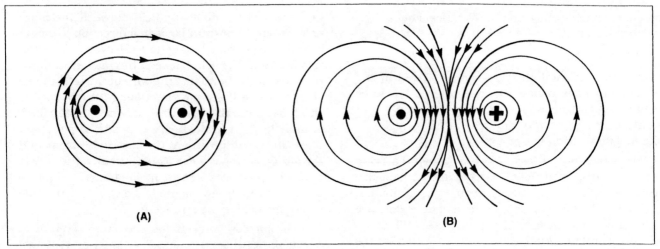

Figure 4-33. Fields surrounding parallel conductors.

b. Developing Torque

If a coil in which current is flowing is placed in a magnetic field, a force is produced which will cause the coil to rotate. In the coil shown in figure 4-34, current flows inward on side A and outward on side B. The magnetic field about B is clockwise and that about A, counterclockwise. As previously explained, a force will develop which pushes side B downward. At the same time, the field of the magnets and the field about A, in which the current is inward, will push side A upward. The coil will thus rotate until its plane is perpendicular to the magnetic lines between the north and south poles of the magnet, as indicated in figure 4-34 by the white coil at right angles to the black coil.

The tendency of a force to produce rotation is called torque. Torque is developed by the reacting magnetic fields about the current-carrying coil just described. This is the torque which turns the coil.

The right-hand motor rule can be used to determine the direction a current-carrying wire will move in a magnetic field. As illustrated in figure 4-35, if the index finger of the right hand is pointed in the direction of the magnetic field and the second finger in the direction of current flow, the thumb will indicate the direction the current carrying conductor will move.

The amount of torque developed in a coil depends upon several factors: the strength of the magnetic field, the number of turns in the coil, and the position of the coil in the field.

c. Basic DC Motor

A coil of wire, through which current flows, will rotate when placed in a magnetic field. This is the technical basis governing construction of a DC motor. Figure 4-36 shows a coil mounted in a magnetic field in which it can rotate. However, if the connecting wires

from the battery were permanently connected to the terminals of the coil and there was flow of current, the coil would only rotate until it lined itself up with the magnetic field. Then, it would stop, because the torque at that point would be zero.

A motor, of course, must continue rotating. It is necessary, therefore, to design a device that will reverse the current in the coil just at the time the coil becomes parallel to the lines of force. This will create torque again and cause the coil to rotate. If the current-reversing device is set up to reverse the current each time the coil is about to stop, the coil can be made to continue rotating as long as desired.

One method of doing this is to connect the circuit so that, as the coil rotates, each contact slides off the terminal to which it connects and slides onto the terminal of opposite polarity. In other words, the coil contacts switch terminals continuously, as the coil rotates, preserving the torque and keeping the coil rotating.

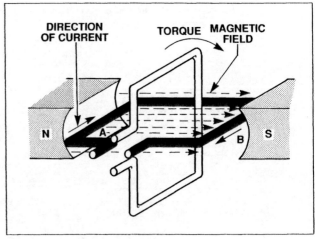

Figure 4-34. Developing a torque.

In figure 4-36, the coil terminal segments are labeled A and B. As the coil rotates, the segments slide onto and past the fixed terminals or brushes. With this arrangement, the direction of current in the side of the coil next to the north seeking pole flows toward the reader, and the force acting on that side of the coil turns it downward. The part of the motor which changes the current from one wire to another is called the commutator.

The torque in a motor containing only a single coil is neither continuous nor very effective, because there are two positions where there is actually no torque at all. To overcome this, a practical DC motor contains a

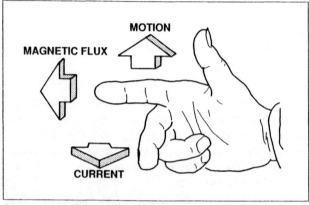

Figure 4-35. Right-hand motor rule.

large number of coils wound on the armature. These coils are spaced so that, for any position of the armature, there will be coils near the poles of the magnet. This makes the torque both continuous and strong. The commutator, likewise, contains a large number of segments instead of only two.

The armature in a practical motor is not placed between the poles of a permanent magnet but between those of an electromagnet, since a much stronger magnetic field can be furnished. The core is usually made of a mild or annealed steel, which can be magnetized strongly by induction. The current magnetizing the electromagnet is from the same source that supplies the current to the armature.

2. DC Motor Construction

The major parts in a practical motor are the armature assembly, the field assembly, the brush assembly, and the end frames.

a. Armature Assembly

The armature assembly contains a laminated, soft-iron core, coils, and a commutator, all mounted on a rotatable steel shaft. Laminations made of stacks of soft iron, insulated from each other, form the armature core. Solid iron is not used, since a solid-ion core revolving in a magnetic field would heat and use energy needlessly. The armature windings are

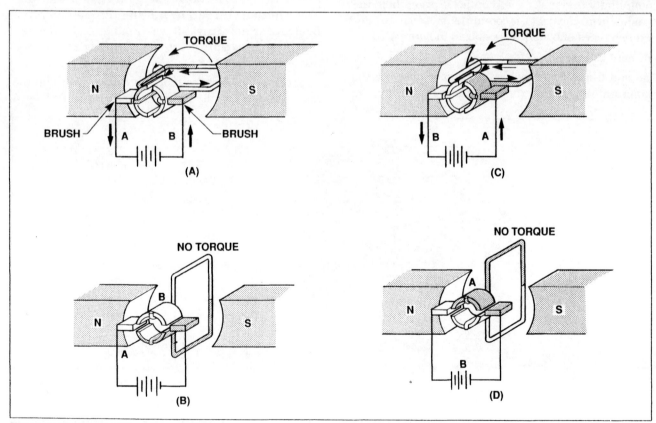

Figure 4-36. Basic DC motor operation.

insulated copper wire, which are inserted in slots insulated with fiber paper to protect the windings. The ends of the windings are connected to the commutator segments. Wedges or steel bands hold the windings in place to prevent them from flying out of the slots when the armature is rotating at high speeds. The commutator consists of a large number of copper segments insulated from each other and the armature shaft by pieces of mica. Insulated wedge rings hold the segments in place.

b. Field Assembly

The field assembly consists of the field frame, the pole pieces, and the field coils. The field frame is located along the inner wall of the motor housing. It contains laminated soft steel pole pieces on which the field coils are wound. A coil, consisting of several turns of insulated wire, fits over each pole piece and, together with the pole, constitutes a field pole. Some motors have as few as 2 poles, others as many as 8.

c. Brush Assembly

The brush assembly consists of the brushes and their holders. The brushes are usually small blocks of graphitic carbon, since this material has a long service life and also causes minimum wear to the commutator. The holders permit some play in the brushes so they can follow any irregularities in the surface of the commutator and make good contact. Springs hold the brushes firmly against the commutator. A commutator and two types of brushes are shown in figure 4-37.

d. End Frame

The end frame is the part of the motor opposite the commutator. Usually, the end frame is designed so that it can be connected to the unit to be driven. The bearing for the drive end is also located in the end frame. Sometimes the end frame is made a part of the unit driven by the motor. When this is done, the bearing on the drive end may be located in any of a number of places.

3. Types of DC Motors

DC motors may be identified by two major factors. Motors are classified by the type of field-armature connection used and by the type of duty they are designed for.

a. Field-armature Connections

There are three basic types of DC motors: series, shunt, and compound motors. They differ largely in the method in which their field and armature are connected.

(1) Series DC Motor

In the series motor, the field windings, consisting of a relatively few turns of heavy wire, are connected in series with the armature winding. The same current flowing through the field winding also flows through the armature winding. Any increase in current, therefore, strengthens the magnetism of both the field and the armature.

Because of the low resistance in the windings, the series motor is able to draw large current in starting. This starting current, in passing through both the field and armature windings, produces a high starting torque, which is the series motor's principal advantage.

The speed of a series motor is dependent upon the load. Any change in the load is accompanied by a

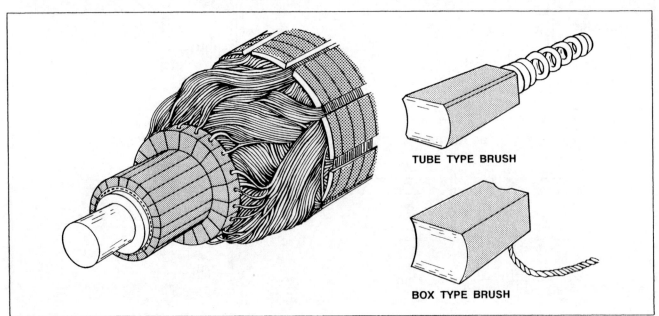

TUBE TYPE BRUSH

BOX TYPE BRUSH

Figure 4-37. Commutator and brushes.

substantial change in speed. A series motor will run at high speed when it has a light load and at low speed with a heavy load. If the load is removed entirely, the motor may operate at such a high speed that the armature will fly apart. If high starting torque is needed under heavy load conditions, series motors have many applications. Series motors are often used in aircraft as engine starters and for raising and lowering landing gear, cowl flaps, and wing flaps.

(2) Shunt DC Motor

In the shunt motor the field winding is connected in parallel, or in shunt with the armature winding. The resistance in the field winding is high. Since the field winding is connected directly across the power supply, the current through the field is constant. The field current does not vary with motor speed, as in the series motor and, therefore, the torque of the shunt motor will vary only with the current through the armature. The torque developed at starting is less than that developed by a series motor of equal size.

The speed of the shunt motor varies little with changes in load. When all load is removed, it assumes a speed slightly higher than the loaded speed. This motor is particularly suitable for use when constant speed is desired and when high starting torque is not needed.

(3) Compound DC Motor

The compound motor is a combination of the series and shunt motors. There are two windings in the field: a shunt winding and a series winding. The shunt winding is composed of many turns of fine wire and is connected in parallel with the armature winding. The series winding consists of a few turns of large wire and is connected in series with the armature winding. The starting torque is higher than in the shunt motor but lower than in the series motor. Variation of speed with load is less than in a series-wound motor, but greater than in a shunt motor. The compound motor is used whenever the combined characteristics of the series and shunt motors are desired.

b. Type of Duty

Electric motors are called upon to operate under various conditions. Some motors are used for intermittent operations; others may operate continuously. Motors built for intermittent duty can be operated for short periods only and, then, must be allowed to cool before being operated again. If such a motor is operated for long periods under full load, the motor will be overheated. Motors built for continuous duty may be operated at rated power for long periods.

4. Motor Speed and Direction

Certain applications may call for motors whose speed or direction are changed. This may include variable speeds for windshield wipers, or changing the direction of the landing gear retraction motor. Certain internal or external changes may be made in the motor design to allow these operations.

a. Reversing Motor Direction

By reversing the direction of current flow in either the armature or the field windings, the direction of a DC motor's rotation may be reversed. This will reverse the magnetism of either the armature or the magnetic field in which the armature rotates. If the wires connecting the motor to an external source are interchanged, the direction of rotation will not be reversed, since changing these wires reverses the magnetism of both field and armature and leaves the torque in the same direction as before.

One method for reversing the direction of rotation employs two field windings wound in opposite directions on the same pole. This type of motor is called a split field motor. The single-pole, double-throw switch makes it possible to direct current to either of the two windings.

Another method of reversal, called the switch method, employs a double-pole, double-throw switch which changes the direction of current flow in either the armature or the field. Current direction may be reversed through the field but not through the armature.

b. Changing Motor Speed

Motor speed can be controlled by varying the current in the field windings. When the amount of current flowing through the field windings is increased, the field strength increases, but the motor slows down since a greater amount of counter emf is generated in the armature windings. When the field current is decreased, the field strength decreases, and the motor speeds up because the counter emf is reduced. A motor in which the speed can be controlled is called a variable speed motor. It may be either a shunt or series motor.

E. AC Motors

Because of their advantages, many types of aircraft motors are designed to operate on AC. In general, AC motors are less expensive than comparable DC motors. In many instances, the AC motors do not use brushes and commutators and, therefore, sparking at the brushes is avoided. They are very reliable and little maintenance is needed. Also, they are well suited for constant-speed applications and certain types are manufactured that have, within limits, variable-speed characteristics. AC motors are designed to operate on poly-phase or single-phase lines and at several voltage ratings.

The subject of AC motors is very extensive, and no attempt has been made to cover the entire field. Only the types of AC motors common to aircraft systems are covered.

The speed of rotation of an AC motor depends upon the number of poles and the frequency of the electrical source of power:

$$RPM = \frac{120 \times Frequency}{Number\ of\ Poles}$$

Since aircraft electrical systems typically operate at 400 Hz, an electric motor at this frequency operates at about seven times the speed of a 60 Hz commercial motor with the same number of poles. Because of this high speed of rotation, 400 Hz AC motors are suitable for operating small high-speed rotors, through reduction gears, in lifting and moving heavy loads, such as the wing flaps, the retractable landing gear, and the starting of engines. The 400 Hz induction type motor operates at speeds ranging from 6,000 RPM to 24,000 RPM.

AC motors are rated in horsepower output, operating voltage, full load current, speed, number of phases, and frequency. Whether the motors operate continuously or intermittently is also considered in the rating.

1. Types of AC Motors

There are three basic types of AC motors: the universal motor, the induction motor, and the synchronous motor. Each of the categories may have many variations on the basic operating principle.

a. Universal Motors

Fractional horsepower AC series motors are called universal motors. A universal motor may be operated on either AC or DC, and resembles a DC motor in that it has brushes and a commutator. They are used extensively to operate fans and portable tools, such as drills, grinders, and saws.

b. Induction Motors

The most popular type of AC motor in use is the induction motor. The induction motor needs no electrical connection to the rotating elements, and therefore there are no brushes, commutators, or slip rings.

Induction motors operate at a fixed RPM that is determined by their design and the frequency of the applied AC. Three-phase induction motors are self-starting and are commonly used when high power is needed. Single-phase induction motors require some form of starting circuit, but once they are started this circuit is automatically disconnected. Single-phase motors operate equally well in either direction of rotation, and the direction they turn is determined by the starting circuit.

Many small appliances such as fans and blowers or record players are driven with a small induction motor called a shaded-pole motor because of the way its rotating field is obtained. These small motors have very low starting torque, but their simplicity and low cost make them desirable for application where torque is not important.

c. Synchronous Motors

The synchronous motor is one of the principal types of AC motors. Like the induction motor, the synchronous motor makes use of a rotating magnetic field. Unlike the induction motor, however, the torque developed does not depend on the induction of currents in the rotor. Briefly, the principle of operation of the synchronous motor is as follows: A multiphase source of AC is applied to the stator windings, and a rotating magnetic field is produced. A direct current is applied to the rotor winding, and another magnetic field is produced. The synchronous motor is so designed and constructed that these two fields react to each other in such a manner that the rotor is dragged along and rotates at the same speed as the rotating magnetic field produced by the stator windings.

F. Engine Starting Systems

1. Reciprocating Engine Starting Systems

The earliest aircraft engines were started by hand "propping". The mechanics swung the propeller by hand to pull the engine through one or two compression strokes, and if everything was as it should be, the engine started. Cold weather made the oil heavy, and the engines were hard to start. As the engines grew larger and the propellers longer, the procedure for starting became more difficult, and several methods were devised to replace the hand-cranking procedure.

a. Inertia Starters

One of the first types of starters coupled to the crankshaft was the hand inertia starter. In this type of starter, a relatively heavy flywheel is spun with a hand crank through a step-up gear arrangement. When the flywheel is spinning at a high rate of speed and lots of kinetic energy, the crank is removed, and the engage handle pulled to extend a ratchet-type jaw of the starter to engage a similar ratchet on the rear end of the crankshaft. A torque-overload clutch is used between the flywheel and the jaws to prevent the sudden engagement damaging either the engine or the starter. With the jaws engaged, the energy stored in the flywheel turns the engine over enough to get it started.

Hand inertia starters were soon improved by mounting an electric motor on the back of the starter to spin the flywheel. When the flywheel was up to speed, the motor was de-energized and the engage handle pulled to engage the flywheel to the engine. This combination electric and hand inertia starter was the standard starter for large engines up until World War II.

b. Direct-cranking Starters

The most widely used starting system on all types of reciprocating engines utilizes the direct-cranking electric starter. This type of starter provides instant and continual cranking when energized. The direct-cranking electric starter consists basically of an electric motor, reduction gears, and an engaging and disengaging mechanism.

(1) Starters for Low Horsepower Engines

Many of the small horizontally opposed aircraft engines use a form of direct-cranking electric starter similar to the one in figure 4-38. This starter uses a small series-wound electric motor with a small gear on the end of its shaft. This small gear meshes with a large gear that is part of an over-running clutch. These starters may be engaged either by a hand-pulled cable or with a solenoid that operates the shift lever.

When the shift lever is pulled, it compresses the meshing spring and forces the pinion to mesh with the starter gear inside the accessory case of the engine. When the pinion and the starter gear are fully meshed, further movement of the shift lever closes the starter motor switch, and the starter cranks the engine. When the engine starts, the over-running clutch allows the pinion to spin without doing any damage, and as soon as the toggle is released or the solenoid is de-energized, the return spring pulls the pinion away from the starter gear.

Avco-Lycoming horizontally opposed engines that have the large diameter starter gear just behind the propeller use a direct cranking electric starter similar to the ones used on automobile engines. These starters are driven through a Bendix drive.

When the starter switch is closed, the series-wound electric motor spins the pinion through the Bendix drive spring. The drive pinion fits loosely over the drive shaft, and as the armature spins, the pinion moves

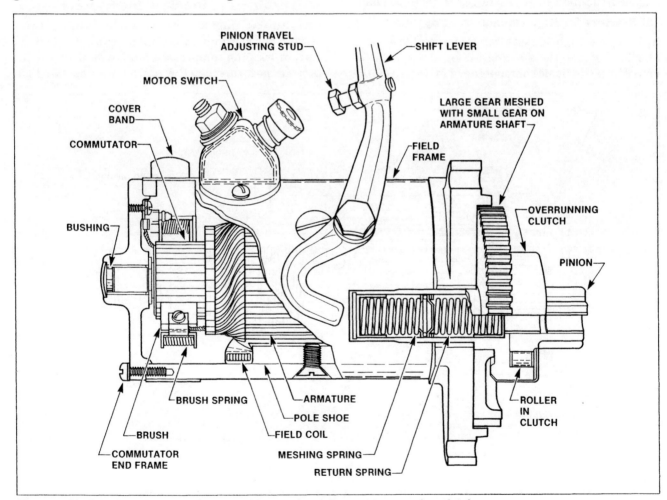

Figure 4-38. Cutaway view of a direct-cranking starter using an over-running clutch.

forward on the helical splines, and it engages the teeth on the periphery of the engine starter gear. The starter then cranks the engine. As soon as the engine starts and the starter gear begins to spin the Bendix drive pinion, the pinion is forced back along the helical splines, and it disengages from the starter gear.

Some of the new generation of Teledyne-Continental aircraft engines use a starter mounted on the side of the accessory case, and it cranks the engine through a right-angle worm-gear-type adaptor.

In figure 4-40, we see the way this system works. The series-wound electric motor drives the starter worm gear, which meshes with the worm wheel. The clutch spring is attached to the worm wheel, and when the worm wheel turns, the spring tightens around a knurled drum on the starter shaft gear, and the starter gear, which is meshed with the crankshaft gear, cranks the engine. As soon as the engine starts, the starter shaft turns faster than the worm wheel, and the spring releases the knurled drum. The generator drive pulley is mounted on the end of the starter gear shaft, and with the clutch spring disengaged, the shaft serves as the generator drive shaft.

(2) Starters for High Horsepower Engines

In a typical high-horsepower reciprocating engine starting system, the direct-cranking electric starter consists of two basic components: a motor assembly

and a gear section. The gear section is bolted to the drive end of the motor to form a complete unit. This type of starter is seen in figure 4-41.

The motor assembly consists of the armature and motor pinion assembly, the bell end assembly, and the motor housing assembly. The motor housing also acts as the magnetic yoke for the field structure.

The starter motor is a non-reversible, series interpole motor. Its speed varies directly with the applied voltage and inversely with the load.

The starter gear section (figure 4-42) consists of a housing with an integral mounting flange, planetary gear reduction, a sun and integral gear assembly, a torque-limiting clutch, and a jaw and cone assembly.

When the starter circuit is closed, the torque developed in the starter motor is transmitted to the starter jaw through the reduction gear train and clutch.

The starter gear train converts the high speed low-torque of the motor to the low-speed high-torque required to crank the engine.

2. Turbine Engine Starting Systems

Gas turbine engines are generally started by a starter power input to the main gearbox which in turn rotates the compressor. On the dual axial compressor gas turbine, the starter rotates the high

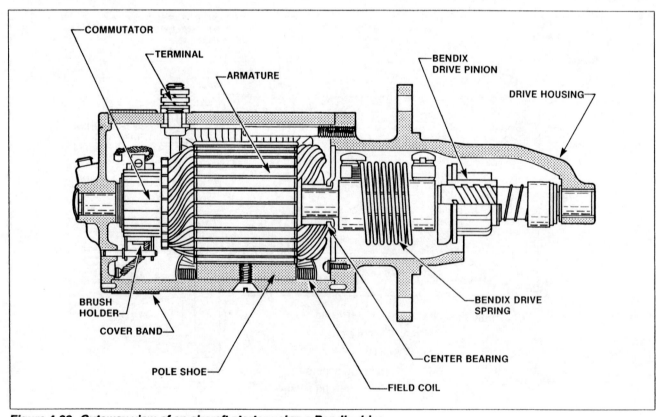

Figure 4-39. Cutaway view of an aircraft starter using a Bendix drive.

speed compressor system only. On free turbine, turboprop, or turboshaft engines, again the compressor rotor system only is rotated by the starter through the accessory gearbox. The usual starting sequence is to energize the starter and then at 5-10% rotor speed, to energize ignition and open the fuel lever. A normal light-off will usually occur in 10 seconds or less. If light-off does not occur within 10 seconds the start would generally be aborted to investigate the malfunction. Such problems as low starting power, weak ignition, or air in the fuel lines can cause starting problems.

Compressor rotation by the starter provides the engine with sufficient air for combustion and also aids the engine in self-accelerating to idle speed after combustion occurs. Neither the starter nor the turbine wheel have sufficient power on their own to bring the engine from rest to idle speed, but when used in combination, the process takes place smoothly in approximately 30 seconds on the typical engine. The start is often automatically terminated by a speed sensor device after self-accelerating speed is reached; at this point, turbine power is sufficient to take the engine up to idle. If the engine is not assisted to the correct speed, a hung start may occur. That is, the engine stabilizes at or near the point of starter cutoff. To remedy this situation, the engine must be shut down for investigation. Any attempt to accelerate by adding fuel will quite often result in a hot start as well as a hung start, because the engine is operating with insufficient airflow to support further combustion.

Turboprop and turboshaft engines are started either in low pitch to reduce drag on the rotor and provide more speed and airflow or they are configured with a free-turbine driving the propeller, which allows for a low drag acceleration in that the compressor rotor system only is being turned by the starter.

a. Electric Starters

Electric starting systems for gas turbine aircraft are of two general types: Direct-cranking electrical systems and starter-generator systems.

(1) Direct-Cranking Starters

Direct-cranking electric starters are not in wide use on flight engines because the combination starter-generator is more feasible for small engines. Also, large engines require such high starting power that

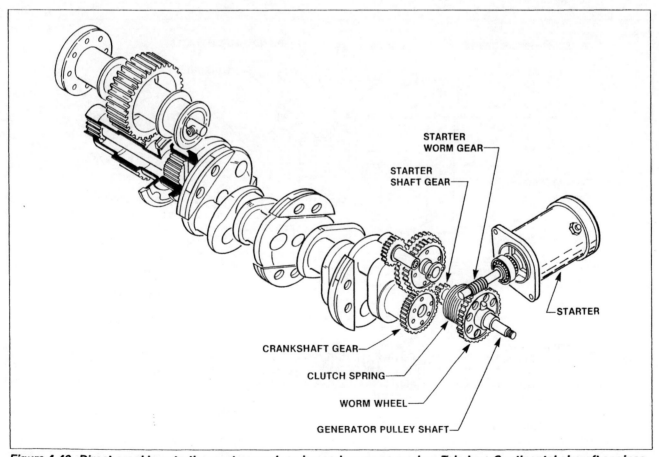

Figure 4-40. Direct-cranking starting system such as is used on some modern Teledyne-Continental aircraft engines.

65

starter weight becomes a problem. However, electric starters are widely used on auxiliary and ground power units, and some small flight engines.

Most electric starters contain an automatic release clutch mechanism to disengage the starter drive from the engine drive. Figure 4-43 shows a clutch assembly that performs two functions. Its first function is to prevent the starter from applying excessive torque to the engine drive. At approximately 130 in.-lbs. of torque, small clutch plates within the clutch housing slip around and act as a friction clutch. This setting is

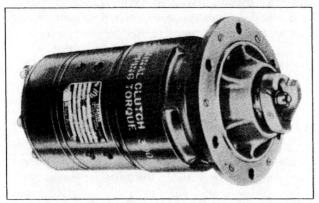

Figure 4-41. Direct-cranking starter for a large aircraft engine.

adjustable. During starting, the friction clutch is designed to slip until engine speed and starter speed increase to develop less than the slip torque setting.

The second function of the clutch assembly is to act as an overrunning clutch. This pawl and ratchet-type mechanism contains three pawls which are spring loaded to the disengage position (figure 4-43(C)). When the starter is rotated, inertia causes the pawls to move inward to engage a ratchet-type engine drive gear. This occurs because the pawl cage assembly, which floats within the pawl clutch housing, tries to remain stationary when the armature starts to drive the clutch housing around. However, the pawl clutch housing quickly forces the pawls inward by a bumping action, overcoming the retracting spring force. When engine speed approaches idle, its speed exceeds that of the starter and the pawls slip out of the tapered slots of the engine drive gear and throw outward, via force of the retracting spring. This overrunning feature prevents the engine driving the starter to burst speed.

(2) Starter-generator Systems

The combination starter-generator is most widely utilized on corporate size jet aircraft due to the weight saving feature of one engine accessory taking the place of two. Because of its dual purpose, the

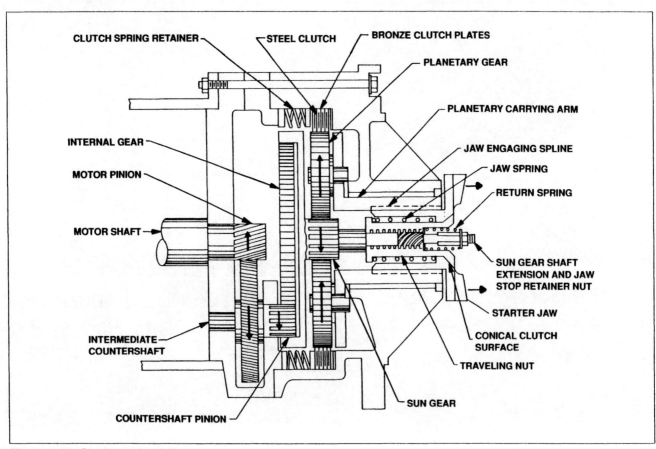

Figure 4-42. Starter gear section.

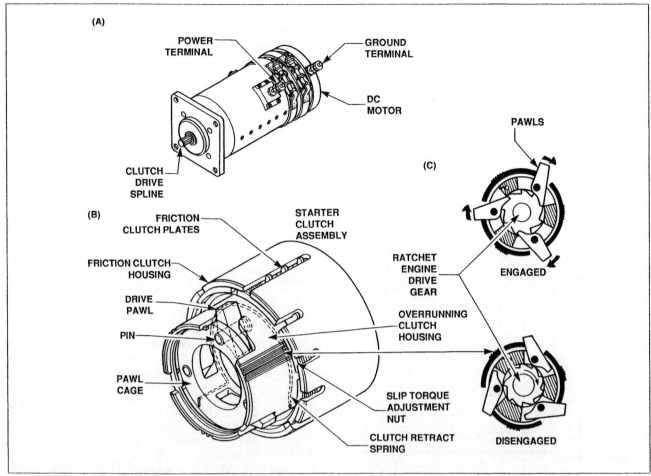

Figure 4-43.
- (A) Direct cranking starter for a turbine engine.
- (B) Starter clutch assembly.
- (C) Overrunning clutch action.

drive mechanism differs from the electric starter. The starter-generator has a drive spline which stays permanently engaged to the engine.

(a) Starter-generator Circuits

An analysis of the example diagram will be made easier by tracing the circuit shown in figure 4-45 in the following steps:

1. Master switch closed (up) allows either battery power or external power to reach the fuel valve, the throttle relay coil, the fuel pumps, and the ignition relay contactor.
2. Battery and start switch closed (up) allows bus power to illuminate the cockpit light, to close the ignition relay, and to close the motor relay. Ignition occurs at this time.
3. Closing the motor relay in turn allows the undercurrent relay to close and the starter to operate.

Figure 4-44. DC aircraft starter-generator used on a gas turbine engine.

4. The battery and start switch can be released and current will continue to flow to the relays via the emergency stop lead. However, as engine speed increases and less than 200 amperes of current is flowing, the undercurrent relay opens to shut down the starter and ignition circuit operation.

5. Pulling the emergency stop button will open the ignition circuit at the same point as the undercurrent relay. This button can be used if a malfunction occurs and the relay contacts stick closed or if continuous high ampere draw from a false start prevents normal cutout.

6. An external power receptacle door microswitch prevents both external power and battery power on the bus at the same time. Some aircraft installations provide no battery start capability or require that battery starting only be used in emergencies to increase service life of the battery.

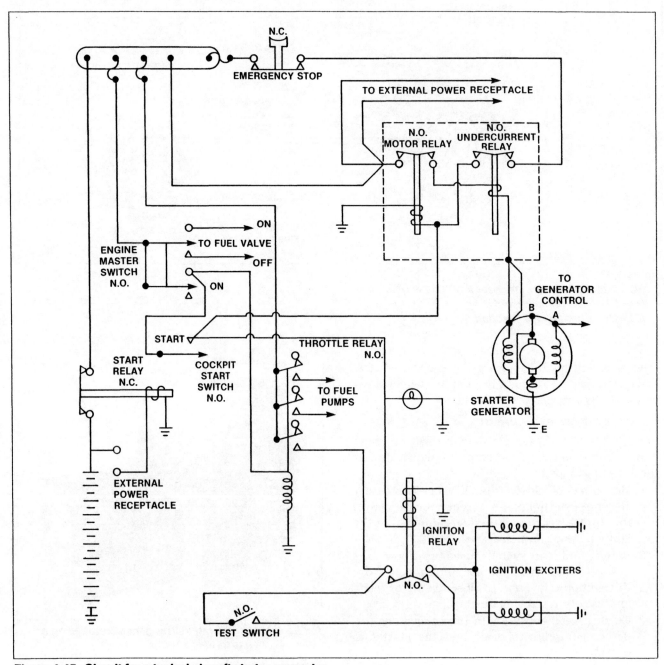

Figure 4-45. Circuit for a typical aircraft starter-generator.

Chapter V

Airborne Sources of Electrical Power

A. DC Power Sources

1. The Battery

a. Lead-acid Battery

The lead-acid battery has been the primary source of electrical energy for starting engines and supplying power in the event of generator failure. Batteries also stabilize and smooth out the generator output during extreme load changes. Today, for many of our high-demand systems, such as turbine-powered aircraft, lead-acid batteries have been replaced with nickel-cadmium batteries. However, the less expensive and less sensitive lead-acid units will continue as a power source for many years to come.

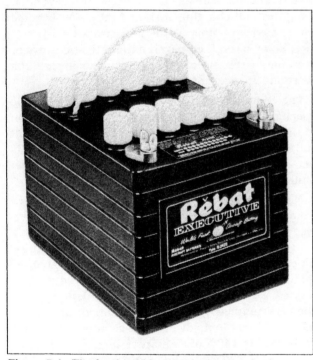

Figure 5-1. The lead-acid battery is the standard battery used in most light aircraft.

(1) Battery Ratings

(a) Voltage

Both 12-volt and 24-volt batteries are available for aircraft. Generally speaking, 12-volt systems are used on single-engine aircraft. Larger aircraft typically employ the 24-volt systems.

The voltage of any battery is a function of its state of charge and the current load placed on the battery. If a 12-volt lead-acid battery has just been removed from the charger, its voltage may be as high as 13.2 volts. This voltage will soon level off to near 12 volts. The same battery may produce only 10 volts under extreme load conditions. In any event, the battery would still be rated at 12 volts.

(b) Ampere-hour Capacity

The number of cells in a battery determines the voltage it will produce. The area of the plates, the amount of active material in the plates, and the electrolyte determine the ampere-hour capacity of the battery. The capacity of a battery is a measure of the battery's ability to produce a current flow.

If a battery is rated at 17 ampere-hours, it is theoretically capable of producing a flow of 1 ampere for 17 hours, or 17 amperes for 1 hour, or any combination of current and time that equals 17 ampere-hours. This is a good reference point, but it is not a linear relationship. The rate at which the current is drawn from the battery determines its actual capacity. The nominal rating is based on the amount of current flow that is needed to drop the closed-circuit voltage of a fully charged battery to 1.2 volts per cell in 5 hours.

If the same 17 ampere-hour battery is loaded so that it will discharge to 1.2 volts per cell in 20 minutes, it will have a capacity of only 10.2 ampere-hours, and if it is discharged in 5 minutes, its capacity will drop to 6.7 ampere-hours. In other words, the quicker one discharges a battery, the less capacity the battery will provide.

BATTERY VOLTAGE	PLATES PER CELL	DISCHARGE RATE					
		5-HOUR		20-MINUTE		5-MINUTE	
		A.H.	AMPS	A.H.	AMPS	A.H.	AMPS
12	9	25	5	16	48	12	140
24	9	17	3.4	10.3	31	6.7	80

Figure 5-2. The ampere-hour capacity of a battery depends on the rate at which it is discharged.

(2) On-board Battery Charging

The aircraft electrical generating system is designed to carry most of the electrical loads and to keep the battery fully charged. The battery has an internal resistance that causes a voltage drop when it is being charged, so in order to fully charge a 24-volt battery, the alternator or generator must produce a higher voltage, normally around 28 volts. A 12-volt battery will typically be charged by a generator producing approximately 14 volts.

The battery is kept charged by the constant voltage method, which means that the alternator output has a constant voltage, and the current flowing into the battery will be high when the battery is discharged. But as it becomes charged and its voltages rises, the current flowing into the battery will decrease, and when it is fully charged, there will be only a small current flow into the battery.

The open-circuit voltage of a lead-acid cell remains fairly constant at about 2.1 volts per cell; therefore, measuring a battery's open-circuit voltage will not accurately indicate the battery's state of charge. The

chemical change that takes place as the battery charges and discharges causes a change in the specific gravity of the battery's electrolyte. This change in specific gravity can be measured to give a good indication of the battery's state of charge. The electrolyte of a fully-charged battery will have a specific gravity of 1.275 to 1.300 at 80°F, and when the battery is fully discharged, its specific gravity will drop to around 1.150.

b. Nickel-cadmium Battery

The high-current demands of turbine engine starting created the need for a battery with a much lower internal resistance than that of the lead-acid battery. The nickel-cadmium battery has met the need and has introduced new servicing and handling techniques.

The low internal resistance of these batteries causes their closed-circuit voltage to remain nearly constant until they are almost completely discharged. This near constant closed-circuit voltage provides the appropriate power required for turbine engine starting. However, this low internal resistance can cause a discharged battery to accept such a high rate of charging current that it can become overheated and start a "thermal runaway". Therefore, many aircraft employ a battery temperature or overcharge sensor to alert the pilot to a potential thermal runaway condition.

The chemistry of these batteries is such that the specific gravity of the electrolyte gives no indication of their state of charge, and since the open circuit voltage changes very little from its 1.55 to 1.80 volts per cell, it is very difficult to determine the exact state of charge of the battery.

Nickel-cadmium batteries are periodically removed from the aircraft and given thorough servicing. Service includes performing an electrical leakage test, a visual inspection, cleaning and recharging. During an electrical leakage test, a leakage greater than 50 milliamperes between any cell terminal and the battery case is considered excessive. The battery must then be completely discharged, cleaned thoroughly, allowed to rest in its discharged condition, and then recharged to 140% of its ampere-hour capacity.

When a nickel-cadmium battery is used, special care must be taken to keep the temperature of the battery within operating range, or there is the possibility of a thermal runaway. Let's assume a condition in which the turbine engine was difficult to start and a large amount of current was taken from the battery. The high flow of current needed to start a turbine engine causes the battery to heat up; the cells located on the outer edge of the battery case can cool more quickly than those in the middle. The

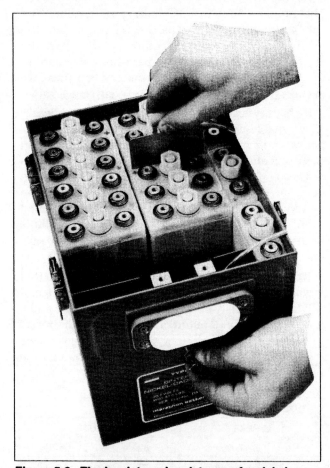

Figure 5-3. *The low internal resistance of a nickel-cadmium battery makes it useful for the high current demands of jet engine starting.*

70

middle cells will become hotter than the outside cells. When the cell heats up, it will accept more current which will cause it to heat even more. This is a self-accelerating cycle that can lead to destruction of the battery and even a fire aboard the aircraft.

To prevent thermal runaways, be sure that the battery is serviced according to the manufacturer's recommendations. The individual cells of the battery must be clean and their electrical connections properly torqued. Ensure all temperature and voltage monitors required for the aircraft are working properly. During flight, if the battery over-current, or over-temperature warning light illuminates, be sure to take the proper precautions. In most cases this means disconnect the battery from the bus and shut down the aircraft as soon as possible.

2. DC Generators and Their Controls

a. Generators

DC generators are constructed much like DC motors. An armature consisting of a series of coils of wire wound on a laminated soft iron core is rotated within an electromagnetic field. As it rotates, AC is generated within the coils and is converted into DC as it is picked up by brushes riding on the copper segments of the commutator.

To start the generation, there is a small amount of residual permanent magnetism in the frame of the generator that produces a low voltage in the rotating coils when the armature first begins to turn. This voltage causes current to flow through the field windings, and as the generator speed increases so

Figure 5-4. An aircraft DC generator produces electricity from electromagnetism and is used as the electrical power source for many aircraft.

does the field current, and the generator output voltage rises. Once the output voltage reaches a predetermined level, it is sent to the aircraft busbar for distribution. The output of the generator is a function of the amount of field current and the speed of armature rotation.

In order to control generator output, a unit called a voltage regulator is used to vary the field current according to engine speed and electrical system demands. The voltage regulator monitors generator output voltage and when it rises above the desired value, changes the resistance of the field circuit, lowering the generators output. All generators employ a reverse-current relay between the generator output terminal and the bus. This prevents the battery discharging through the generator. As soon as the generator voltage rises above that of the battery, the relay automatically closes and puts the generator on the line. The reverse-current relay may be contained in the voltage regulator or it may be a separate unit.

b. Generator Controls

(1) For High-output Generators

The voltage produced by a DC generator is regulated by controlling the field current as a function of the generator output voltage. There are two methods of connecting the shunt field of a generator to the armature, and the method of connection determines the action and placement of the voltage regulator.

If the internal field connection is made to the (positive) brush or brushes, the voltage regulator acts as a variable resistor between the external field connection and ground. But if the internal field connection is made to the grounded brush, the voltage regulator is placed between the external field connection and the armature output.

Many older generators requiring a considerable amount of field current often use carbon-pile voltage regulators. A stack of carbon discs is assembled in a ceramic tube, and pressure is applied with a spring to hold the discs tightly together. An electrical connection is made to each end of the stack, and current from the generator output flows through the carbon stack and the field coils to ground at the ground brush inside the generator.

An electromagnet draws current from the generator output to sense the output voltage. When the engine is started and the generator begins to turn, the residual magnetism in the generator frame provides the magnetic field to start output current flowing, and as this current flows through the compressed carbon pile and the field windings, increases the field strength and the output voltage rises. The increased voltage causes more current to flow through the regulator's electromagnet and begins to pull on the armature which opposes the spring, and loosens the carbon pile. Loosening the pile increases its resistance and decreases the field current so that the generator output voltage drops.

Most high-output electrical systems use some form of differential-voltage, reverse-current relay that serves a dual function: it acts as a remotely controlled switch for the pilot or flight engineer to open the generator output circuit, and it automatically connects the generator to the electrical system bus when the generator voltage is a specified amount higher than the battery voltage. It also disconnects the generator from the system when its output voltage drops below a specified value.

The main contactor is in series with a reverse-current coil and is installed in the main line between the generator output and the aircraft power bus. When the generator switch is closed and the generator is turning, current flows through the voltage coil. When the generator voltage is high enough, the magnetic strength of this coil closes the voltage contacts, and current can flow between the battery and the generator through the differential voltage

coil. As soon as the generator voltage rises to a preset value above the battery voltage, the magnetic strength of the differential voltage coil closes the differential voltage contacts so current can flow to the main contactor coil and close the main contactor. This puts the generator on the system bus.

The generator remains on the line as long as its output voltage is higher than that of the battery, or until the pilot or engineer opens the generator switch. When the engine speed decreases enough to drop the generator output voltage below that of the battery, current flows from the battery into the generator, and as it does, it flows through the reverse-current coil. The magnetic field from this reverse-flowing current cancels the field from the differential voltage coil, and a spring opens the differential voltage contacts. This opens the circuit to the main contactor coil and de-energizes it so that it loses its magnetic pull on the contactors and they spring open, disconnecting the generator from the power bus. This is necessary to keep the generator from discharging the battery in the event of a generator failure.

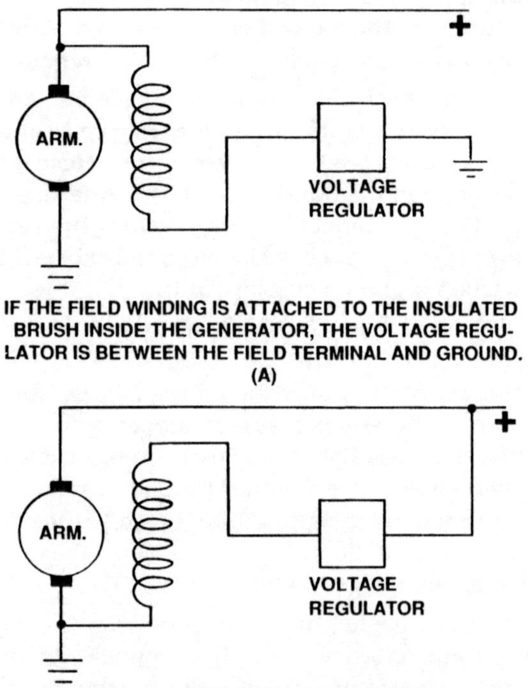

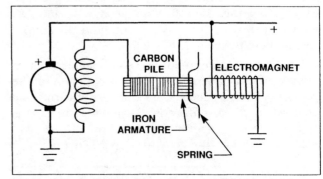

Figure 5-6. A carbon-pile voltage regulator is used with generators requiring a large amount of field current.

IF THE FIELD WINDING IS ATTACHED TO THE INSULATED BRUSH INSIDE THE GENERATOR, THE VOLTAGE REGULATOR IS BETWEEN THE FIELD TERMINAL AND GROUND.
(A)

IF THE FIELD WINDING IS ATTACHED TO THE GROUNDED BRUSH INSIDE THE GENERATOR, THE VOLTAGE REGULATOR IS BETWEEN THE FIELD TERMINAL AND THE GENERATOR OUTPUT.
(B)

Figure 5-5. Voltage regulator placement in DC generator circuits.

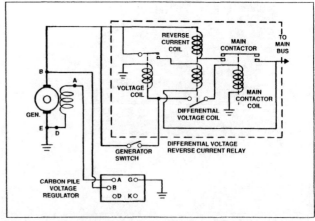

Figure 5-7. A differential reverse-current relay connects the generator to the battery when the generator output voltage is higher than battery voltage.

72

(2) For Low-output Generators

Most low-output DC generators are found on older single engine and light twin-engine aircraft. These systems typically employ a 3-unit-vibrator-type control unit. The three units are, the voltage regulator, the current limiter and the reverse-current cutout relay.

(a) Voltage Regulator

A typical vibrator-type voltage regulator senses the voltage output of the generator by an electromagnet, winding C on the voltage regulator (figure 5-8). This electromagnet exerts a pull on a set of contacts that are spring-loaded in their closed position.

The generator field winding is connected to ground through these contacts when they are closed. When the ground is connected, current flows through the field windings to create the field magnetism needed to produce the generator output voltage.

When the output voltage rises to its regulated value, the pull on the voltage regulator contact points becomes strong enough to open them, and the field current must flow through the resistor R to get to ground. This resistor decreases the field current, and the generator output voltage drops. The contacts vibrate open and closed many times each second to maintain the output voltage at the value for which they are adjusted.

(b) Current Limiter

Low-output electrical systems typically use an automatic current limiter to prevent electrical loads exceeding the generator rating. An electromagnet made up of a few turns of heavy wire in series with the generator output creates the current limiter relay coil. The magnetism from this coil exerts a pull on a set of contacts that are spring-loaded to their closed position. The magnetic strength is proportional to the amount of current flowing out of the generator, and the spring holding the contacts closed is calibrated so that when the rated current flows through the current limiter coil, the magnetic pull will open the contacts.

The current limiter contacts are in the generator field circuit, in series with the contacts in the voltage regulator. If the current demands exceed the output rating of the generator, the contacts will open and the field current will have to flow through the resistor to ground. This will decrease the field current and lower the generator output voltage so it cannot produce enough current to exceed the generator rating.

(c) Reverse-current Cutout Relay (RCR)

The RCR used in most low-output generators is simply an electromagnet with two windings. One winding, called the voltage winding, is made up of many turns of fine wire and is in parallel with the generator output.

The other, a current winding, is in series with the current limiter coil and connects to the normally open contacts of the relay. When the engine is not running and there is no current through the voltage coil, a spring holds the contacts open. When the engine starts and the generator begins to produce voltage, current flows through the voltage coil. And when the voltage rises to a preset value, which, for a 12-volt system is usually between 11.8 and 13 volts, the pull produced by the voltage coil will close the contacts. With the contacts closed, the generator is connected to the aircraft electrical system, and current flowing through the current coil helps hold the contacts tightly closed. If the generator output voltage becomes less than the battery voltage, current will flow through the current coil in a reverse direction. The magnetic field this current produces will oppose the field of the voltage coil, and the spring will open the contacts, removing the generator from the electrical system.

3. Starter/Generators

Starter/generators are dual purpose units typically found on turbine powered aircraft. This unit provides both power for starting the engine and electrical power to the aircraft bus after the engine is started. The advantages of the starter/generator are that it does the work of two units in the space and weight of one, and it is directly coupled to the engine through the gear box, eliminating any disengagement mechanism needed for conventional starters. During the start mode, the starter/generator receives power to both the armature and the series field windings. This produces a high motor torque needed for starting. During run operations the unit receives power to its shunt field which, along with the rotating armature, produces an output voltage in the same manner as a low-output generator.

Typically, starter/generators have a control system similar to that found on high-output generator systems as discussed earlier. The control unit for a modern twin-engine aircraft starter/generator system would contain circuits for voltage regulation,

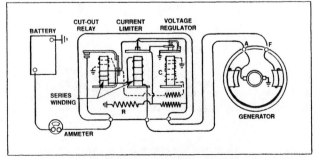

Figure 5-8. A vibrator-type voltage regulator is used with many of the low-output DC generators.

over-voltage protection, reverse-current protection, over-excitation protection load sharing and paralleling. Paralleling of generators is necessary when two or more generators are used to supply electrical power to the aircraft bus. Paralleling circuitry ensures that at any given time during normal flight the aircraft's electrical loads are carried equally by all operating generators.

4. DC Alternators and Their Controls

a. Alternator

The 3-phase alternator with a built-in solid-state rectifier has almost become the standard source for aircraft DC electrical power. A generator has several disadvantages an alternator does not have. All of the AC load current is produced in the rotating armature of a generator and must be changed into DC, or rectified, by a mechanical switch called the commutator and brush assembly. The heavy load current must all flow through the brush-to-commutator contact. Since this is a moving contact, it is difficult to get a good electrical connection; hence, the brushes and commutator typically require regular maintenance. In a DC alternator the AC load current (up to 150 amps) is produced in the fixed stator winding rather than in the moving winding of the generator, and is rectified by semiconductor diodes so that all of the connections through which this current flows are solid. The low field current (approximately 5 amps) flows through brushes and smooth slip rings into the rotor, where it produces several sets of north and south magnetic poles. The multi-polar rotor produces a usable output at a much lower engine RPM than the generator, which has fewer sets of field poles.

The stator of an alternator has three sets of windings connected into a Y-type circuit, whose output

is connected to a 6-diode full-wave rectifier. The output from the rectifier is almost pure DC, with a high-frequency, low-amplitude ripple.

b. Solid-state Voltage Regulator

The principle of generation is the same with an alternator as it is with a generator. There is a relative motion between a magnetic field and a conductor. The voltage produced in the conductor is determined by the rate at which the lines of flux are cut, and this depends on the speed of the rotating member and the strength of the magnetic field. In the alternator, the rotating element, the rotor, carries the field current. The voltage regulator senses the alternator output voltage and controls the field current to keep this voltage within the desired range. Modern solid-state electronics have done away, to a great extent, with moving parts to sense and control current and voltage. And while it is possible to use a vibrator-type voltage regulator with an alternator, most of the modern systems use a solid-state voltage regulator.

When the alternator switch is turned on, the field relay closes and current flows through transistor T_1 and the rotor field coil. As soon as the engine starts, the alternator begins to put out voltage, and when the voltage rises to the regulating value, the zener diode ZD, begins to conduct. Then, through the action of transistor T_2, T_1 shuts off the field current and the output voltage drops. As soon as the voltage across ZD drops below its zener voltage and stops conducting, T_1 turns back on, allowing field current to flow again. This solid-state device provides smooth and consistent control of the system voltage with no moving parts.

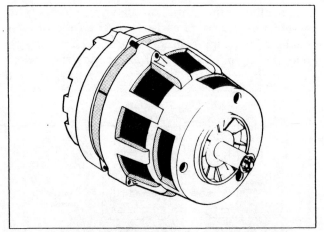

Figure 5-9. Aircraft alternators are used instead of generators because of their higher current output at low engine RPM.

Figure 5-10. A solid-state voltage regulator controls the voltage of an aircraft alternator and has no moving parts.

The solid-state rectifier used in the alternator prevents the flow of any current from the load bus back to the alternator stator winding so there is no need for reverse-current relay with an alternator. The field current is taken from the regulated bus voltage rather than directly from the alternator output, and this makes the alternator self-limiting with regard to current output, so there is no need for a current limiter. There is a need, however, for a relay or switch in the alternator field to prevent current flowing through the field winding when the engine is not running. This field relay or switching transistor is typically contained in the voltage regulator or alternator control unit.

B. AC Power System

1. Alternator

Most of the larger aircraft use AC for their primary electrical power. DC is supplied from the AC alternators through a transformer-rectifier unit, commonly called a T-R unit. The T-R unit steps down the AC voltage using a transformer and then changes the AC to DC using a full-wave rectifier. DC power is necessary on all aircraft for certain equipment and battery charging.

A typical AC alternator for a large jet transport aircraft has a rating of between 40 to 90 KVA and has a 3-phase output, with the phases normally connected in a Y-arrangement producing a 400 CPS current. There are two basic types of alternators in use, brushless and the brush-type. Modern aircraft typically use the brushless alternator system employing an integrated oil cooler to help eliminate the heat generated during operation.

The brushless alternator uses a small amount of exciter current to induce a larger alternator field

current in the rotor. The exciter field magnetism induces a current into the rotating exciter armature. The exciter armature sends its current through six diodes in the rotor that convert the intruded AC into DC for use in the field coil. The alternator field then induces a voltage into the main AC armature in the stator of the unit. This system eliminates the need for a rotating electrical connection between the rotor and the stator of the alternator.

The 3-phase output of AC alternators typically have a voltage of 120 volts across each of the phase windings, and with the windings connected in a Y, the output between each of the terminals is 208 volts.

2. Alternator Drive

It is essential that the alternator output have a nominal frequency of 400 Hz with a tolerance usually from 380 to 420 Hz. This is accomplished throughout the engine operating speed range by using a hydraulically operated constant-speed drive unit between the engine and the alternator. A CSD consists of an axial-piston hydraulic pump and motor, connected together so that regardless of the engine speed, the CSD output will be constant. This constant speed is required for the alternator to have an output of 400 Hz. Many modern aircraft employ an Integrated Drive Generator (IDG)

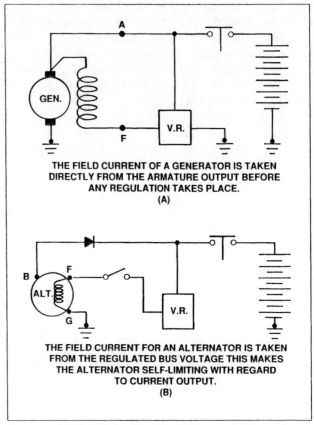

THE FIELD CURRENT OF A GENERATOR IS TAKEN DIRECTLY FROM THE ARMATURE OUTPUT BEFORE ANY REGULATION TAKES PLACE.
(A)

THE FIELD CURRENT FOR AN ALTERNATOR IS TAKEN FROM THE REGULATED BUS VOLTAGE THIS MAKES THE ALTERNATOR SELF-LIMITING WITH REGARD TO CURRENT OUTPUT.
(B)

Figure 5-12. Typical voltage regulator arrangements for generators and alternators.

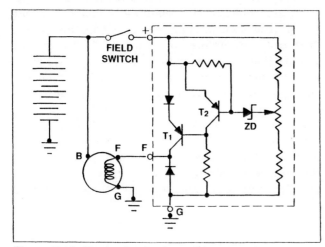

Figure 5-11. Basic circuit of a solid-state voltage regulator for a DC alternator.

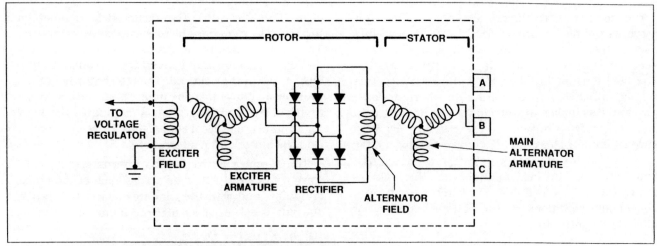

Figure 5-13. Circuit of a brushless AC alternator for large aircraft.

which contains both the alternator and CSD in one compact unit. This compact unit is mounted to a quick-attach-detach (QAD) adaptor which facilitates removal and replacement. This quick replacement helps the airlines maintain flight schedules even when a problem occurs within the IDG.

If the AC frequency should drop below approximately 350 Hz, the inductive reactance will decrease enough that the current can become excessive. To prevent damage to the circuit components, if the CSD should ever allow the alternator frequency to drop, the AC alternator (generator) control unit incorporates an under-frequency compensating circuit that will decrease the alternator field current and drop the output voltage enough to prevent excessive current flow.

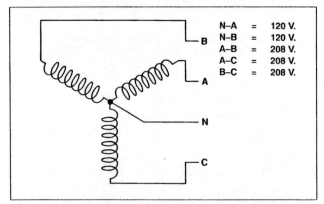

N–A	=	120 V.
N–B	=	120 V.
A–B	=	208 V.
A–C	=	208 V.
B–C	=	208 V.

Figure 5-14. The Y-connected, 3-phase output of an aircraft alternator has 120 volts across each phase winding and 208 volts across any two windings.

3. AC Voltage Regulator

The complex nature of AC power systems in an aircraft requires more considerations for voltage regulation than are required for DC systems. The voltage control circuit must sense the voltage output of all three phases in the alternator, and if they are not equal and within limits, adjust them accordingly. There must be provisions in the regulator to reduce the alternator voltage if the frequency drops below a specified level, and the control system must have provisions for equalizing both the real and the reactive loads among the generators. Many aircraft use a Generator Control Unit (GCU) to perform these functions as well as performing system testing and fault isolation.

4. Constant Speed Variable Frequency (VSCF) Alternators

The VSCF systems are the latest attempt to eliminate moving parts from the various electrical components on the aircraft. This system utilizes a large DC alternator which is not reliant on a constant input speed. The mechanically complex constant speed drive unit is therefore not required. The DC output voltage from the alternator is sent to a solid-state device which converts the DC to an AC voltage of a constant 400 CPS. This unit is typically referred to as an invertor. The electronic control circuitry for VSCF system is quite complex; however, the reliability of the electrical system should out-perform the CSD needed for the typical AC alternator. It is very likely that future AC power systems will rely on the VSCF system due to their enhanced reliability.

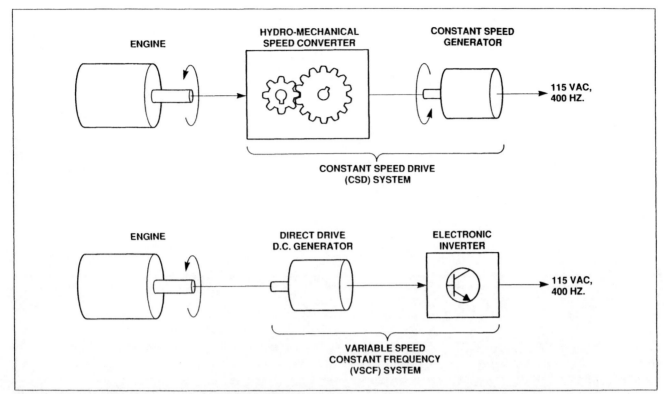

Figure 5-15. Block diagram of a typical VSCF system.

Chapter VI

Aircraft Electrical Systems

Originally all aircraft flew without an electrical system. Electrical power was produced, but its sole purpose was to create the spark necessary for combustion within the piston engine. Soon came the need for better navigation and communication systems. Electrically operated radios and navigational aids became commonplace.

Today modern aircraft could not fly without an electrical system. A typical commercial airliner contains miles of wire connecting hundreds of components. Aircraft require electrical power for fuel pumps, fuel valves, engine instruments and the landing gear, as well as for the starter, lights, and communication and navigation radios.

It is essential to understand not only the theory of electricity, but its practical application. In this chapter, we consider the practical aspects of the airframe electrical system. We will consider the generation and regulation of power from our on-board electrical power sources, then look at typical electrical systems, wiring installation and electrical system components.

A. Wiring Diagrams

1. Block Diagrams

The block diagram uses very few component symbols, but rather uses blocks to tell how a particular portion of the system operates. In figure 6-1, we have a block diagram of the power system of a Boeing 727. From this diagram we can tell nothing about the wires required nor the types of components, but the interrelation between the parts of the system is very clear. We can tell what each generator does and visualize the way each of the relays and breakers tie the system together and the way in which to isolate portions of the circuit. A block diagram gives us an overview of a system in the simplest way.

2. Pictorial Diagrams

The symbols used on an electrical schematic are actually a language of their own and are often unintelligible to persons not schooled in their use. In figure 6-2, we have a pictorial diagram of a popular single-engine aircraft electrical system. This is sort of a mixture of a block diagram and a schematic. You can identify such components as the alternator (7), the starter (16), the battery (1), and the ignition switch (17), but you do not know the wire sizes needed, or part numbers of any of the components. This type of drawing is extremely helpful for understanding the operation of a system and of seeing the interrelationship between parts.

3. Schematic Diagrams

From a schematic diagram, we can get the information needed to troubleshoot and service the equipment, and since this type of diagram is used in the manufacturer's maintenance manuals, they are FAA-approved data. In the typical diagram of figure 6-3, we have the information we need to service this particular flashing beacon light. In the equipment table, we can find the part number of each of the components, and in the wire table we have the wire gauge and a list of the various electrical connectors.

The symbols used for aircraft schematics vary somewhat from one manufacturer to the next, but the symbols shown in figure 6-4 are typical of the ones you are most likely to encounter.

B. Small Single-engine Aircraft

The electrical systems for most of the small single-engine aircraft are relatively simple. The power is distributed to the various loads through the aircraft busbar, or bus. The bus receives power from the battery or aircraft alternator. Aircraft systems have a master switch to disconnect the battery from the electrical system when the generator is not in use, and there is also a switch to open the generator or alternator field and shut off its output in case of an electrical system malfunction.

Most of the aircraft service manuals have all of the electrical circuits broken down with only one basic circuit per page. This makes troubleshooting much easier by isolating the individual circuit. The term "schematic" is often used to refer to the electrical diagrams found in such manuals. The intent of these diagrams is to show the aircraft technician the relationship between all the electrical components and their associated wiring of a particular system. The electrical diagrams do not show the physical location of components; they do however sometimes contain code numbers which help locate a component on the aircraft.

1. Battery Circuit

The electrical systems for most small aircraft use lead-acid batteries rated at either 12 or 24 volts, and, almost without exception, all use a negative-ground, single-wire system. This means that the negative terminal of the battery is connected directly to the aircraft structure, and places the entire metal aircraft structure at a negative potential. All electrical components need only a single wire from the positive voltage source to supply them, and their negative terminals connected to the metal structure to provide a return (negative) path for the current. The exception to this system occurs when the aircraft is built using composite materials in place of aluminum. The composite materials are non-conductive. On composite aircraft, or portions of the aircraft made of composites, a 2-wire system must be used. One wire is needed for the positive connection and one for the negative connection.

In figure 6-5, we have a typical battery circuit for a light aircraft. The positive terminal of the battery connects to the battery contactor, which is a normally-open heavy-duty relay. One end of the control coil of the contactor connects internally to the main terminal, and the other end is sent to ground through the battery master switch on the instrument panel. A clipping diode is installed across the coil of the relay to eliminate spikes of voltage that are induced when the master switch is opened and the magnetic field from the contactor coil collapses. The voltage spikes may damage sensitive electronic components if they are not controlled using the clipping diode.

Most aircraft have some circuits that require power whether the master switch is on or not. Low-current components, such as the clock and the flight-hour meter circuit, are connected to the main terminal of the battery contactor and receive current any time a battery is installed in the aircraft. These circuits often employ an in-line fuse or one mounted adjacent to the battery to protect the circuit.

The battery and battery contactor on a light aircraft may be located on the engine-side of the

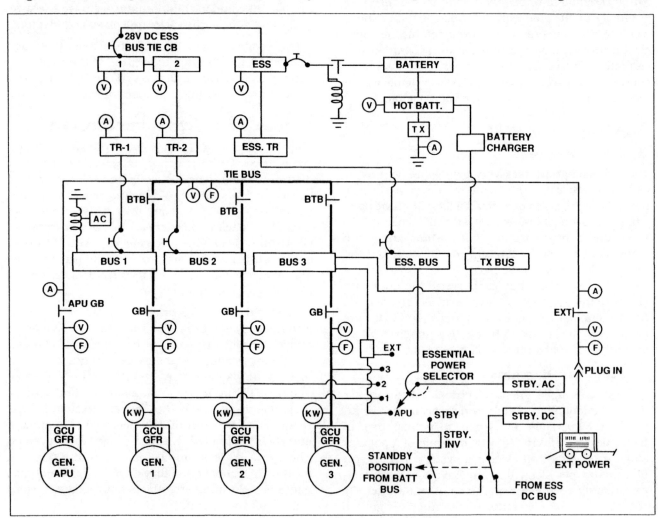

Figure 6-1. Block diagram of the electrical system of a Boeing 727 jet transport aircraft.

firewall, or they may be in the rear baggage compartment. To reduce the amount of large wire needed, the starter contactor, which is always on the engine-side of the firewall, normally serves as a junction point for the heavy wire from the battery contactor and ground service circuit, as well as for the wire that supplies the aircraft electrical loads through the ammeter.

2. Generator Circuit

An aircraft generator or alternator is a primary source of electrical energy. It must have sufficient capacity to supply all of the electrical loads and keep the battery fully charged.

It is possible for an aircraft to have electrical demands that exceed the rating of the generator. If this occurs for two minutes or less, no action must be taken. If the overload continues, the aircraft must have placards that tell what equipment can be used.

Most smaller electrical systems use a current limiter in the generator control to limit the generator current. Aircraft which use a DC alternator typically have a circuit breaker as their current limiter. An ammeter is typically installed in either the alternator output lead or battery positive lead. An ammeter installed in the battery lead should not show

discharge except during the momentary operation of high-current devices such as landing gear motors or flaps. If a discharge is shown on the ammeter, the generator/alternator is incapable of supplying enough current to meet demands. If the ammeter is installed in the alternator output lead, the meter will indicate a positive value whenever the alternator is working correctly.

Some installations, instead of having an ammeter, use a load-meter which is similar to an ammeter but is marked in percentage rather than in amps. The flight crew should never allow the electrical load to exceed 100% on the meter. The shunt for the load-meter is matched to the generator output to indicate 100% when the generator rated current is flowing.

In an installation where there is no way to monitor the load, and where it is important that the battery be kept charged in flight, the total continuous load connected to the generator should not exceed 80% of the generator's rated output.

In figure 6-7, we have a typical light-aircraft generator circuit. The generator output goes to the voltage regulator and through the reverse current relay inside the regulator box to the main bus. It must pass through a circuit breaker of adequate capacity to protect the generator in case the current

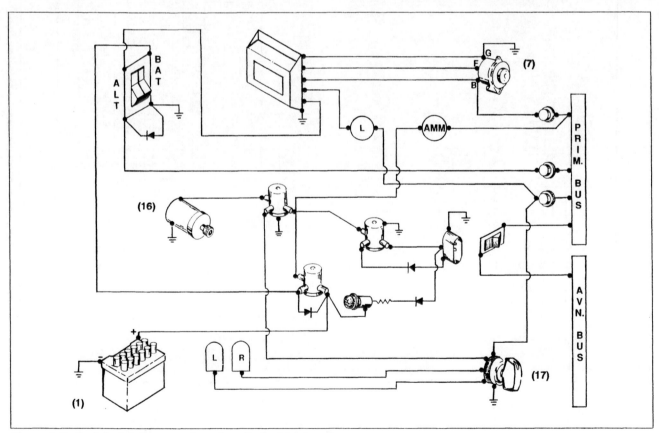

Figure 6-2. A pictorial diagram of an aircraft electrical system.

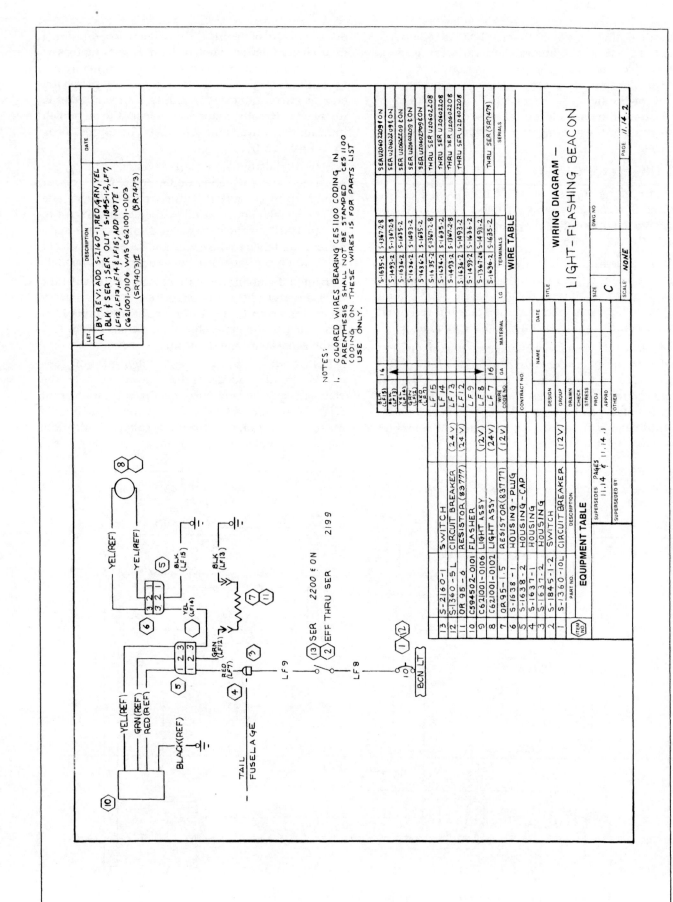

Figure 6-3. A schematic diagram of a portion of an aircraft electrical system.

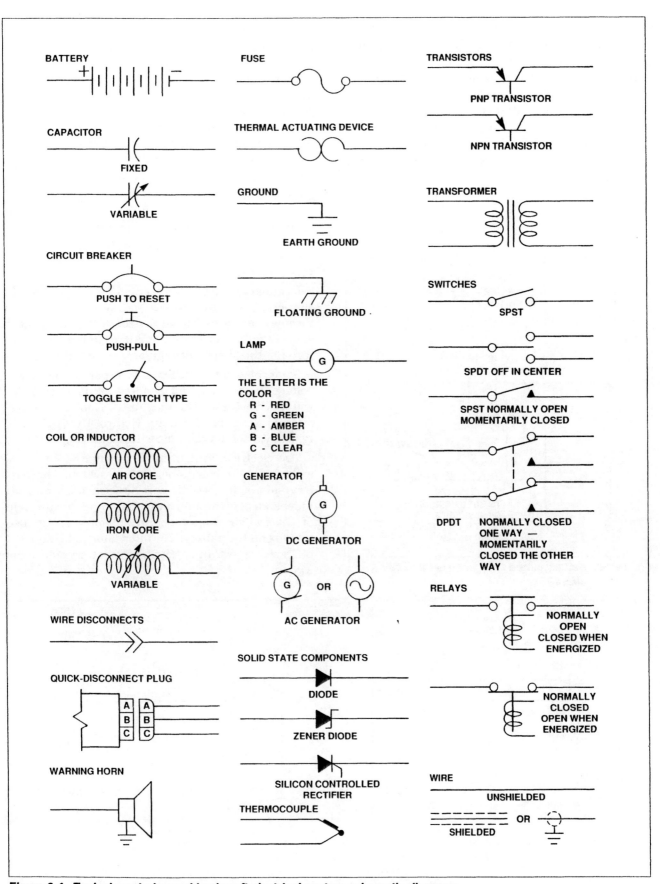

Figure 6-4. Typical symbols used in aircraft electrical system schematic diagrams.

limiter should malfunction. The field current flows from the field terminal of the generator, through one side of the master switch to the F-terminal of the voltage regulator, and to ground inside the regulator.

The generator and the battery are in parallel with their common terminal at the main bus. The ammeter measures only the current flowing into or out of the battery.

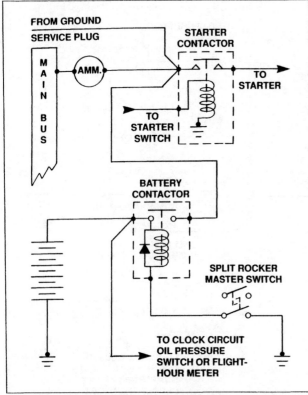

Figure 6-5. *Battery circuit for a small single-engine aircraft.*

3. Alternator Circuit

The advantages of more current for less weight has made the alternator the modern choice for DC electrical power on most aircraft. The exception to this is the use of starter generators found on turbine-powered aircraft. The external circuit of a DC alternator is similar to that used by a generator, with a few exceptions. In figure 6-8, we have a typical DC alternator circuit for a light aircraft.

The G-terminal of the alternator is connected to ground at the G-terminal of the voltage regulator. The B-terminal of the alternator is its positive output terminal, and it connects to the aircraft main power bus through a circuit breaker that protects the alternator from exceeding its current limits. The F-terminal of the alternator connects directly to the F-terminal of the voltage regulator, and this circuit continues out the B-terminal of the regulator, through the over-voltage sensor to the alternator side of the master switch and then to the main bus through the alternator regulator circuit breaker.

Some alternator systems incorporate the over-voltage sensor, an under-voltage sensor, and the voltage regulator into one unit. This unit, often referred to as an Alternator Control Unit (ACU), is typically a solid-state unit with no moving parts.

The electrical system master switch is an interlocking double-pole, single-throw switch. The battery side of the switch can be turned on and off independent of the alternator, but the alternator side of the switch cannot be turned on without also turning on the battery. The alternator can be turned off, however, without affecting the battery side of the switch.

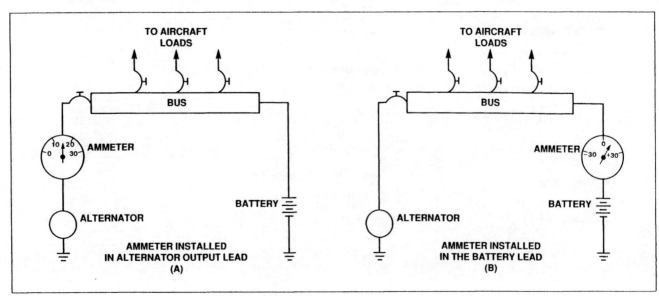

Figure 6-6. *Typical ammeter installations for a DC alternator.*

84

An over-voltage relay in the field circuit senses the output voltage, and if it becomes excessive, it will open the field circuit, shutting off the alternator output. It also turns on a warning light on the instrument panel informing the pilot that the generator is off the line because it has produced an excessively high voltage.

A solid-state diode is placed across the master switch from the field connection of the alternator side to the ground terminal of the battery side. This allows any spikes of voltage that are induced into the system when the field switch is opened to pass harmlessly to ground rather than getting to the main power bus.

4. External Power Circuit

Because of the heavy drain the starter puts on the battery, many aircraft are equipped with external power receptacles where a battery cart, or external power supply, may be plugged in to furnish power for engine starting.

Power is brought from the battery cart through a standard 3-terminal plug. Two of the pins in the aircraft receptacle are larger than the third, and they are also longer. When the cart is plugged in, a solid contact is made with the two larger plugs. The external power relay in the aircraft remains open and no current can flow from the external source until the plug is forced all the way into the receptacle and the smaller

pin makes contact. This small pin then supplies power through the reverse-polarity diode to the external power relay which closes, connecting the external power source to the aircraft bus.

The reverse-polarity diode is used in the circuit to prevent an external power source with incorrect polarity from being connected to the aircraft's bus. The diode simply blocks current from flowing to the external power relay if the applied power is connected backwards or offering reverse polarity.

It is possible that the aircraft battery can be so completely discharged that the battery contactor cannot get enough current to close. This would prevent the external power source from charging the battery. A circuit consisting of a diode, a current-limiting resistor, and a fuse is connected between the positive terminal of the external power plug and the battery side of the battery contactor. With this arrangement, enough current can flow from the external power source to energize the battery contactor coil so that it can close and allow the battery to be charged. The diode D_2 is in the circuit to prevent the positive pin in the external power receptacle from being "hot" when no external power plug is connected.

With many of the smaller aircraft having 12-volt systems while others have 24-volt systems, it is

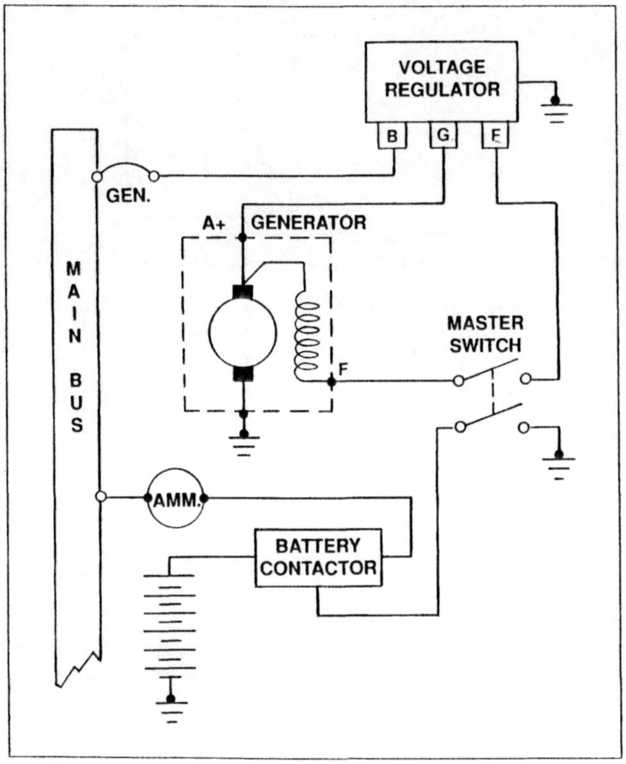

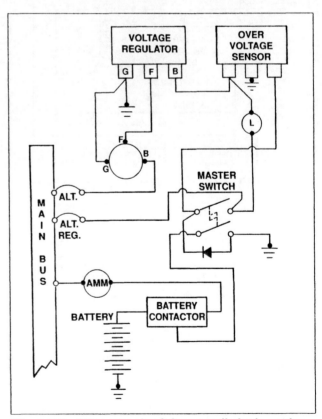

Figure 6-7. Generator circuit for a small single-engine aircraft.

Figure 6-8. Alternator circuit for a small single-engine aircraft.

extremely important that the correct voltage be used with an external power source. Diode D_1 prevents the external power relay closing if a power source has the wrong polarity, but there is normally no protection against the improper voltage.

5. Starter Circuit

In most aircraft, the starter is activated through a solenoid by ignition switch or start button found on the instrument panel. A spring-loaded START position on the switch sends current from the main bus to the coil of the starter contactor. The term contactor is often used to define a heavy current solenoid. When the starter contactor closes, the high current required for the starter motor flows from either the battery or the external power source to the starter.

6. Avionics Power Circuit

The vast majority of the avionics equipment used today has solid-state components, which can be damaged by voltage spikes such as those produced when a magnetic

field collapses and sends its induced voltage into the system. To prevent this type of damage to the avionics equipment, the radios often receive power from a separate bus that may be isolated from the main bus when the engine is being started or when the external power source is connected.

The avionics bus may be connected to the main bus with a split-bus relay, which is a normally-closed relay that is opened by current from the ignition switch when it is in the START position, and from the control pin of the external power receptacle. Diodes are used in the circuit to both of the sources of current to isolate one when the other is being used.

The avionics bus of some aircraft is isolated from the main bus by a circuit breaker switch rather than with a relay. When an avionics power switch is installed, it is the responsibility of the pilot to be sure this switch is turned off before the master switch is either turned on or off and any time the engine is started or external power is connected to the aircraft.

This arrangement has a couple of very definite advantages. The circuit breaker-type switch can be used as a master switch for all of the avionics equipment so their individual switches will not have

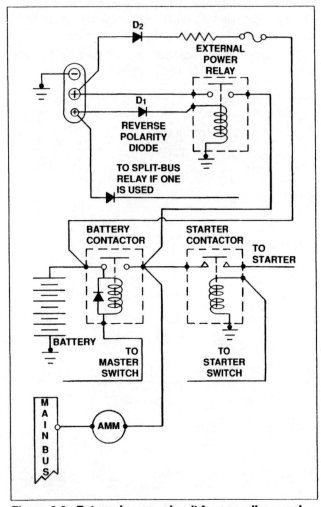

Figure 6-9. *External power circuit for a small general aviation aircraft.*

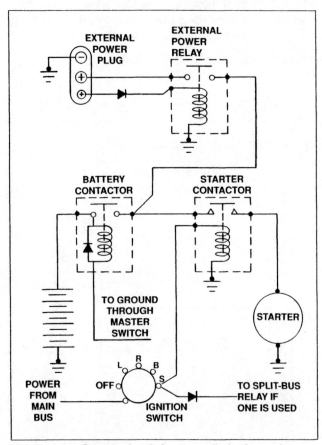

Figure 6-10. *Starter circuit for a small single-engine aircraft.*

to be used. And in the case of a fault in any of the avionics equipment, this circuit breaker will open to protect the avionics wiring.

7. Landing Gear Circuit

In figure 6-13, we have the landing gear circuit for a typical twin-engine general-aviation airplane. The landing gear is hydraulically operated by a reversible DC electric motor. It turns in one direction to lower the gear and in the opposite direction to raise it.

Consider the airplane to be in the air with the landing gear down and locked, but with the landing gear selector switch in the GEAR UP position (figure 6-13(A)). The down-limit switches in each of the three landing gear are in the DOWN position and the up-limit switches are all in their NOT UP position. Current flows through the NOT UP side of the up-limit switches through the FLIGHT side of the squat switch and through the hydraulic pressure switch to the gear up relay.

The squat switch in the circuit is mounted on one of the struts such that it is in one position when the weight of the airplane is on the landing gear and in the other position when there is no weight on the wheels. The purpose of the squat switch in this circuit is to prevent the gear from being retracted while the aircraft is still on the ground. The hydraulic pressure switch is used to turn off the pump motor in the event hydraulic pressure exceeds its limits.

This switch is closed when the hydraulic pressure is low, but opens when the hydraulic pressure rises to a preset value.

From the pressure switch, the current goes through the coil of the LANDING GEAR UP relay and to ground through the landing gear selector switch. This flow of current creates a magnetic field in the LANDING GEAR UP relay and closes it, so that current can flow from the main bus through the relay contacts and the windings that turn the motor in the direction to raise the landing gear. As soon as the landing gear is fully up, the up-lock switches in each gear move to the UP position and current is shut off to the landing gear motor relay and the motor stops. The down-limit switches have moved to the NOT DOWN position, and the three down-and-locked lights go out. If the throttle is closed when the landing gear is not down and locked, the warning horn will sound.

The landing gear may be lowered in flight by moving the landing gear selector switch to the GEAR DOWN position. Follow this in figure 6-13(B). Current flows through the NOT DOWN side of the down-limit switches, through the coil of the LANDING GEAR DOWN relay, and to ground through the landing gear selector switch. The motor turns in the direction needed to produce hydraulic pressure to lower the landing gear.

When the landing gear is down and locked, (figure 6-13(C)), current flows through the DOWN sides of the down-limit switches, and the green GEAR DOWN AND LOCKED lights come on. In the daytime, current from these lights goes directly to ground through the closed contacts of the light dimming relay. At night when the navigation lights are on, current from this light circuit energizes the relay, and current from the indicator lights must go to ground through the resistor. This makes the lights illuminate dimly so they will not be distracting at night.

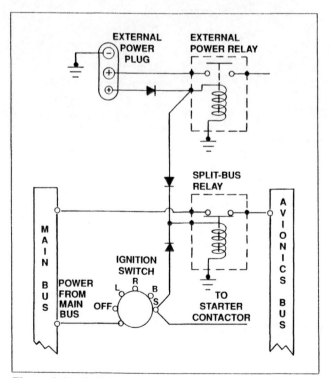

Figure 6-11. Avionics power source using a split-bus relay.

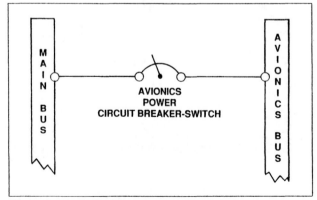

Figure 6-12. Avionics power source using a circuit-breaker switch.

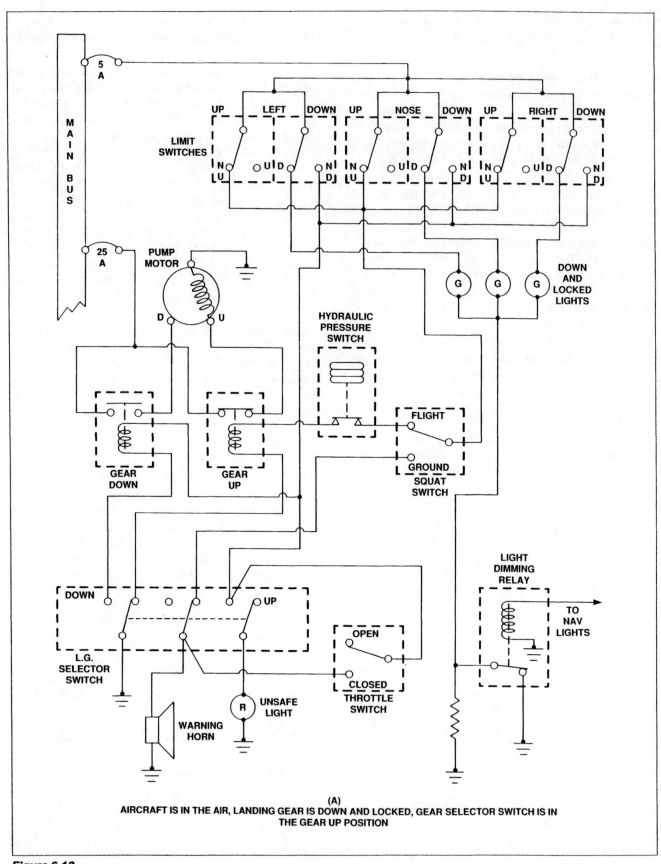

Figure 6-13.
(A)   (1 of 3) Landing gear circuit.

88

If any of the limit switches are in a NOT UP or a NOT DOWN position, a red UNSAFE light will illuminate. But when the landing gear selector switch is in the LANDING GEAR DOWN position and all three gears are down and locked, the light will be out. If the selector switch is in the LANDING GEAR UP position and all three gears are in the up position, the light will also be out.

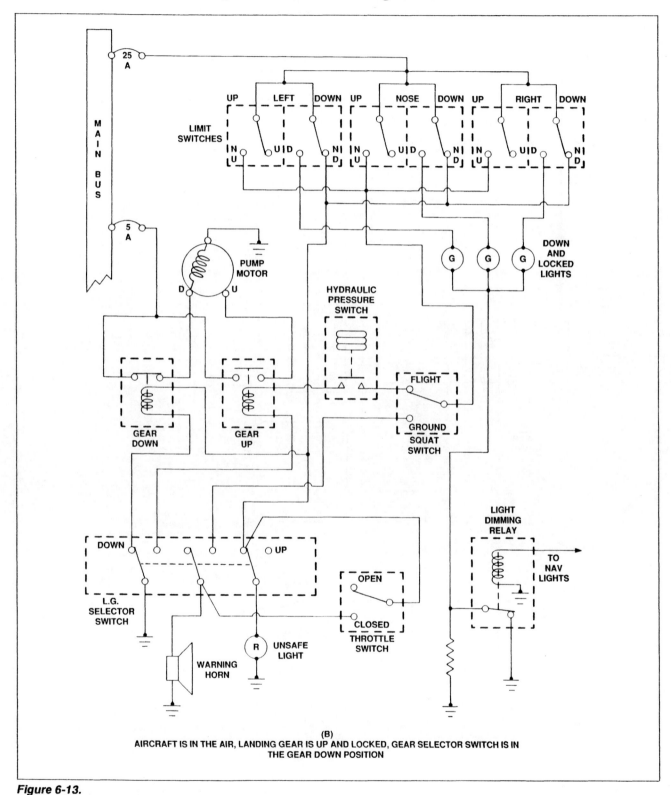

Figure 6-13.
(B) (2 of 3) Landing gear circuit.

If the airplane is on the ground with the squat switch in the GROUND position, and the landing gear selector switch is moved to the LANDING GEAR UP position, the warning horn will sound but the landing gear pump motor will not run.

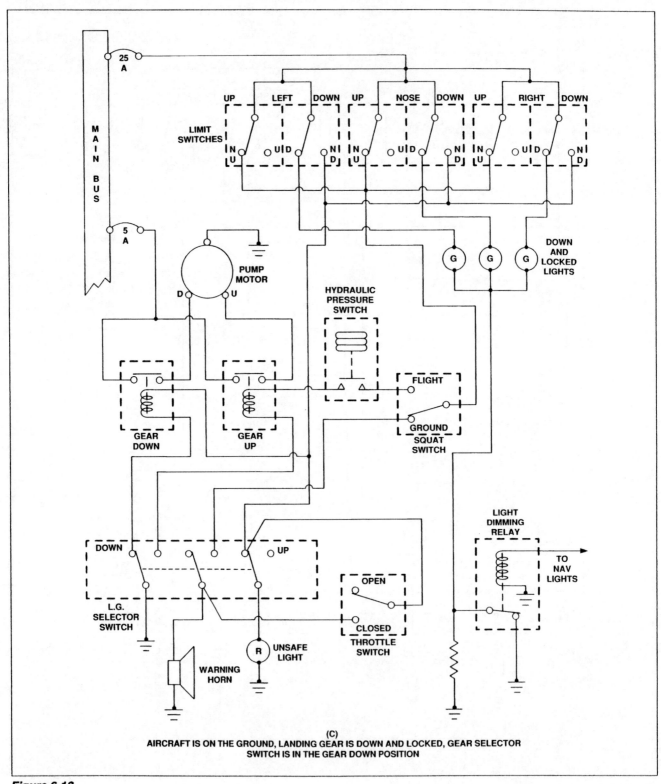

(C)
AIRCRAFT IS ON THE GROUND, LANDING GEAR IS DOWN AND LOCKED, GEAR SELECTOR SWITCH IS IN THE GEAR DOWN POSITION

Figure 6-13.
(C)   (3 of 3) Landing gear circuit.

8. Alternating Current Supply

Small aircraft for which DC is the primary source of electrical power have little use for alternating current except for certain instruments that require 26-volt, 400-Hz AC and some lighting circuits known as Electro Luminescent Panels. Most aircraft needing this type of power are equipped with solid-state, or static, invertors. These units consist of a solid-state sine-wave oscillator followed by a transformer that produces the required power. Some instruments that use 26-volt AC have built-in invertors and can be operated with a DC input voltage.

Before solid-state electronics became such an important factor in aircraft instrumentation, most DC-powered aircraft got their AC for instruments from small single-phase rotary invertors which had a small DC motor driving an AC generator. These units may still be found in some of the older aircraft, but because they are noisy, subject to mechanical problems and are electrically inefficient, the rotary invertors in most cases are being replaced by solid-state invertors.

C. Small Multi-engine Aircraft

The vast majority of light twin-engine aircraft use two generators or alternators and have their voltage controlled so that when they are connected together on the power bus, the regulators work together to

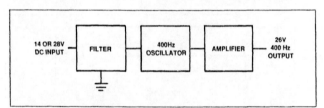

Figure 6-14. A solid-state invertor uses an oscillator to produce 400-Hz AC, which is amplified so it can drive AC instruments.

Figure 6-15. A rotary invertor used to produce AC from DC.

keep the output voltages of the two sources the same. This is called paralleling.

1. Paralleling with Vibrator-type Voltage Regulators

Some of the lower-output electrical systems use vibrator-type voltage regulators with provisions for paralleling the two generators. These generator controls work in the same way as the 3-unit controls for a single-engine installation, except that the voltage regulator relay has an extra coil that is connected through either a paralleling switch or relay to a similar coil in the voltage regulator of the other engine.

In figure 6-16, we have the basic principle of the paralleling circuit for a twin-engine system using vibrator-type regulators. With the paralleling switch open, each generator acts in exactly the same way it would act in a single-engine system. The generator with the highest voltage will produce the most current. But, assume that the paralleling switch is closed when the left generator is producing a higher voltage than the one on the right engine. Current will flow from the left-engine regulator to the regulator on the right engine through both paralleling coils. The flow through the left coil produces a magnetic field that assists the voltage coil, and the contacts open sooner, inserting the field resistor more often and lowering the output voltage of the left generator. This same current flows through the paralleling coil in the right voltage regulator, except that it flows in the direction that will cause its magnetic field to oppose the field from the voltage coil. This allows more field current to flow through the right generator and increase its voltage.

The only current that flows in the paralleling coils is that caused by the difference in the output voltages of the two generators, and this small current will produce just enough magnetic field difference to keep the generators putting out the same voltage and thus sharing the load equally. This theory of operation applies to vibrating-type voltage regulators, however transistorized regulators can provide the same paralleling functions using solid-state devices.

2. Paralleling with Carbon-pile Voltage Regulators

Light twin-engine aircraft with generators of greater output than can be controlled with a vibrator-type voltage regulator use carbon-pile voltage regulators. As we have explained for the single-engine installation, the field current is controlled by varying the pull of an electromagnet on the voltage regulator armature. The higher the output voltage, the more current through the electromagnet and the more pull on the armature. This loosens the carbon pile, increasing its resistance and decreasing the field current.

The only difference between a carbon-pile voltage regulator used on a single-engine installation and that used for a twin-engine system is a paralleling coil. This coil is connected in the same way as the paralleling coil of a vibrator-type regulator; the basic difference being that the current that flows through it is produced by the voltage drop across paralleling resistors in the ground leads to the armatures of both generators. All of the generator output flows through these resistors. If the left generator puts out more current than the right, the voltage drop across the left paralleling resistor will be higher than that across the right and electrons will flow through the paralleling coils of both voltage regulators. The magnetic field of the left paralleling coil will assist the left voltage coil and loosen the carbon pile. This will decrease the field current in the left generator and lower its voltage. At the same time, the field of the right paralleling coil will oppose that of its voltage coil and the spring will compress the carbon pile and increase the output voltage of the right generator.

3. Paralleling Twin-engine Alternator Systems

Most modern light twin-engine aircraft contain DC alternator systems for electrical power generation. These alternators are typically controlled through two relatively complex solid-state alternator control units (ACU). The alternator control units receive input from both alternators in order to provide paralleling. The ACU also provides voltage and current regulation as well as over-and-under voltage sensing and protection. In the event of a fault condition, the ACU would automatically isolate the defective alternator and alert the flight crew.

D. Large Multi-engine Aircraft

There are two basic types of large aircraft power distribution systems: the split-bus and the parallel system. The split-bus system is found on twin engine aircraft such as the Boeing 757 and 767, the McDonnell Douglas MD-80 and the Airbus A320. The parallel system is typically used on aircraft containing three or four engines such as the DC-10 and Boeing 727. Most 4-engine aircraft employ a modified split-bus system.

Figure 6-18 shows a simplified version of a split-bus power distribution system. This schematic shows that the AC generator power from the right engine is connected to the right distribution bus and isolated from the left bus by the bus tie breakers (BTB). The left AC generator supplies power only to the left bus. In the event of a generator failure, the failed generator is isolated by the generator breaker (GB) and BTB 1 and 2 close to connect the isolated

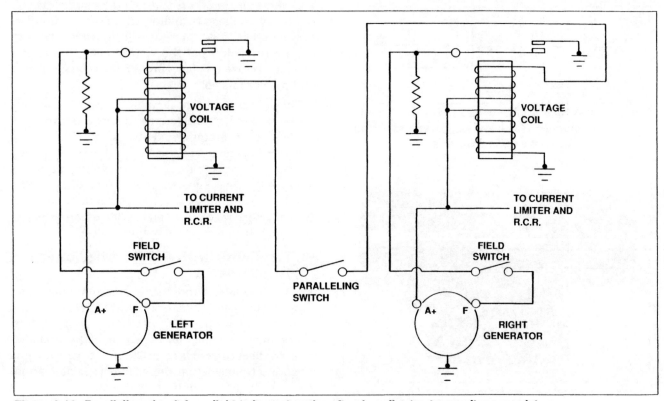

Figure 6-16. Paralleling circuit for a light twin-engine aircraft using vibrator-type voltage regulators.

bus. On some aircraft, the Auxiliary Power Unit (APU) generator could be started during flight and used to carry the load of the failed generator. In that case the left and right busses would once again be isolated.

A parallel power distribution system is shown in figure 6-19. With this system all three generators are connected to a common bus and share the electrical loads equally. In the event of a generator failure, the failed unit would be isolated from the bus by its generator breaker and the flight would continue with two generators supplying the electrical power.

A modified split-bus system found on some 4-engine aircraft connect the two right-side generators in a parallel configuration. The two left-side generators

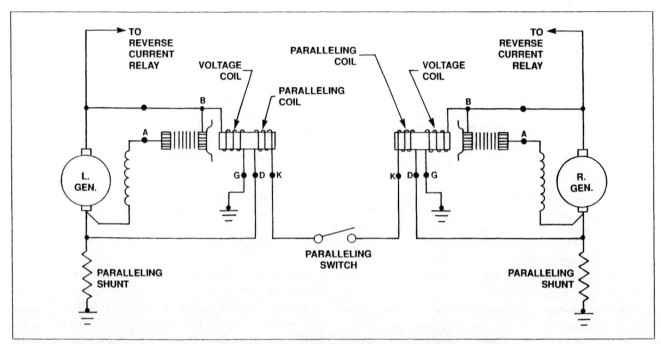

Figure 6-17. Paralleling circuit for a twin-engine aircraft using carbon-pile voltage regulators.

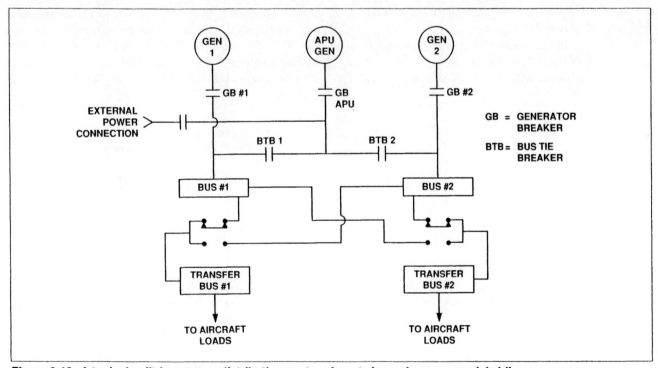

Figure 6-18. A typical split-bus power distribution system for a twin-engine commercial airliner.

are also paralleled. The right- and left-side busses are kept isolated by a split-system breaker. In the event of a generator failure the associated paralleled generator will carry the entire load for that bus. If both generators on the same side should fail, the split-system breaker would close and send power to the inoperative bus from the working generators.

The Boeing 727 is one of the most popular jet airliners, and its electrical system is typical for this type of aircraft. The B727 uses a parallel power distribution system where each of the three engines drives a 3-phase alternator through a hydraulic constant-speed-drive (CSD) unit. Each alternator produces 115 volts at 400 Hz. Single-phase transformers reduce some of this power to 28 volts AC to operate most of the lights, and there are three transformer-rectifier (T-R) units that convert the 115 volts AC to 28 volts DC for emergency lights and system control circuits. The 28-volt DC is also used for charging the battery.

A gas turbine-powered APU located in the wheel well drives a 3-phase, 115-volt alternator identical to the ones driven by the engines. The APU is used to supply all of the needed electrical power when the aircraft is on the ground. Unlike some aircraft, the 727's APU cannot be operated when the aircraft is in the air.

Each engine-drive alternator feeds its own bus through a generator breaker, and all three buses can be tied to a common sync, or tie, bus through bus tie breakers when the alternators are synchronized. In this way the alternators can divide the electrical load among themselves.

While most of the electrical power used by this aircraft comes directly from the AC alternators, the aircraft is equipped with a battery to start the APU

and to provide power for certain essential lighting, avionics and instrument equipment. In normal operation the battery is disconnected from the DC loads. DC power is supplied by transformer-rectifier units connected to the main AC buses. The battery is kept fully charged by a battery-charger circuit that draws its power from the AC transfer bus.

Equipment that is essential for flight gets its power from an AC and a DC essential bus, and the flight engineer has a selector on the upper panel that allows them to supply the essential buses from any of the three main AC buses, the external power supply, or the APU. In the event that all three AC generators fail, the engineer can select the STANDBY position of the selector switch, and the standby AC and DC buses are supplied directly from the battery bus with a standby invertor providing the AC.

1. AC Alternator Drive

Each of the alternators is driven through a hydraulic constant-speed drive unit, and the flight engineer has controls that allow him to disconnect the CSD in case of an alternator malfunction. The CSD has its own lubrication system, and the flight engineer has a low oil pressure warning light and an oil temperature gauge for the unit. The temperature gauge can either indicate the temperature of the oil entering the CSD unit, or it can show the amount of temperature rise as the oil passes through the drive unit to give an indication of the load that is being carried by the CSD.

The paralleling process of two or more alternators requires that the flight engineer connect the generators to the tie bus. If there are no other power sources connected to the tie bus the first alternator can be connected without complications by simply

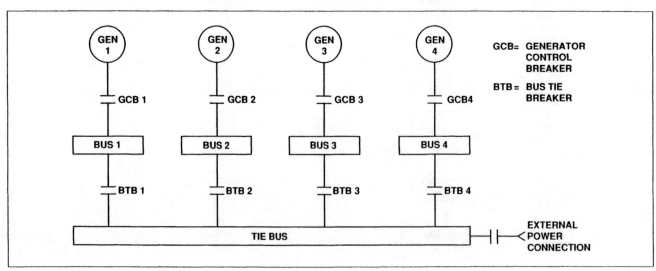

Figure 6-19. A typical parallel power distribution system for a 3-engine commercial airliner.

closing its BTB. But, before the second or third alternator can be placed on the tie bus, they must be synchronized with regard to voltage output, phase and frequency. The phase rotation is determined when the alternator is installed and it will not change in flight. The voltage is controlled by the generator control unit to hold the output to 115 volts, plus or minus 5 volts, and the frequency is maintained by the CSD. There is a control on the flight engineer's panel that allows the frequency to be adjusted for paralleling. The CSDs maintain the frequency at 400 Hz ±8 Hz. It is the flight engineers job to determine that all generators are producing equal values before they are connected to the tie bus. If a generator is paralleled improperly, damage may occur to the generator or the CSD.

2. Alternator Instrumentation and Controls

A frequency meter and an AC voltmeter may be selected to monitor the voltage and frequency of the APU, the external power source, or any of the three alternators as well as that of the tie bus. A push-button beside the voltmeter allows it to read residual voltage, which is the voltage produced by the selected alternator when no field current is flowing. If there is residual voltage, you know the alternator is turning, but no voltage tells you the CSD has been disconnected or the residual has been lost.

Two synchronizing lights on the panel illuminate when the selected alternator is not synchronized with the power on the tie bus, and it must not be connected until it is synchronized. The alternator frequency should be adjusted until the lights blink at their slowest rate and the bus tie breaker closes when both lights are out.

The generator control unit used with each of the engine-driven alternators and with the APU contain all of the circuitry needed to maintain a constant voltage as the load current varies The control unit will open the bus tie breaker, the generator breaker, or the generator field relay if a fault occurs in either the system or the alternator. The

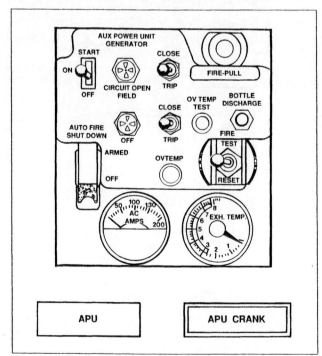

Figure 6-20. *Control panel for the auxiliary power unit of a Boeing 727. The APU can be started from this panel and the output of its alternator monitored.*

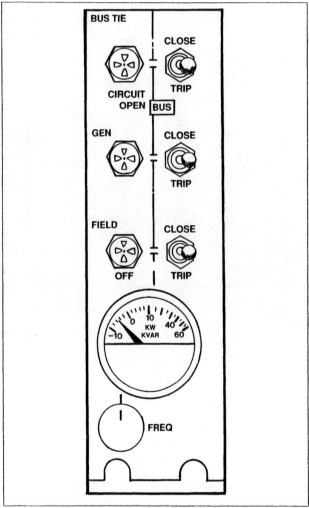

Figure 6-21. *Generator control panel for a Boeing 727. The switches control the bus tie breaker, the generator breaker, and the field relay. The KW-KVAR meter indicates the power the generator is putting out, and the frequency control varies the output of the CSD unit to control the generator frequency.*

control unit will also alert the flight engineer as to the defect, in order that corrective action can be taken.

Each of the three main alternator control panels have a control for the bus tie breaker and a light that is on when the breaker is open, a generator breaker switch, and the generator field switch. There is a light that is on when the generator breaker is open, and one when the field is off. The generator field switch connects voltage to the generator field through the voltage regulator. The generator breaker connects the generator output leads to the correct AC power distribution bus. The bus tie breaker connects the number 1, 2 or 3 AC bus to the tie bus.

Each alternator is equipped with a KW-KVAR meter that normally indicates the amount of electrical power being produced by the alternator in kilowatts. When a button on the instrument panel is pressed, the indicator shifts circuits and indicates the reactive power in kilo-volt-amps. This indication is to inform the flight crew of the real power of the generator. Real power is the measure of both the resistive and reactive loads.

3. Automated AC Power Systems

Many of the latest generation commercial aircraft use automated systems for controlling the various AC power distribution functions previously mentioned. The use of automated systems has made it possible to reduce flight crew work loads enough that most modern commercial airliners require only 2 flight crewmembers. The flight engineers position has been replaced by automated electronic systems. The generator control panel shown in figure 6-25 illustrates the simplicity of a modern power distribution system.

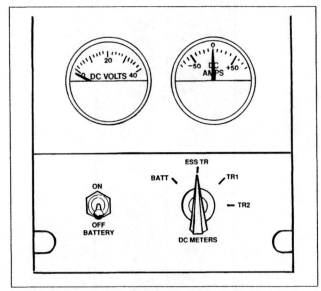

Figure 6-22. The DC electrical panel of a Boeing 727.

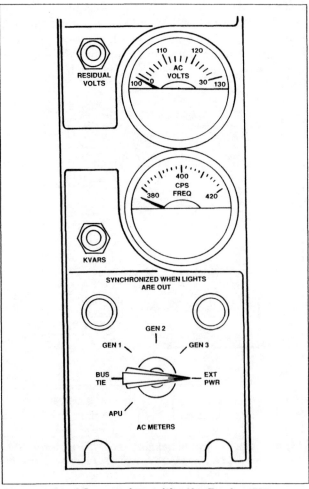

Figure 6-24. AC control panel for the Boeing 727.

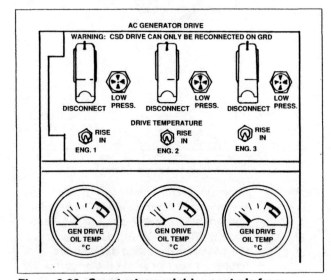

Figure 6-23. Constant-speed drive controls for a Boeing 727.

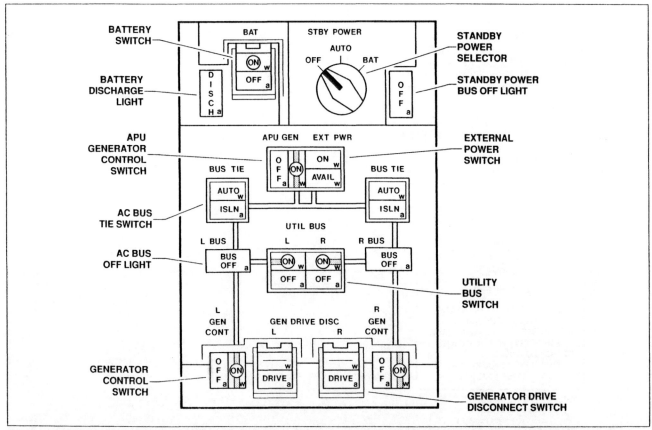

Figure 6-25. The generator control panel for a B757. The simplicity of the system helps reduce the flight crew work load.

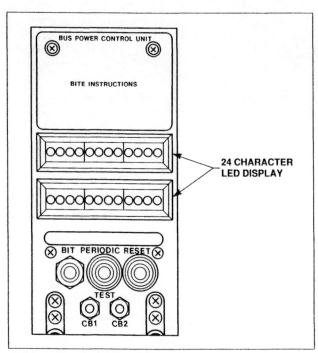

Figure 6-26. The generator control unit from a B757. This unit contains a 24-character LED display for visual display of system faults.

The automated systems not only are designed to lighten flight crew loads, they also incorporate built-in test circuitry to ease maintenance troubleshooting. The Built In Test Equipment (BITE) circuitry is typically contained in the control units located in the aircraft's electrical equipment bay. The control units, known as Line Replaceable Units (LRU), are easily removable to facilitate maintenance. The BITE system employs an LED display which can be viewed by maintenance personnel during system troubleshooting. The technician then refers to a code book to determine the defective component and necessary repairs. Figure 6-26 shows the generator control unit and the associated BITE displays.

It should be noted that the complex electronic circuitry which makes the automated systems possible are very sensitive to stray electrical currents. The current produced from static electricity could be harmful to the LRU. Avoid any electrical component which is labeled as Electro Static Discharge Sensitive (ESDS). Be sure to look for a symbol as shown in figure 6-27 which identifies this type of component.

ATTENTION
STATIC SENSITIVE DEVICES
HANDLE ONLY AT STATIC
SAFETY WORK STATIONS

CAUTION

CONTENTS SUBJECT TO DAMAGE
BY STATIC ELECTRICITY

DO NOT OPEN

EXCEPT AT APPROVED STATIC-
FREE WORK STATION

ATTENTION

THIS UNIT CONTAINS STATIC
SENSITIVE DEVICES.
CONNECT GROUNDING WRIST
STRAP TO ELECTROSTATIC
GROUND JACK LOCATED AT THE
LOWER RIGHT HAND SIDE OF
THIS UNIT

**ATTENTION
ELECTROSTATIC
GROUND
JACK**

*Figure 6-27. The commonly used Electro Static
Discharge Sensitive (ESDS) symbols.*

Chapter VII

Aircraft Lighting Systems

As aircraft grew in complexity and the airspace became more crowded, the number of lighting systems required for safe flight and passenger comfort increased. Lighting systems illuminate everything from cargo compartments to the pilots instrument panel. Exterior lights are required to ensure safe operations during night flights.

A. Exterior Lights

There are a variety of exterior lighting systems. These include position, landing, taxi, anti-collision and wing inspection lights.

1. Position Lights

Position lights are used to indicate the position of an aircraft during night operations. If pilots can identify the position of another aircraft from its position lights, they may safely navigate around that aircraft, hence position lights are often referred to as navigation lights. One or more position lights must be located on each wing tip and the tail of the aircraft. The right wing tip must have a green colored light, the left a red light and the tail must have a white light. These lights are required on any aircraft certified for night flight. The actual light bulb is covered with a clear glass, the color is achieved by placing a red or green lens over the bulb. Most navigation

lights operate in one mode only; however, some older model aircraft have dimmer or flasher circuits incorporated with position lights. A typical position light circuit is shown in figure 7-1.

2. Anti-collision Lights

Anti-collision lights are of two basic types and the difference typically is a function of age. Older aircraft were originally equipped with rotating beacons either on top of the vertical stabilizer or on top or bottom of the fuselage. Newer systems utilize solid state electronics to create a flashing- or strobe-type anti-collision light. The rotating beacon system typically contained a stationary light bulb and a rotating reflector covered by a red glass lens as shown in figure 7-2.

The strobe-type flashing anti-collision light has an extremely bright flash produced by a xenon tube which requires approximately 400 volts. The high voltage is produced by the strobe power supply which uses a capacitor charging system to achieve the high voltage. Modern aircraft are required to have a minimum of three anti-collision lights. Typically, two white wing tip strobe lamps and one red tail strobe are used. Figure 7-3 shows the power supply and wiring arrangement for an aircraft strobe.

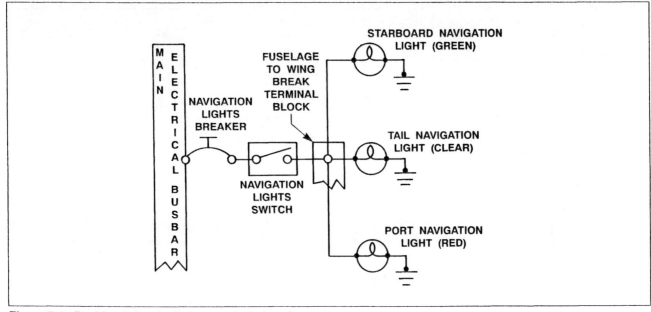

Figure 7-1. Position light circuit for a typical aircraft.

3. Landing and Taxi Lights

In order to provide night visibility for landing and taxiing, two or more sealed beam lamps are mounted on the aircraft facing forward. These lights can be mounted in the leading edge of the wing, in the cowling or on landing gear struts. Some aircraft employ a retractable light which extends from the wing during use. Since the airplane is in a nose-high attitude during landing, lights must point forward and slightly down. Taxi lights point mostly straight forward of the airplane.

Since both landing and taxi lights are relatively high power components, they are often controlled by a solenoid. The pilot activates the appropriate cockpit switch; this engages the solenoid and turns on the lamp.

4. Wing Inspection Lights

Wing inspection lights are typically flush mounted in the fuselage or engine nacelle and are directed towards the leading edge of the wing. If the pilot suspects the formation of ice, the wing can be illuminated and the proper inspection made.

B. Interior Lights

There are a variety of interior lights in use, including instrument lights, overhead lights, step lights and reading lights to mention a few. In general, these lights can be divided into two basic categories: incandescent and fluorescent. Incandescent lights use a small coil of wire (filament) which glows in a white light when current flows through it.

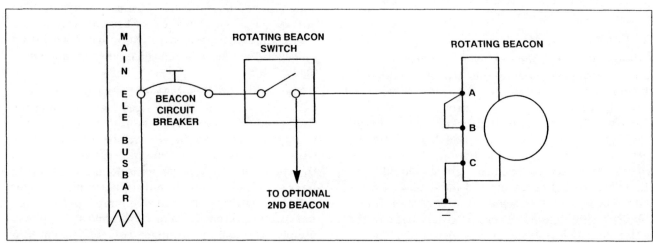

Figure 7-2. Motor driven rotating beacon.

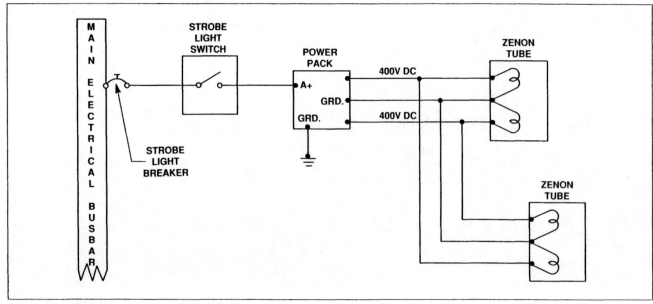

Figure 7-3. Strobe-type anti-collision light.

Fluorescent lights are made of a gas-filled glass tube which glows when a high AC voltage is applied to electrodes at each end that emit free electrons. The free electrons strike atoms of mercury vapor in the tube and produce an ultraviolet light. The ultraviolet light strikes the phosphorous coating on the inside of the tube and glows with white light. The conversion of one kind of light to another is known as fluorescence. Fluorescent lamps are much more efficient than incandescent lamps, however they require transformers and AC voltage.

Both incandescent and fluorescent lamps can operate in a bright or dimmed position. Incandescent lamps are often dimmed using a solid-state circuit to control the current to the lamps. As illustrated in figure 7-4, a potentiometer is used to control the input signal to the transistor, con-

trolling the current to the light. In figure 7-5, the fluorescent tube is in the dim position when only a single voltage source is applied to the ballast transformer. In the bright position, an additional voltage is applied and the ballast and more current is sent to the fluorescent tube.

Another type of interior lighting system has recently been introduced to aircraft instrument panels. The Electro Luminescent (EL) panel contains a fluorescent paste sandwiched between two layers of plastic. The paste glows when an AC voltage is applied to the panel. The light glows through the unpainted areas of the plastic, typically displaying letters and/or numbers. Since Electro Luminescent panels operate only with alternating current, most light aircraft with EL systems use a static invertor specifically designed for the panel.

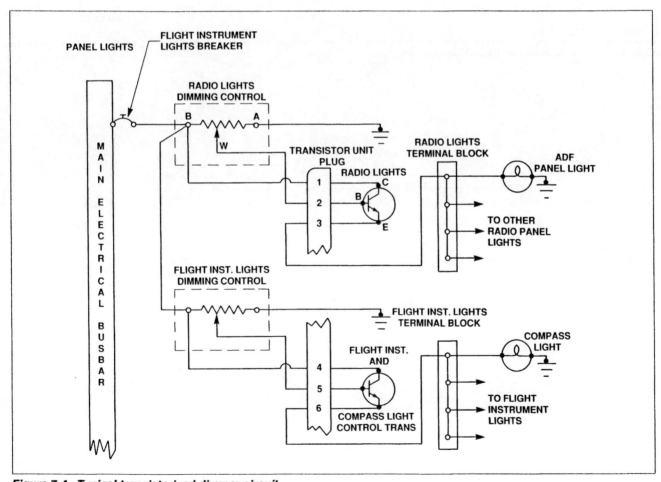

Figure 7-4. Typical transistorized dimmer circuit.

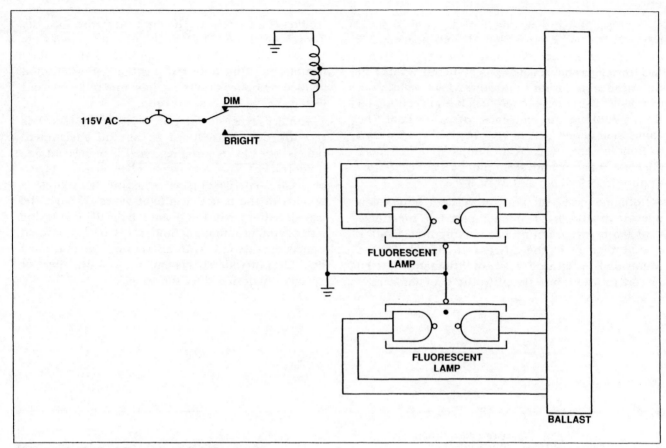

Figure 7-5. Typical fluorescent lighting system.

Chapter VIII

Engine Ignition and Electrical Systems

A. Reciprocating Engine Ignition Systems

The basic requirements for reciprocating engine ignition systems are the same, regardless of the type of engine involved or the make of the components of the ignition system. All ignition systems must deliver a high-tension spark to each cylinder of the engine in a predetermined firing order. Automobile engines have high rotational speed requiring a great many sparks each second, but aircraft reciprocating engines turn more slowly and do not need high speed ignition. However, with aircraft engines an extremely high degree of reliability is essential.

Aircraft systems are required by Federal Aviation Regulations Part 33 to have "at least two spark plugs for each cylinder and two separate electrical circuits with separate sources of electric energy, or have an ignition system of equivalent in-flight reliability."

The requirements for two separate sources of electric energy have traditionally been met by using two separate magnetos. The relatively slow turning aircraft engines do not require the complexity of the breakerless ignition systems nor the high energy produced by the capacitor discharge system.

A magneto ignition system produces its voltage by two self-contained AC generators, which have

permanent magnets for their rotating fields. As with any permanent magnet generator, the faster the generator turns, the more voltage it produces. The main problem with the magneto system is that of producing a sufficiently intense spark for starting the engine when the magneto is rotating very slowly.

1. Battery Ignition System

To overcome the limitation of a magneto producing a weak spark for starting, some of the ignition systems used with early aircraft engines had a magneto to fire one of the spark plugs in each cylinder and a battery ignition system to fire the other plug. To start the engine, only the battery system was used. A spark was provided with this system that allowed the engine to start and build up sufficient speed for the magneto to produce a hot spark. For all normal operations, both the magneto and the battery system worked together. In figure 8-1, we have the schematic of a typical battery ignition system.

When the ignition switch is turned on (closed) and the breaker points are closed, current flows from the battery through the coil and the breaker points to ground. As this current flows, a magnetic field builds up around the turns of wire in the primary winding. The lines of flux in this field expand to the maximum

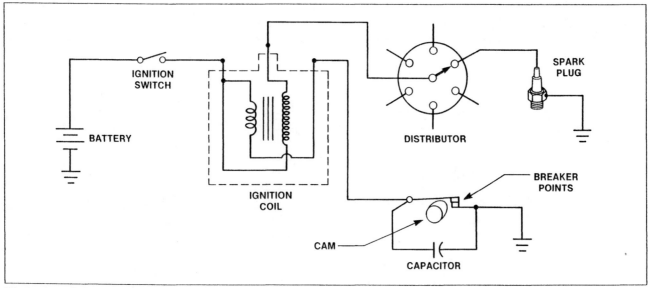

Figure 8-1. Typical battery ignition system.

103

as current flows through the coil. When the breaker points are opened by the cam, the current stops flowing and the magnetic field collapses. As the field collapses, the lines of flux cut across the turns in the secondary winding and induce a high voltage in it.One end of the secondary coil is connected to the primary coil, and the other end is carried outside the coil housing through the high-voltage terminal.

The high tension secondary voltage is carried into the distributor which acts as a selector switch to direct the voltage to the proper spark plug. In the spark plug, the high voltage causes current to flow across the gap and produce the spark needed to ignite the fuel-air mixture.

Inductance is a characteristic of a coil that opposes any change in the rate of flow of current. When the breaker points close, inductance prevents the current reaching its maximum flow rate immediately, and when the points open, inductance tries to keep the current flowing. The amount of voltage induced into the secondary winding is determined by the rate of collapse of the magnetic field around the primary winding. If the current could stop flowing immediately, there would be a higher voltage induced into the secondary winding. To increase the speed with which the current stops flowing, a capacitor is installed in parallel with the breaker points.

When the points open, the current from the battery stops flowing, and the magnetic field around the primary winding begins to collapse. As it collapses, the field cuts across the turns of the windings and induces a voltage in them that causes an induced current to flow. This induced current flows in the same direction as the battery current. If there were no capacitor in the circuit, as the points began to open, the current flow through the points would cause a spark to jump between the points. This spark ionizes the air between the points and makes it conductive so that current can continue to flow even though the points are open. This flow, in the form of an arc, not only slows down the collapsing of the magnetic field, but deposits metal from one breaker point to the other and shortens the life of the points.

To speed up the collapse of the field and prevent arcing, a capacitor is installed across (in parallel) the points. As the points begin to open, the electrons see the capacitor as an easy path to ground and flow into it. By the time the capacitor is charged enough to prevent the flow of electrons, the points are opened sufficiently wide to prevent arcing and the current stops flowing.

2. Magneto Ignition Systems

Certificated aircraft reciprocating engines use magnetos as the source of electrical energy to ignite the fuel/air mixture inside the cylinders. In the history of the magneto, there have been several types.

a. High and Low Tension

Aircraft magneto systems include high-tension and low-tension systems.

All ignition systems provide a high voltage at the spark plug to jump the gap and ignite the fuel/air mixture. During World War II, it was discovered that when flying at high altitudes, the high voltage inside the distributor of the magneto could jump between the distributor electrodes and cause failure of the spark plugs to fire. This caused rough engine operation and loss of power.

Several design changes were made to prevent arcing inside the distributor. Some magneto manufacturers made their distributors physically larger to increase the distance the spark would have to jump. Others pressurized the distributor with compressed air to make it more difficult for the spark to jump. These measures were only partially effective. The most success in overcoming the arcing, or flashover problem, came with the low-tension magneto.

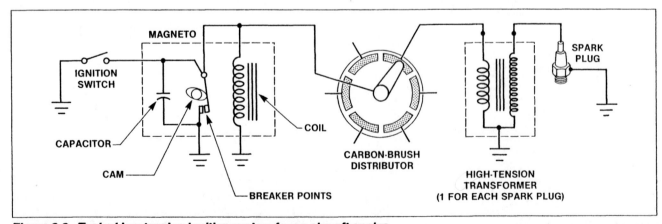

Figure 8-2. Typical low-tension ignition system for an aircraft engine.

In this system, the coil inside the magneto has only a primary winding. There is another coil with a primary and a secondary winding mounted on the cylinder head, near the spark plug. This unit is called the high-tension transformer. Electrical current from the magneto is directed by the distributor to the primary winding of this transformer where it induces a high voltage into the secondary winding. This high voltage is carried to the spark plug through a very short lead. There is no flashover in this system, because the only place the high voltage exists is in the transformer, the short spark plug lead, and the spark plug itself.

Low-tension ignition systems were originally built for the large radial engines, but in later years this type of ignition system was used on some smaller horizontally opposed engines.

All ignition systems for currently manufactured certificated reciprocating engines are the high-tension type. These systems consist of a magneto with a built-in distributor, an ignition harness connecting the distributor to each of the spark plugs, an ignition switch, and an auaxiliary start unit.

A high-tension magneto uses a permanent-magnet alternating current generator to produce the primary current. This current flows through the primary winding of the high-voltage step-up coil. A cam-operated set of breaker points interrupts the flow of current through the primary winding of the coil, and the collapse of the magnetic field around the primary winding induces a high voltage in the secondary winding. This high voltage is carried to the distributor rotor by a carbon brush and then to the proper spark plug through the appropriate ignition cable. The ignition switch grounds the primary circuit to stop the magneto from functioning.

b. Single and Dual-Type Magnetos

The rotating-magnet magneto is the type used currently and has been in use for almost 60 years. Today it is available in both single and dual-type systems.

The single magneto consists of a permanent magnet having 2, 4, or 8 poles rotating inside a laminated iron frame. The flux from the magnet flows through the frame and cuts across the primary winding of the magneto coil that is mounted on the frame. The cam which opens the breaker points is attached to the rotating drive shaft, and the gear that drives the distributor rotor is also driven from the same drive shaft. A typical high-tension, single-type magneto is seen in figure 8-4.

The Federal Aviation Administration requires that all certificated aircraft engines have an ignition system with two separate sources of electrical energy. A concession in the interpretation of this regulation allows the use of dual-type magnetos. Dual magnetos have one housing, one rotating magnet, and one cam, but there are two separate and independent systems that contain all of the other parts of the ignition system. There are two coils, each having its own primary and secondary winding, two capacitors, two sets of breaker points, two distributors, two sets of ignition leads.

3. Magneto Operating Principles

The rotating-magnet magneto has four basic systems. The mechanical system is that portion of the magneto that includes the housing, bearings, oil seals, and all non-electrical portions of the magneto. The magnetic system consists of the rotating magnet, the pole shoes, and the core of the magneto coil. The primary electrical system consists of the primary winding of the coil, the breaker points, the capacitor, and the ignition switch. And the secondary electrical system consists of the secondary winding of the coil,

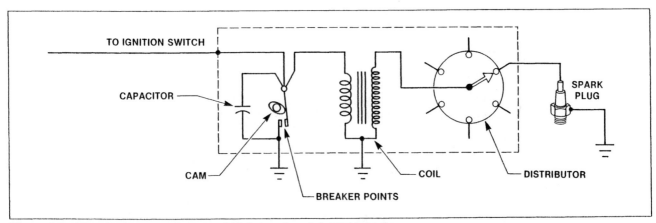

Figure 8-3. Electrical circuit of a typical high-tension aircraft magneto.

the distributor, the ignition harness, and the spark plugs.

a. The Mechanical System

Most magnetos have the rotating magnet supported in ball or needle bearings pressed onto the shaft.

Magnetos are mounted on the engine by base mounting or flange mounting. Base mounted magnetos are bolted rigidly to the engine accessory case, and the rotating magnet is coupled to the engine drive with a vernier coupling. A vernier coupling is a toothed coupling with more teeth on one side than on the other. By disconnecting the coupling and rotating it, the timing between the magneto and the engine can be changed in very small increments. The more common flange mounted magnetos are bolted to the engine with the attachment bolts passing through banana shaped slots in the magneto case. Either method will allow the magneto to be rotated slightly for fine adjustment of the magneto-to-engine timing.

b. The Magnetic Circuit

Most magnetos for 4- or 6-cylinder aircraft engines use a 2-pole magnet made of a very high permeability alloy steel.

The pole shoes for the magnetic circuit are made of laminated steel and are usually cast into the magneto housing. The core of the magneto coil is also part of the magnetic circuit, and is wedged tightly against the pole shoe extensions so that it will make a good magnetic path for the flux to flow with a minimum of reluctance.

In figure 8-6, we see the paths the lines of magnetic flux take as they flow through the magnetic circuit of the magneto. In view A, the magnet is in what is called its full register position, with all of the lines of flux from the magnet passing through the coil core from left to right. In view B, the magnet has rotated 90° and there is no flux in the coil core. This is called the neutral position. In view C, the magnet is again in its full register position, but this time the lines of flux pass through the coil core from right to

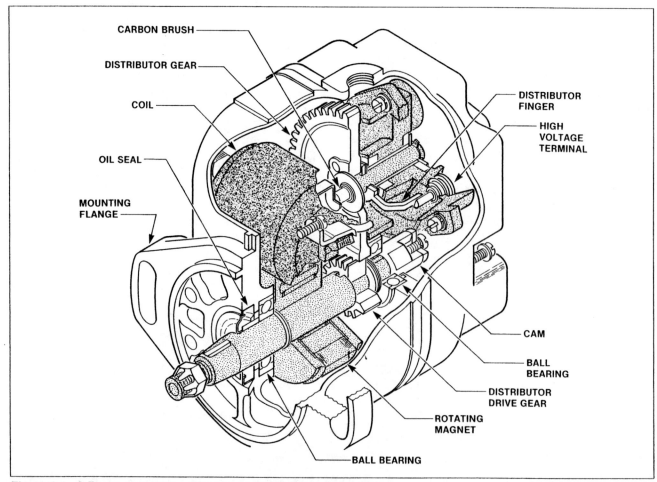

Figure 8-4. A flange-mounted rotating-magnet-type aircraft magneto.

left. The magnetic field has expanded to a maximum, collapsed and expanded again to a maximum, but in the opposite direction. The primary winding of the magneto coil is cut by the flux each time the magnetic field expands and collapses and current is induced in the primary winding.

When current flows in a conductor, it produces a magnetic field. The current generated as the field collapses will produce a magnetic field that will try to sustain the collapsing field. The current generated as the magnetic field builds up will produce a magnetic field that opposes the build-up.

If we close the primary circuit so current can flow in it, the flux from the magnetic field produced by current flowing in the primary winding combines with the flux caused by the rotating magnet. When these fields combine, the greatest change in flux does not occur when the magnet passes through its neutral position as it does when there is no primary current. The maximum rate of change occurs a few degrees of magnet rotation beyond the neutral position. If the breaker points are opened when they cause the greatest change in the resultant flux, the most intense spark will be produced. The point at which the breaker points open is called the E-gap angle. The resultant flux curve of a magneto is shown in figure 8-7.

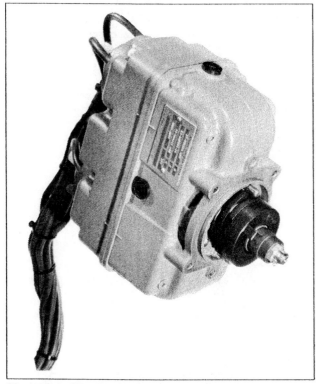

Figure 8-5. The Bendix D-3000 dual magneto.

c. The Primary Electrical Circuit

The primary winding on the magneto coil consists of around 180 to 200 turns of relatively heavy copper wire coated with an enamel insulation. It is wound directly over the laminated iron core that forms a part of the magnetic circuit. The inside end of the

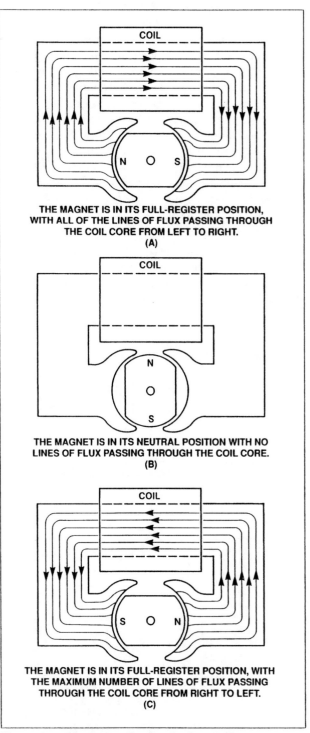

THE MAGNET IS IN ITS FULL-REGISTER POSITION, WITH ALL OF THE LINES OF FLUX PASSING THROUGH THE COIL CORE FROM LEFT TO RIGHT.
(A)

THE MAGNET IS IN ITS NEUTRAL POSITION WITH NO LINES OF FLUX PASSING THROUGH THE COIL CORE.
(B)

THE MAGNET IS IN ITS FULL-REGISTER POSITION, WITH THE MAXIMUM NUMBER OF LINES OF FLUX PASSING THROUGH THE COIL CORE FROM RIGHT TO LEFT.
(C)

Figure 8-6. The magnetic circuit of a rotating-magnet magneto.

primary winding grounds to the iron core and also to a ground lead. The outside end of the primary winding connects to the inside end of the secondary winding and is brought out of the coil through a lead that is connected to the insulated breaker point.

The breaker points are normally held closed by a leaf-type spring and are opened by the cam that is mounted on the end of the rotating drive shaft. The cam allows the points to close when the magnet is in its full register position. As the magnet moves away from the full register position, the flux through the coil core begins to decrease and a voltage is induced in the primary winding that causes current to flow through the breaker points to ground. This current causes a magnetic field which prevents the flux in the coil core following the static flux curve. The two magnetic fields, the one from the rotating magnet and the one from the primary current, cause the flux to follow the resultant flux curve we saw in figure 8-7.

When the magnet rotates a few degrees beyond its neutral position (the E-gap angle), the cam will open the breaker points and the primary current will stop flowing. This sudden stoppage of the primary current causes the magnetic field in the coil core to collapse. It is the rate of flux change that determines

the amount of voltage induced by a magnetic field, and because this flux change is so fast, a high voltage is induced into the primary winding.

Any time moving contact points interrupt a flow of current, an arc is produced between the points. As the points begin to separate, the resistance increases and the current flowing through the resistance produces heat. This heat becomes so intense that it ionizes the air and current flows through it, causing an arc that not only delays the decrease in current flow, but transfers metal from one breaker point to the other and can even weld the points together.

To prevent this arcing, a capacitor is installed in parallel with the points. As the contacts begin to open and the resistance across them begins to increase, the electrons see the capacitor as a low resistance path to ground and flow into it. By the time the capacitor is charged enough to stop the flow of electrons, the points have opened far enough that no aracing will occur.

In some magnetos, the capacitor serves a dual function. It is in parallel with the breaker points to prevent arcing as they open, and is also in series with the ignition switch to prevent electromagnetic radiation from the primary lead causing radio interference. This type of capacitor serves as a feed-through for the ignition lead. The pigtail inside the magneto connects to the insulated breaker point, and the lead from the ignition switch in the cockpit connects to the capacitor terminal outside of the magneto. The metal case of the capacitor is connected to the outside of the plates in the capacitor, and any radio frequency energy that is induced into

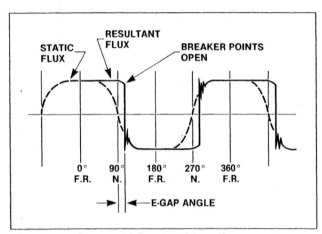

Figure 8-7. Change in flux density as the magnet rotates.

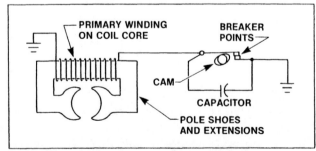

Figure 8-8. The primary electrical circuit of a high-tension magneto.

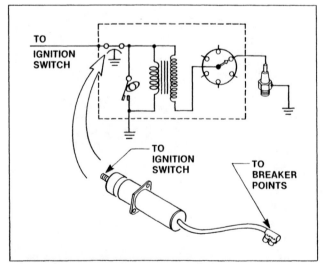

Figure 8-9. A feed-through capacitor used in the primary circuit of some magnetos.

the primary lead by the points opening is carried to ground before it can leave the magneto.

d. The Secondary Electrical Circuit

A coil made up of thousands of turns of very fine wire is wound on top of the primary coil in the magneto coil assembly. The inside end of this secondary coil is connected to the outside end of the primary winding, and the outside end is brought out of the coil assembly at a high voltage contact usually on the side of the coil.

A spring-loaded carbon brush in the center of the distributor gear presses against the high voltage contact and conducts the high secondary voltage into the distributor rotor. The distributor finger, which is a conductive arm in the rotor, carries the high voltage from the coil to the contact for the proper spark plug lead in the distributor block.

Heavily insulated, shielded spark plug leads carry the high voltage from the distributor to the spark plug. Current flows across the gap in the spark plug and produces the spark that ignites the fuel/air mixture inside the cylinder.

4. Ignition Harness

The high voltage generated in a magneto should cause an adequate spark to jump the gap in the spark plug, but if this high voltage is not delivered to the spark plug without losses, engine performance will be less than optimum.

Communication and navigation equipment must be able to function without interference caused by the ignition system. Since all high voltage ignition systems generate extraneous radio frequency (RF) signals, they must be contained within the harness and grounded. Otherwise, there will be enough energy radiated to interfere with radio reception.

a. Construction

Ignition leads are usually made of stranded copper or stainless steel wire, enclosed in a rubber or silicone insulation. This insulation is covered with a braided metal shield, protected by a tough plastic outer covering.

Slick Electro, Inc. produces a very popular ignition harness that, instead of using stranded wire, uses a continuous spiral of wire. This spiral is impregnated with a high voltage silicone rubber insulation.

There have been two sizes of ignition leads used in aircraft engine ignition harnesses, 5 mm and 7 mm. Practically all of the modern harnesses use the smaller size lead. Many of the older radial engines used un-shielded wire run inside separate shielding. When it was necessary to replace a lead, the old lead was pulled from the shielding and a new lead was pulled through in its place. With the more modern installations, the entire lead, shielding and all is replaced.

Modern ignition harnesses are available with terminal ends to fit either the standard ⅝-24 shielded spark plug or the ¾-20 all-weather spark plug. Many operators, when having to replace both the spark plugs and the harness at the same time are converting the ignition system to the all-weather configuration.

The large bend radius required by the older 7 mm ignition leads made angled lead terminals important. There are elbows with 70°, 90°, 110°, and 135°

Figure 8-11. A typical stranded ignition lead.

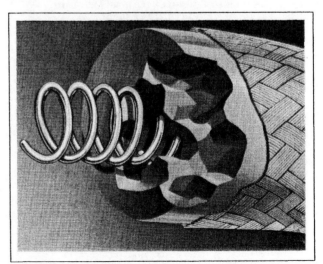

Figure 8-12. The coiled conductor in a Slick Electro ignition lead.

Figure 8-10. The high-tension terminal in a coil of an aircraft magneto.

bends, so the lead can be installed without straining the terminal end. The smaller leads may also use the angled elbows, but some harnesses are fitted with straight terminals. When it is necessary to have an angle between the lead and the terminal, a bracket

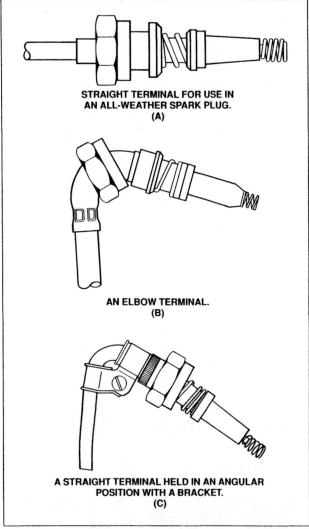

Figure 8-13. Typical spark plug lead terminals.

STRAIGHT TERMINAL FOR USE IN
AN ALL-WEATHER SPARK PLUG.
(A)

AN ELBOW TERMINAL.
(B)

A STRAIGHT TERMINAL HELD IN AN ANGULAR
POSITION WITH A BRACKET.
(C)

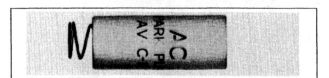

Figure 8-14. A ceramic terminal insulator for an ignition harness.

is used to hold the lead with an adequate bend radius. The bracket prevents the lead being strained (figure 8-13).

Some of the older harnesses used a phenolic or a ceramic tube with a coil spring at its end for the terminal connection inside the spark plug. These are called cigarettes. The insulation is cut back from the stranded conductor far enough to allow the wires to stick through the small hole in the end of the terminal. The ends of the wire are fanned out to provide a good electrical contact and to secure the cigarette to the wire. A cigarette is seen in figure 8-14.

Some modern harnesses use silicone rubber for the terminal connectors. In this case, the terminal is crimped to the wire rather than spreading the strands. The springs screw over the end of the terminal, and may be replaced when they become damaged. The components of this type of lead are illustrated in figure 8-15.

One main source of radio interference from a shielded ignition harness comes from improper securing of the shielding at the ends of the leads. Figure 8-16 shows the components used to secure the shielding at the magneto end of an ignition lead. The shielding is secured by clamping it between an outer and an inner ferrule, and the two ferrules are pressed together so the shielding becomes an integral part of the lead, and it is electrically grounded at each end.

5. Spark Plugs

The function of the spark plug in an ignition system is to conduct a short impulse of high voltage current through the wall of the combustion chamber. Inside the cylinder it provides an air gap across which this impulse can produce an electric spark to ignite the fuel/air charge. While the aircraft spark plug is simple in its construction and operation, it is nevertheless the direct or indirect cause of many malfunctions in aircraft engines. But they provide a great deal of trouble-free operation, considering the adverse conditions under which they operate.

Aviation spark plugs are made in two sizes of shell threads, 14 mm and 18 mm. With the exception of the Franklin engine, all aircraft engines use the 18 mm spark plug.

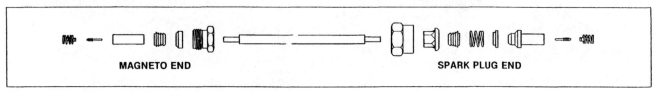

MAGNETO END

SPARK PLUG END

Figure 8-15. The typical components of an ignition lead.

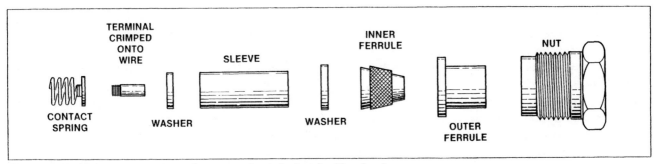

Figure 8-16. The components on the magneto end of an ignition lead.

There are two types of shielded spark plugs used in aircraft engines. The older type has a 5/8-24 thread on the shield (figure 8-17). The newer type, called the high altitude or all-weather spark plug, uses a 3/4-20 thread on the shield. As you can see in figure 8-18, the ceramic insulator in the all-weather plug does not extend to the top of the shell. This provides room for the resilient grommet on the ignition lead to form a watertight seal that prevents rain from entering the terminal end of the spark plug and causing misfiring.

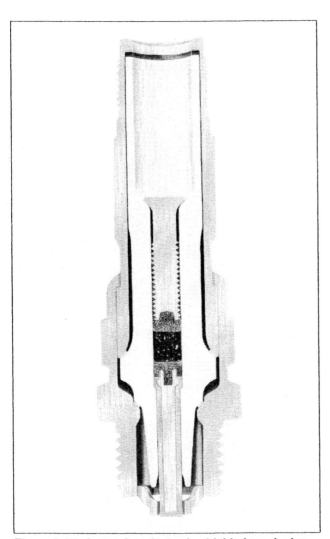

Figure 8-17. A massive-electrode shielded spark plug with 5/8-24 shielding.

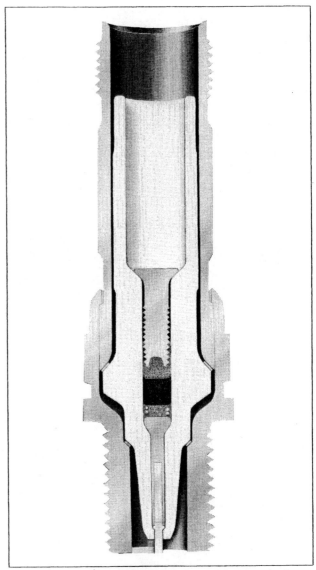

Figure 8-18. A fine-wire electrode shielded spark plug of the all-weather type.

a. Reach

The length of the threads on the shell classifies a spark plug according to is reach. A short reach plug has ½" of threads on its shell, and a long reach plug has 13⁄16" of threads.

The reason for the two different reaches is the physical construction of the cylinder heads. When the spark plug is properly installed, the bottom of the threads is flush with the combustion chamber. Figure 8-19 illustrates common problems relating to spark plug reach. If a long reach plug is installed in an engine requiring one with a short reach (view A), or if the correct spark plug is installed without a gasket (view B), the end of the threads will extend into the combustion chamber. Heat will damage the bottom threads and carbon will fill the thread grooves so that removal of the spark plug will be difficult.

If the reach is too short for the engine (view C), or if two gaskets are used (view D), the threads in the spark plug insert of the cylinder will be exposed and they will fill with carbon. When the correct spark plug is screwed into the hole, it will bottom on the carbon and the correct torque will be reached without the spark plug seating against its gasket. This loose installation will allow hot gases to leak past the threads and will damage the cylinder head.

Some cylinder head temperature gauges take their reading from a gasket-type thermocouple pickup under one of the spark plugs. If this type of pickup is used, no regular gasket is used with the thermocouple gasket.

Additionally, exposed threads in the combustion chamber may become hot enough to glow "red" which may lead to pre-ignition.

b. Heat Range

The heat range of a spark plug refers to the ability of the insulator and center electrode to conduct heat away from its tip. Hot spark plugs have a long heat path and are used in engines whose cylinder temperatures are relatively low. A cold spark plug has a short heat path and is used in hot running, high compression engines.

It is important when selecting replacement spark plugs for an engine to choose the correct heat range for the operating conditions. The Type Certificate Data Sheet for the engine will list all of the spark plugs that are approved for the engine.

c. Resistor-Type Spark Plugs

Shielded ignition will reduce radio interference, but may cause accelerated wear of the spark plug electrodes. This is because the shield acts as a capacitor, storing electrical energy that is released when the spark jumps the gap in the spark plug.

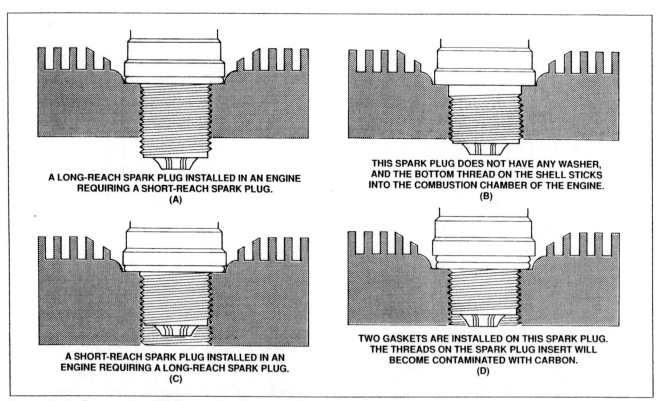

A LONG-REACH SPARK PLUG INSTALLED IN AN ENGINE REQUIRING A SHORT-REACH SPARK PLUG.
(A)

THIS SPARK PLUG DOES NOT HAVE ANY WASHER, AND THE BOTTOM THREAD ON THE SHELL STICKS INTO THE COMBUSTION CHAMBER OF THE ENGINE.
(B)

A SHORT-REACH SPARK PLUG INSTALLED IN AN ENGINE REQUIRING A LONG-REACH SPARK PLUG.
(C)

TWO GASKETS ARE INSTALLED ON THIS SPARK PLUG. THE THREADS ON THE SPARK PLUG INSERT WILL BECOME CONTAMINATED WITH CARBON.
(D)

Figure 8-19. Common installation problems pertaining to spark plug reach.

As this spark tries to die away, the energy that is stored in the capacitance of the ignition harness is returned, and continues to supply energy to sustain the spark. This long duration spark is not needed since the fuel/air mixture has already been ignited, and causes the spark plug electrodes to erode faster.

To minimize this problem, shielded spark plugs have a resistor of about 1,500 ohms installed inside the spark plug insulator, between the spark plug lead and the center electrode.

d. Servicing

Spark plugs should be removed for inspection and servicing at intervals recommended by the manufacturer. Since the rate of gap erosion varies with different operating conditions, engine models, and type of spark plug, engine malfunction traceable to faulty spark plugs may occur before the regular servicing interval is reached. Normally, in such cases, only the faulty plugs are replaced.

6. Auxiliary Systems for Starting

One of the problems with using magnetos as the source of electrical energy for aircraft engine ignition is that they do not produce a hot spark when turning at a very slow speed. This requires some form of auxiliary system to provide the spark for starting the engine. This spark must have a high intensity, and

occur later than normal, about the ? reaches top center. This will pre kicking back when being started damage the starter and cause injury.

There are a number of systems that have used for supplying this hot and late spark for starting. We will consider the two systems that are most popular today.

a. "Shower of Sparks" Ignition System

This is a modern version of the induction vibrator that is used with many horizontally opposed engines.

This system works essentially the same as the induction vibrator system, except that the magnetos used have an extra set of breaker points in parallel with the normal points. These points are called the retard points and are timed so that they open later than the normal points.

In figure 8-22(A), we have a typical electrical circuit for the Bendix "Shower of Sparks" ignition system. The right magneto used in this system is of standard construction, but the left magneto has two sets of breaker points operated by the same cam.

The advance set of points operates in exactly the same way as the points in the right magneto. They are in parallel with the capacitor and are connected to the LEFT terminal of the ignition switch, and they are in the ignition circuit at all times. The retard

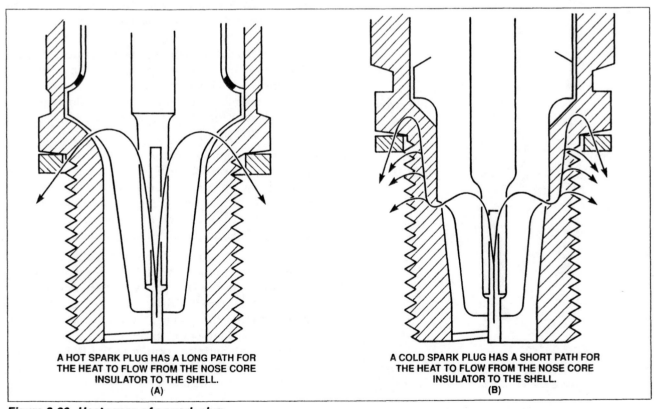

A HOT SPARK PLUG HAS A LONG PATH FOR THE HEAT TO FLOW FROM THE NOSE CORE INSULATOR TO THE SHELL.
(A)

A COLD SPARK PLUG HAS A SHORT PATH FOR THE HEAT TO FLOW FROM THE NOSE CORE INSULATOR TO THE SHELL.
(B)

Figure 8-20. Heat range of a spark plug.

oints are connected to the LR (left-retard) terminal of the ignition switch. This portion of the switch is normally open and is closed only when the ignition switch is held in the START position (figure 8-22(B)).

A starting vibrator is used with this system to produce pulsating DC from the DC supplied by the aircraft battery. You will notice in figure 8-22(B) that when the ignition switch is held in the Start position, current from the battery flows through both the contacts and the coil of the starting vibrator. It then flows through the BO and the LR contacts in the ignition switch, and to ground through both the retard and the advance set of breaker points in the left magneto. As soon as the current flows in the vibrator coil, a magnetic field is produced that pulls the contacts open and interrupts the flow of current so the spring can close the contacts and current will again flow through the coil.

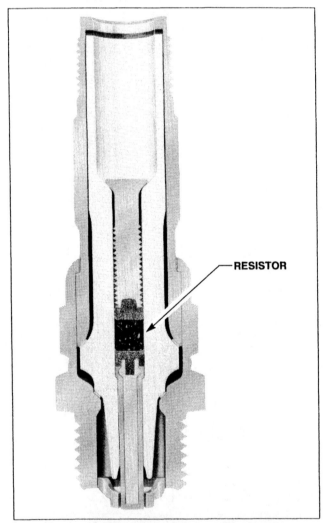

Figure 8-21. A resistor is used in a spark plug to increase the life of the electrodes.

This continual making and breaking of the current causes pulsating DC to flow through the magneto breaker points. The capacitor in parallel with the vibrator contacts prevents the points arcing as they interrupt the flow of current. Electrons flow into the capacitor as the contacts begin to open rather than flowing across the contacts and causing a spark. By the time the capacitor is charged to the battery voltage, the contacts are open far enough that no spark can jump the gap.

When the ignition switch is placed in the Start position, the right magneto is grounded so its normally advanced timing cannot cause a spark that could cause the engine to kick-back. The starter is energized so the engine will begin turning and the pulsating DC from the starting vibrator flows to ground through both sets of breaker points in the left magneto.

As the crankshaft turns, the advance points in the left magneto open, and all pulsating DC must flow to ground through the retard points. The crankshaft continues to rotate, and about 20 degrees after the advance points open, the piston reaches the top of its stroke and the retard points open. Now, with both sets of points open, the pulsating DC can get to ground by flowing through the primary coil of the left magneto. When this pulsating current flows through the primary coil, it induces a high voltage into the secondary winding, and as long as both sets of breaker points are open, a "shower of sparks" will jump across the spark plug that is connected to the distributor terminal being supplied by the distributor rotor. This procedure continues, distributing to each cylinder hot and late ignition until the engine is running and the ignition switch is returned to the BOTH position.

When the ignition switch is placed in the BOTH position (figure 8-22(C)), all of the contacts are open. The starter solenoid is de-energized, the starting vibrator gets no more current, the retard breaker points are out of the left magneto circuit, and the primary of neither magneto is grounded.

When the ignition switch is not held in the spring loaded Start position, it functions as any other ignition switch. In the OFF position, both magnetos are grounded. In the RIGHT position, the left magneto is grounded and the primary circuit of the right magneto is open. In the LEFT position, the right magneto is grounded and the primary circuit for the left magneto is open. In the BOTH position, the primary circuit for both magnetos are open.

d. Impulse Couplings

Many 4- and 6-cylinder horizontally opposed aircraft engines use an impulse coupling on one or both magnetos to produce a hot and late spark for starting the engine.

An impulse coupling is a small spring-loaded coupling between the magneto shaft and the engine drive gear. When the engine is not running but is turned over by hand or by the starter, flyweights in the impulse coupling contact a stop pin in the magneto housing. This pin holds the magnet shaft still as the engine continues to rotate. By the time the engine has rotated far enough for the piston to reach top center, a projection on the body of the impulse coupling wedges the flyweight off of the stop pin and the spring spins the magneto shaft fast enough to produce a hot and late spark.

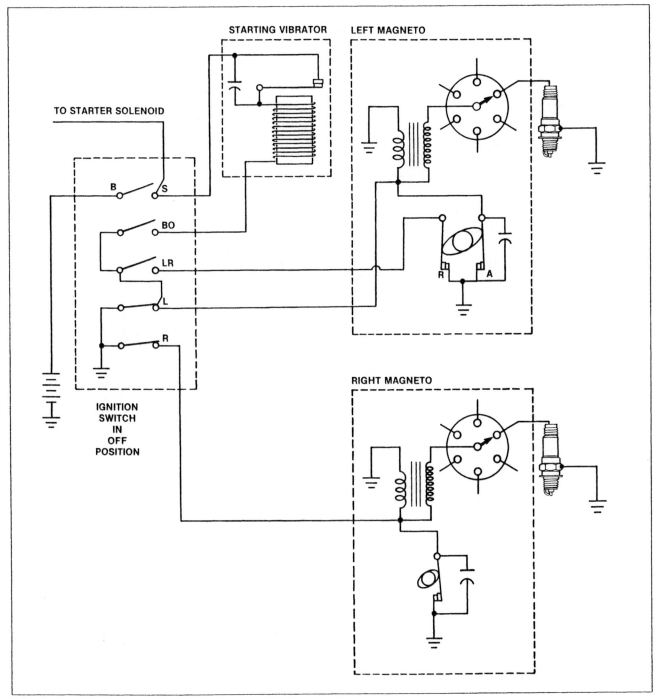

Figure 8-22.

(A) (1 of 3) The Bendix "Shower of Sparks" system with the ignition switch in the OFF position.

115

This action takes place for every spark the magneto produces until the engine starts running and turning fast enough for centrifugal force on the flyweights to hold them away from the stop pin. Then the impulse coupling acts as a straight coupling for the magneto.

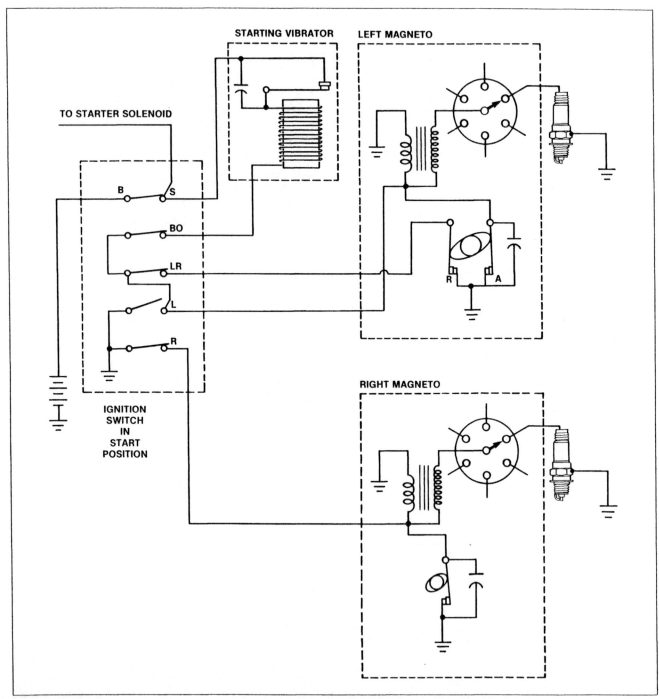

Figure 8-22.
(B) (2 of 3)The Bendix "Shower of Sparks" system with the ignition switch in the START position.

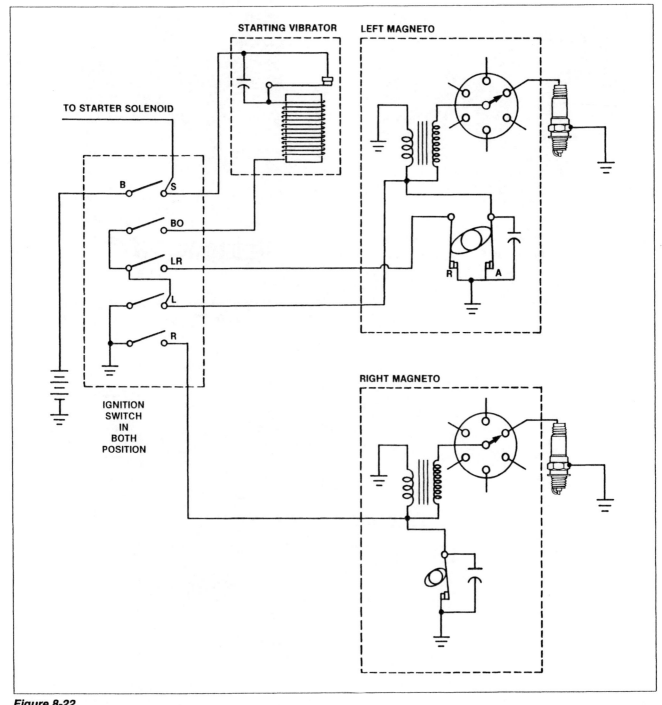

Figure 8-22.
(C) (3 of 3) The Bendix "Shower of Sparks" system with the ignition switch in the BOTH position.

Figure 8-23. Starting vibrator, such as is used with the Bendix "Shower of Sparks" system.

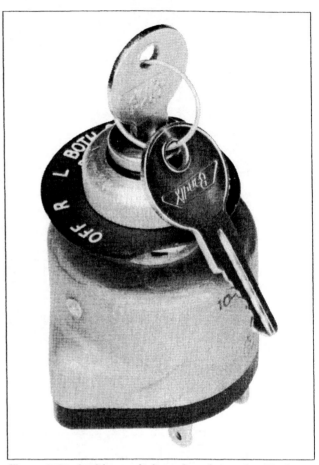

Figure 8-24. Ignition switch such as is used with the Bendix "Shower of Sparks" system.

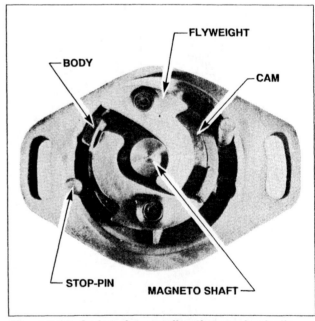

Figure 8-25. An impulse coupling that mechanically provides a hot and late spark for starting an aircraft engine.

PART II

Aircraft Hydraulic and

Pneumatic Systems

Chapter IX

Hydraulic and Pneumatic Power Systems

The word hydraulics is based on the Greek word for water, and originally meant the study of physical behavior of water at rest and in motion. Today, the meaning has been expanded to include the physical behavior of all liquids including hydraulic fluids.

A. Aircraft Hydraulic Systems

Hydraulic systems are not new to aviation. Some early aircraft used hydraulic brake systems. As aircraft became more sophisticated, newer systems with greater complexity were developed.

Although some aircraft manufacturers make greater use of hydraulic systems than others, the hydraulic system of the average modern aircraft performs many functions. Among the units commonly operated by hydraulic systems are landing gear, wing flaps, speed and wheel brakes, and flight control surfaces.

Hydraulic systems have many advantages as a power source for operating various aircraft units. They combine the advantages of light weight, ease of installation, simplification of inspection, and minimum maintenance requirements. Hydraulic operations are almost 100% efficient, with only a negligible loss due to fluid friction.

Aircraft hydraulic systems belong to that branch of physics concerned with fluid power/mechanics. They do their work by moving fluid, and the fluid they use is incompressible. Pneumatic systems work in much the same way, obeying many of the same laws, but the fluid they use (air) is compressible.

To better understand how a hydraulic system accomplishes its task, a brief review of the physics involved is necessary.

1. Pascal's Law

This is the basic law we use when we think of transmitting power by a hydraulic system. The French mathematician Blaise Pascal observed that any increase in the pressure on a confined liquid was transmitted equally and undiminished to all parts of the container, and acts at right angles to the enclosing walls of the container. This means simply that if we have an enclosed vessel full of liquid, and we apply a force to a piston in the vessel to raise the pressure, this increase in pressure will be the same anywhere in the system. Each of the gauges attached

to the container shown in figure 9-1 will have the same reading.

2. The Hydrostatic Paradox

The pressure produced by a column of liquid is directly proportional to its density and the height of the column, and in no way depends upon the shape of the container or the amount of liquid the container holds. For example, 1 cu. in. of water weighs 0.036 lb. A tube that is 231" tall with a cross section of 1 sq. in. will hold 1 gal. of water (1 gal. = 231 cu. in.). If the tube is

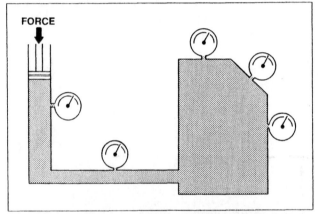

Figure 9-1. *Pressure exerted on a fluid in an enclosed container is transmitted equally and undiminished to all parts of the container and acts at right angles to the enclosing walls.*

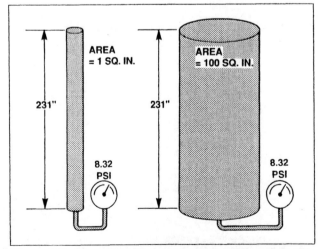

Figure 9-2. *The pressure exerted by a column of liquid is determined by the height of the column and is independent of its volume.*

standing straight up, the 1 gal. of water will exert a pressure of 8.32 PSI at the bottom of the tube.

If the tube were 231" high and had an area of 100 sq. in., it would hold 100 gal. of water, but the pressure at the bottom would still be 8.32 PSI. The force exerted by the column of water is, of course, equal to the pressure acting on each square inch times the number of square inches, or 832 lbs.

It makes no difference as to the shape or size of the vessel that contains the liquid; it is the height of the column that is the critical factor. In figure 9-3, the pressure (P) read by the gauges will be the same in all four instances, since the height (H) is the same. Naturally, all of the vessels must be filled with the same liquid.

3. Relationship Between Pressure, Force, and Area

Pressure is a measure of the amount of force that acts on a unit of area. In most American hydraulic systems, pressure is measured in pounds per square inch (PSI).

The relationship between force, pressure, and area may be expressed by the formula:

$$\text{Force} = \text{Pressure} \times \text{Area}$$

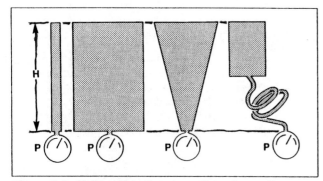

Figure 9-3. Neither the shape nor the volume of a container affects the pressure.

This may be visualized by looking at figure 9-4. The bottom half represents the product of the area in square inches and the pressure in PSI. This gives us the amount of force in pounds, which is represented by the top half of the circle.

In order to find pressure, divide the force by the area:

$$\text{Pressure} = \frac{\text{Force}}{\text{Area}}$$

In order to find the area, divide the force by the pressure:

$$\text{Area} = \frac{\text{Force}}{\text{Pressure}}$$

4. Relationship Between Area, Distance, and Volume

Another relationship in hydraulics is between the area of the piston, the distance it moves, and the volume of the fluid displaced. We can visualize this relationship in figure 9-5. One half of the circle represents the volume in cubic inches, and the other half of the circle the area in square inches and the distance the piston moves in inches. Distance is also known as stroke.

The relationship between volume, area, and distance may be expressed by the formula:

$$\text{Volume} = \text{Area} \times \text{Distance}$$

To find the area divide the volume by the distance:

$$\text{Area} = \frac{\text{Volume}}{\text{Distance}}$$

To find the distance divide the volume by the area:

$$\text{Distance} = \frac{\text{Volume}}{\text{Area}}$$

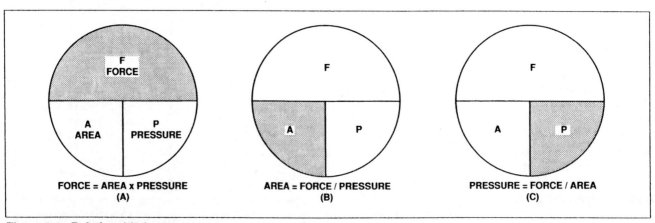

Figure 9-4. Relationship between area, pressure, and force.

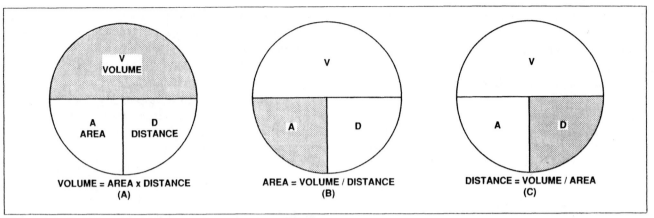

Figure 9-5. *Relationship between volume, area, and distance.*

5. Mechanical Advantage in a Hydraulic System

A hydraulic system has two major advantages over other types of mechanical systems. One is the ease with which force can be transmitted over large distances and into and out of sealed compartments. The other is the mechanical advantage made possible by varying the size of pistons.

In figure 9-6, we see the way mechanical advantage is achieved in a hydraulic system. If we have a piston whose area is 1 sq. in. pressing down with a force of 1 lb., it will produce a pressure of 1 PSI, and for every inch it moves, will displace 1 cu. in. of fluid.

If the cylinder containing this piston is connected to one having a piston with an area of 20 sq. in., every square inch will be acted on by the same 1 PSI pressure, and a force of 20 lbs. will be produced. The 1 cu. in. of fluid displaced when the small piston

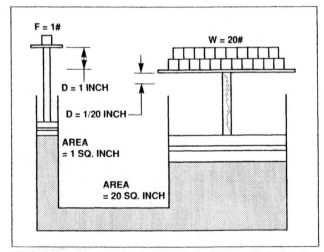

Figure 9-6. *The product of the force times the area of the large piston is equal to the product of the weight times the area of the small piston.*

moves down 1 in. spreads out under all 20 sq. in. of the large piston, and will move up only 1/20".

This may be expressed as:

$$A \text{ (small)} \times D \text{ (small)} = A \text{ (large)} \times D \text{ (large)}$$

$$1 \times 1 = 20 \times \tfrac{1}{20}$$

$$1 = 1$$

All hydraulic systems are essentially the same, whatever their function. Regardless of application, each hydraulic system has a minimum number of components, and some type of hydraulic fluid.

B. Hydraulic Fluid

While we may not normally think of fluid as being a component, the fluid used in aircraft hydraulic systems is most important. This fluid must flow with a minimum of opposition, and be incompressible. It must have good lubricating properties to prevent wear in the pump and valves. It must inhibit corrosion and not chemically attack seals used in the system. And it must not foam in operation, because air carried into the components will give them a spongy action.

Manufacturers of hydraulic devices specify the type of fluid best suited for use with their equipment. Working conditions, service, temperatures, pressures, possibilities of corrosion, and other conditions must be considered. Some of the characteristics that must be considered when selecting a satisfactory fluid for a particular system are discussed in the following paragraphs.

1. Viscosity

One of the most important properties of any hydraulic fluid is its viscosity. Viscosity is a measure of internal resistance to flow. A liquid such as gasoline flows easily (has a low viscosity) while a liquid such as tar flows slowly (has a high viscosity). Viscosity increases as temperature decreases.

The viscosity of a liquid is measured with a viscosimeter. There are several types, but the instrument most often used is the Saybolt universal viscosimeter (figure 9-7). This instrument measures the number of seconds it takes for a fixed quantity of liquid (60 cc) to flow through a small orifice of standard length and diameter at a specific temperature. This time of flow is measured in seconds, and the viscosity reading expressed as SSU (seconds, Saybolt universal).

2. Chemical Stability

Chemical stability is another property which is important in selecting a hydraulic fluid. It is the ability of the liquid to resist oxidation and deterioration for long periods. Mostl liquids tend to undergo unfavorable chemical changes during severe operating conditions. This is the case when a system operates for a considerable period of time at high temperatures.

Excessive temperatures have an adverse effect on the life of a liquid. The temperature of the liquid in the reservoir of an operating hydraulic system does not always represent a true state of operating conditions. Localized hot spots occur on bearings, gear teeth, or at the point where liquid under pressure is forced through a small orifice. Continuous passage of a liquid through these points may produce local temperatures high enough to carbonize or sludge the liquid, yet the liquid in the reservoir may not indicate an excessively high temperature. Liquids with a high viscosity have a greater resistance to heat than light

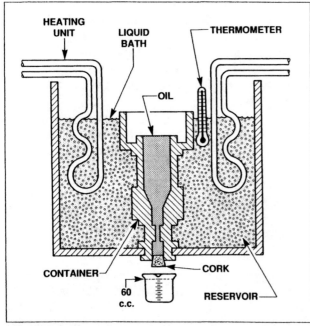

Figure 9-7. Saybolt viscosimeter.

or low viscosity liquids which have been derived from the same source. Fortunately, there is a wide choice of liquids available for use within the viscosity range required of hydraulic systems.

Liquids may break down if exposed to air, water, salt, or other impurities, especially if in constant motion or subject to heat. Some metals, such as zinc, lead, brass, and copper have an undesirable chemical reaction on certain liquids.

These chemical processes result in the formation of sludge, gums, carbon or other deposits which clog openings, cause valves and pistons to stick or leak, and give poor lubrication to moving parts. As soon as small amounts of sludge or other deposits are formed, their rate of formation generally increases. As they are formed, certain changes in the physical and chemical properties of the liquid take place. The liquid usually becomes darker in color, higher in viscosity, and acids are formed.

3. Flash Point

Flash point is the temperature at which a substance gives off vapor in sufficient quantity to ignite momentarily (flash) when a flame is applied. A high flash point is desirable for hydraulic fluids because it indicates a good resistance to combustion and a low degree of evaporation at normal temperatures.

4. Fire Point

Fire point is the temperature at which a substance gives off vapor in sufficient quantity to ignite and continue to burn when exposed to a spark or flame. Like flash point, a high fire point is required of desirable hydraulic fluids.

5. Types of Hydraulic Fluid

To assure proper system operation and to avoid damage to nonmetallic components of the hydraulic system, the correct fluid must be used.

When adding fluid to a system, use the type specified in the aircraft manufacturer's maintenance manual or on the instruction plate affixed to the reservoir or unit being serviced. There are three types of hydraulic fluids currently being used in civil aircraft.

a. Vegetable-base Fluid

MIL-H-7644 fluid has been used in the past when hydraulic system requirements were not as severe as they are today. This fluid is essentially castor oil and alcohol. Although it is similar to automotive brake fluid it is not interchangeable. This fluid is used primarily in older type aircraft. It is dyed blue for identification. Natural rubber seals are used with vegetable base fluid. If this system is contaminated with petroleum base or phosphate ester base fluids, the seals will swell, break down and block the system. The system may be flushed with alcohol. This type of fluid is flammable.

b. Mineral-base Fluid

MIL-H-5606 is the most widely used hydraulic fluid in general aviation aircraft today. It is basically a kerosene-type petroleum product, having good lubricating properties and additives to inhibit foaming and prevent corrosion. It is quite stable chemically and has very little viscosity change with temperature. MIL-H-5606 fluid is dyed red for identification, and systems using this fluid may be flushed with naphtha, varsol, or Stoddard solvent. Neoprene seals and hoses may be used with MIL-H-5606 fluid. This type of fluid is flammable.

c. Synthetic Fluid

Non-petroleum base hydraulic fluids were introduced in 1948 to provide a fire-resistant hydraulic fluid for use in high performance piston engine and turbine powered aircraft.

The most commonly used fluid of this type is MIL-H-8446 or, Skydrol® (a registered trade name of the Monsanto Chemical Co.). This fluid is colored light purple, is slightly heavier than water, and has a wide range of operating temperatures from around –65°F to over 225°F for sustained operation. Currently there are two grades of Skydrol in use, Skydrol 500B4, and Skydrol LD. Skydrol LD has a lower density and offers some advantage in jumbo jet transport aircraft where weight is a prime factor.

Skydrol is not without its problems however, as it is quite susceptible to contamination by water from the atmosphere and must be kept tightly sealed. When servicing a system using Skydrol, be extremely careful to use only seals and hoses having the proper part number. Skydrol systems may be flushed out with trichlorethylene.

6. Intermixing of Fluids

Due to the difference in composition, vegetable base, petroleum base and phosphate ester base fluids will not mix. Neither are the type of seals for any one fluid usable with or tolerant of any of the other fluids. Should an aircraft hydraulic system be serviced with the wrong type of fluid, immediately drain and flush the system and maintain the seals according to the manufacturer's specifications.

7. Compatibility with Aircraft Materials

Aircraft hydraulic systems designed for Skydrol fluids should be virtually trouble-free if properly serviced. Skydrol does not appreciably affect common aircraft metals as long as the fluid is kept free of contamination.

Due to the phosphate ester base of synthetic hydraulic fluids, thermoplastic resins, including vinyl compositions, nitrocellulose lacquers, oil base paints, linoleum and asphalt may be softened chemically by these fluids. Skydrol will attack polyvinyl chloride, and must not be allowed to drip on to electrical wiring, as it will break down the insulation. However, this chemical reaction usually requires longer than just momentary exposure; and spills that are wiped up with soap and water do not harm most of these materials.

Skydrol is compatible with natural fibers and with a number of synthetics, including nylon and polyester, which are used extensively in many aircraft.

Petroleum oil hydraulic seals of neoprene or Buna-N are not compatible with Skydrol and must be replaced with seals of butyl rubber or ethylene-propylene elastomers for units that are intended for use in systems utilizing phosphate ester base hydraulic fluid. These seals are readily available from suppliers.

8. Health and Handling

Skydrol fluid does not present any particular health hazard in its recommended use. Skydrol has a very low order of toxicity when taken orally or applied to the skin in liquid form. It causes pain on contact with eye tissue, but animal studies and human experience indicate that it causes no permanent damage. First aid treatment for eye contact includes flushing the eyes immediately with large volumes of water and the application of an anesthetic eye solution. If pain persists, the individual should be referred to a physician.

In mist or fog form, Skydrol is quite irritating to nasal or respiratory passages and generally produces coughing and sneezing. Such irritation does not persist following cessation of exposure.

Silicone ointments, rubber gloves, and careful washing procedures should be utilized to avoid excessive repeated contact with Skydrol in order to avoid solvent effect on skin.

C. Basic Hydraulic Systems

A hydraulic system is much like an electrical system. It must have a source of power, a means of transmitting this power, and finally some type of device to use the power.

1. Open Hydraulic Systems

The most basic form of an open hydraulic system is that used by hydroelectric power plants. Large dams block streams of water to form lakes that store billions of gallons of water. This stored water represents the potential energy in the system. This potential energy is converted to kinetic energy as the water flows downward through penstocks, or pipes, to the turbine. The kinetic energy of the flowing water is converted to mechanical energy as it turns the turbine used to drive the generator.

The open hydraulic system works well for the production of electrical energy, but has no practical application to airborne systems.

2. Closed Hydraulic Systems

To apply hydraulic power to aircraft systems we must enclose the fluid, move it through a system of rigid lines and flexible hoses, and put its energy to use in various types of actuators and hydraulic motors.

Among the first hydraulic systems used on airplanes was the hydraulic brake. This type of system may be seen in figure 9-8. Most airplanes use disc brakes, but the hydraulic systems for both disc and shoe brakes are similar.

The hydraulic cylinder inside the wheel has 2 rubber cups which act as pistons. They are both pushed into the cylinder as the brake return spring pulls the shoes away from the drum. The piston in the master cylinder is pushed back by a spring so it just uncovers the compensator port and opens the passage between the vented reservoir and the inside of the master cylinder.

When the pilot applies the brakes, the first movement of the piston in the master cylinder covers the compensator port and traps the fluid in the line to the wheel cylinder. As the piston continues to move, the fluid is forced into the wheel cylinder where it moves the pistons out and pushes the brake shoes against the drum. When the brake pedal is released, the spring in the wheel pulls the shoes away from the drum, and at the same time, the spring inside the master cylinder moves the piston back, uncovering

the compensator port. If any fluid is lost, it will be automatically replaced from the reservoir. And if the fluid in the brake line expands due to heat, the expanded fluid will back up into the reservoir and not cause the brakes to drag.

D. Hydraulic Power Systems

As aircraft have become more complex, the demand for hydraulically operated equipment has increased. Retractable landing gear, wing flaps, engine cowl flaps, passenger doors and stairs, windshield wipers, and even motors to operate air conditioning compressors are but a few of the functions that can be efficiently done with hydraulics.

Each of these systems needs the same basic components. As the systems grow in complexity, the components themselves become more elaborate, and we must add auxiliary devices to make the basic components operate more effectively.

All hydraulic systems must have a fluid that is capable of flowing through the system with a minimum of friction. There must be a reservoir to hold enough fluid to actuate all of the components. A pump is needed to move the fluid against the opposition of the system, and there must be actuators to convert the pressure of the fluid into a mechanical force to perform work. There must be flow control valves to direct the fluid to the correct component, and pressure control valves to maintain the correct pressure within the system. Finally, there must be both rigid and flexible fluid lines to carry the fluid where it is needed.

1. Evolution of the Hydraulic System

We will begin with the example in figure 9-9. Here we have a vented reservoir, a hand-operated pump

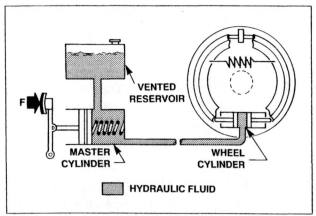

Figure 9-8. Hydraulic brakes operated by a simple hydraulic systems.

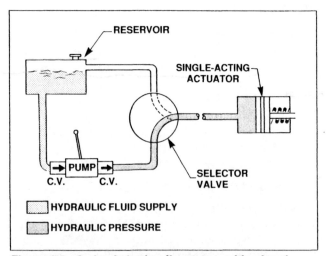

Figure 9-9. A simple hydraulic system with a hand pump operating a single-acting actuator.

with a check valve at both its inlet and outlet, and a selector valve that will direct fluid either from the pump into the actuator or from the actuator back into the reservoir. This actuator is a simple single-acting unit that uses fluid to force the piston out, but a spring to return the piston when the fluid is released back into the reservoir.

This basic system has several limitations. First, it requires manual operation of the pump, and it can apply hydraulic pressure to only one side of the actuator.

In figure 9-10, we have replaced the actuator with a double-acting cylinder that uses hydraulic pressure on both sides of the piston. The selector valve has also been replaced. This one has four ports, and in one position (dotted lines), directs fluid from the pump to the lower side of the piston while the upper side of the piston is connected to the reservoir. When the selector valve is rotated 90° (solid lines), the upper side of the piston is connected to the pump outlet, and the fluid from the lower side is returned to the reservoir.

An improvement we can make in this system is to replace the hand pump with an engine-driven pump (figure 9-11) and install a pressure relief valve.

To actuate this system, the pilot puts the selector valve in the desired position. The pump directs fluid into one side of the actuator while the fluid on the opposite side of the piston returns to the reservoir. The pump continues to move fluid after the piston reaches the end of its travel, and the pressure rises enough to unseat the relief valve. This valve allows fluid to return to the reservoir and maintain a pressure below the

bursting pressure of the lines, or below the pressure that could damage the pump.

In order to maintain pressure on the system without causing the engine to continually work against the pressure, we need two new types of components: an unloading valve and an accumulator.

The hydraulic pump moves the non-compressible fluid through the hydraulic system. There is no pressure generated until this flow of fluid is opposed. The fluid can move the piston of an actuator from one end of its travel to the other with very little rise in pressure, just enough to overcome the friction. When the piston reaches the end of its travel, the pressure rises immediately because there is no longer a place for the fluid to go. If there is no relief valve in the system, this sudden rise in pressure will cause damage.

In figure 9-12, we have installed an unloading valve between the pump and the selector valves. This valve has a return line to the reservoir. We have shown a check valve after the unloading valve to prevent any reverse flow of fluid from the pressure manifold back to the reservoir. This valve, however, is normally built into the unloading valve.

We have also added the accumulator. This is a device having two compartments separated by a

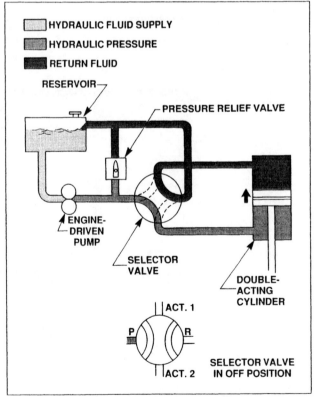

Figure 9-11. A basic aircraft hydraulic system using an engine-driven pump with a pressure relief valve.

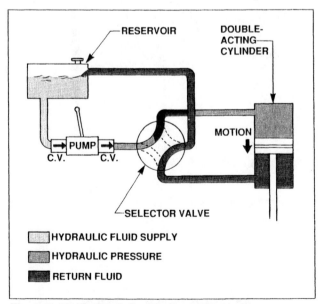

Figure 9-10. A simple hydraulic system using a double-acting linear actuator.

127

movable partition: either a piston, a diaphragm, or a bladder. One compartment is connected directly to the pressure manifold, and the other is sealed and filled with either compressed air or nitrogen. The air (or nitrogen) pressure is initially about one-half of the system operating pressure. When the pump forces fluid into the pressure manifold, some of it flows into the accumulator and moves the partition over, further compressing the air, giving it the same pressure as that of the fluid. When the system pressure reaches the desired value, the unloading valve automatically "kicks out", which means that it opens the return line to the reservoir and unloads the pump. No fluid can flow back from the pressure manifold through the unloading valve because of the check valve, and the air in the accumulator holds pressure on the fluid in the manifold.

As soon as any component connected to the pressure manifold is actuated, the pressure will drop, and the unloading valve will detect this drop through the sensor line (this, like the check valve, is actually built into the unloading valve) and the valve will "kick in",

putting the pump on the line until the pressure rises to the kick-out pressure. The shock-absorbing action of the accumulator will prevent the pressure from changing so rapidly that it could damage the system.

As we continue to evolve our hydraulic system (figure 9-13), we can add a hand pump to provide emergency hydraulic pressure. We have also made a slight change in the reservoir. The engine-driven pump no longer receives its fluid from the bottom of the reservoir, but takes it from a standpipe. If a line breaks, the engine-driven pump can exhaust the reservoir only down to the top of the standpipe and there will still be enough fluid available to the hand pump to lower the landing gear.

To keep the fluid in the system clean, we need a filter through which all of the fluid will pass. A typical location for the filter is in the return line to the reservoir.

We have also installed thermal relief valves. If fluid trapped in the line should expand due to heat, these valves will offseat just enough to relieve the pressure.

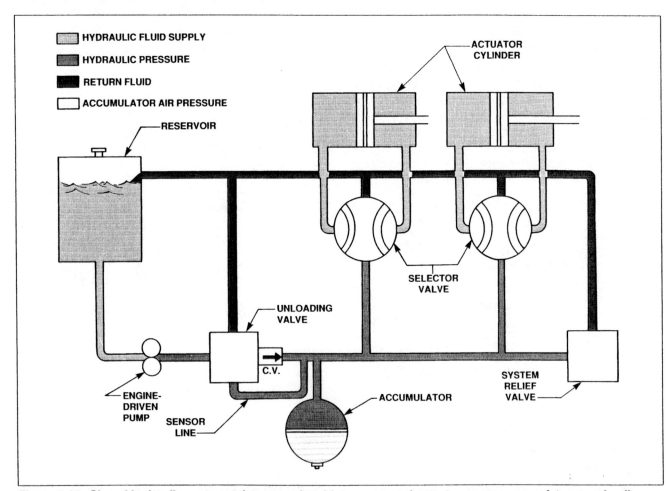

Figure 9-12. Closed hydraulic system using an engine-driven pump and a system pressure regulator or unloading valve.

128

2. Special Types of Aircraft Hydraulic Systems

The hydraulic system described above can be expanded with the addition of various components to accommodate all of the systems of a large aircraft. To allow smaller aircraft to take advantage of hydraulic power, but utilize a less complex system, open-center hydraulic systems and hydraulic power pack systems have been developed.

a. Open-center System

Many of the lighter aircraft use a hydraulic system that performs the functions of the more complex systems with relatively simple components. One of the smaller twin-engine aircraft uses an open-center hydraulic system such as the one seen in figure 9-15. The reservoir, pumps, filter, and system relief valve all function in the same way as in the closed-center system, the main difference being that the two selector valves are in series, while those in the closed-center system of figure 9-14 are in parallel.

The open-center valves serve the function of both selector valve and unloading valve. When the selector handle is in the neutral position, fluid flows straight through the valve. Since all of the valves in the system are in series, the fluid flows out of the

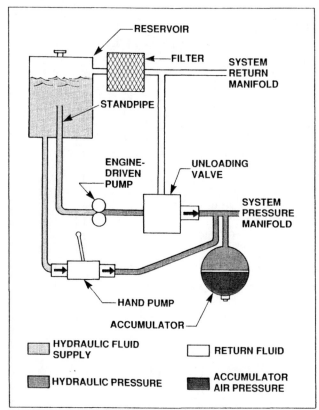

HYDRAULIC FLUID SUPPLY   RETURN FLUID

HYDRAULIC PRESSURE   ACCUMULATOR AIR PRESSURE

Figure 9-13. Hydraulic power system using an engine-driven pump and a hand pump as a backup.

tank, through the pump, through both selector valves, and back into the reservoir through the filter.

When the pilot moves the landing gear selector to the GEAR DOWN position, fluid flows from the pump to the actuator and moves the piston over. Fluid that is forced out of the other side of the cylinder flows through the other selector valve back to the reservoir. When the landing gear are down and locked, the valve is moved to its neutral position so that fluid can flow straight through it.

3. Hydraulic System Components

We have introduced the components of typical hydraulic systems, and their basic function. In this section, we will examine each of the major components, in detail, and study the common variations in their design.

a. Reservoirs

There is a tendency to envision a reservoir as an individual component; however, this is not always true. There are two types of reservoirs and they are:

Integral — This type has no housing of its own but is merely a space within some major component to hold a supply of fluid. A familiar example of this type is found within most brake master cylinders.

In-Line — This type has its own housing, is complete within itself, and is connected with other components in a system by tubing or hose.

In an in-line reservoir, a space is provided in the reservoir, above the normal level of the fluid, for fluid expansion and the escape of entrapped air. Reservoirs are never intentionally filled to the top with fluid. Most reservoirs are designed so the rim of the filler neck is somewhat below the top of the reservoir to prevent overfilling during servicing. Most reservoirs are equipped with a dipstick or a glass sight gauge by which fluid level can be conveniently and accurately checked.

Reservoirs are either vented to the atmosphere or closed to the atmosphere and pressurized.

(1) Unpressurized Reservoirs

Aircraft that fly in the lower altitudes normally have hydraulic systems supplied with fluid from unpressurized reservoirs. One such reservoir is illustrated in figure 9-16. These reservoirs must be large enough to hold all of the fluid in any condition of the actuation cylinders.

The fluid return into the reservoir is usually directed in such a way that foaming is minimized, and any air in the fluid is swirled out, or extracted. Some reservoirs have filters built into them at the return line so that all of the fluid entering the tank is strained.

Many reservoirs have two outlets. One is located in the bottom and the other is either part way up the side, or is connected to a standpipe that sticks up inside the reservoir. This outlet feeds the engine-driven pump. In the event of a break in the system that allows the engine pump to lose all its fluid, the hand pump can still pick up enough fluid to lower the landing gear and flaps and actuate the brakes.

(2) Pressurized Reservoirs

Jet aircraft that operate at altitudes where there is not enough air pressure to assure a positive feed of fluid to the pump have the hydraulic reservoirs pressurized. This assures that an adequate supply of fluid, free from foaming, is always available at the pump inlet. There are three ways of pressurizing these reservoirs.

One system uses an aspirator in the return line from the main system filter to the reservoir. The aircraft uses variable displacement hydraulic pumps, from which there is always some fluid flow back to the reservoir. Fluid flowing through the

aspirator pulls either cabin or ambient air by jet action into this return fluid. A pressure regulator maintains a pressure of between 30-35 PSI in the reservoir. This system is illustrated in figure 9-17.

Figure 9-18 shows a system using bleed air from the aircraft's turbine engines to maintain a pressure in the main hydraulic reservoir of 40-45 PSI.

A third type of reservoir may be pressurized by hydraulic system pressure acting on the small area inside the piston as seen in figure 9-19. This high pressure moves the piston inside the reservoir and exerts pressure on the fluid. Pressure ratios of near 50:1 are common for this type of reservoir. This means that a 3,000 PSI system can pressurize the fluid to about 60 PSI. The quantity of fluid in this type of reservoir is indicated by the amount the piston sticks out of the body of the reservoir.

b. Filters

The extremely small clearances between components in many hydraulic pumps and valves make effective filtering of the fluid extremely important. A

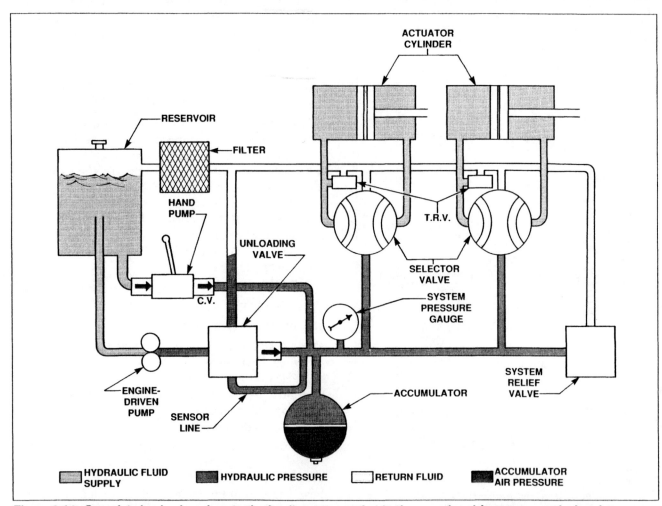

Figure 9-14. Complete basic closed center hydraulic system using both an engine-driven pump and a hand pump.

130

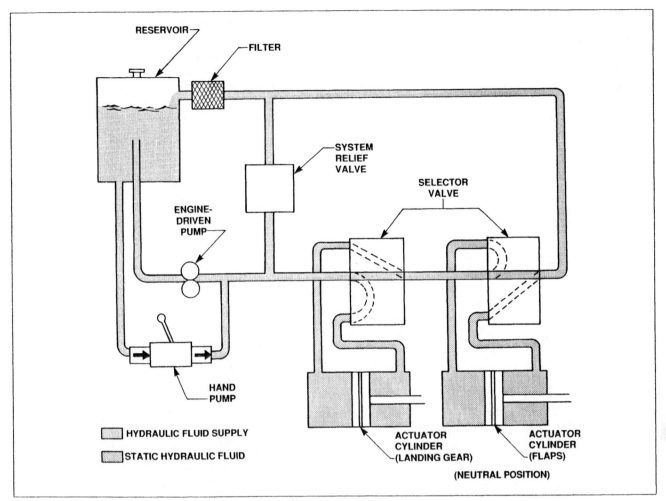

Figure 9-15. Open-center hydraulic system.

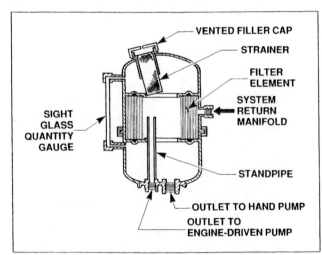

Figure 9-16. Non-pressurized hydraulic reservoir.

filter is rated in the size of particles it will remove, and these sizes are measured in microns, with 1 micron equal to 1 millionth of a meter or 0.000039". To get an idea of how small this is, the unaided eye can see something as small as 40 microns, and white blood cells are about 25 microns. In figure 9-20, we see the relative size of the particles a filter will remove.

One of the more efficient types of filters used in aircraft hydraulic systems is made of specially treated paper folded into pleats to increase its surface area. This pleated paper micronic element, as it is called, is wrapped around a spring steel wire coil to prevent its collapsing. These filters, such as the one seen in figure 9-21, often have a bypass valve across the filtering element so that if the filter ever plugs up, the fluid will bypass the element. This type of filter is usually installed in the fluid return line.

Some filters have elements made of stainless steel wire woven into a mesh and wrapped around a wire frame. We see this type of filter in figure 9-22.

A special 2-stage filter is used in the return line for some large aircraft hydraulic systems in place of the standard single element unit. This type of filter allows the use of an extremely fine element at low flow rates without causing an excessively high pressure drop.

In figure 9-23, we have a schematic and cutaway drawing of this filter. The first stage element has a filter rating of 0.4 to 3 micron and the second stage filter has a rating of 1.5 to 15 microns. All flow less than 5 gal./min., which is adequate for normal cruise flight operation, passes through both the first- and second-stage elements and back into the reservoir. During the higher flow operations, such as during

actuation of the landing gear or flaps, the flow is divided with up to 5 gal./min. passing through both elements, while all in excess of this bypasses the first-stage element and passes through the second-stage element only. This allows the pressure drop across the filter to be held to a reasonable value during conditions of high flow rate.

There are differential pressure indicators on top of the filter that indicate when the element is contaminated and needs to be replaced. There are also relief valves across both elements to prevent over-pressurizing the return line if, for any reason, the pressure drop across the elements becomes excessive.

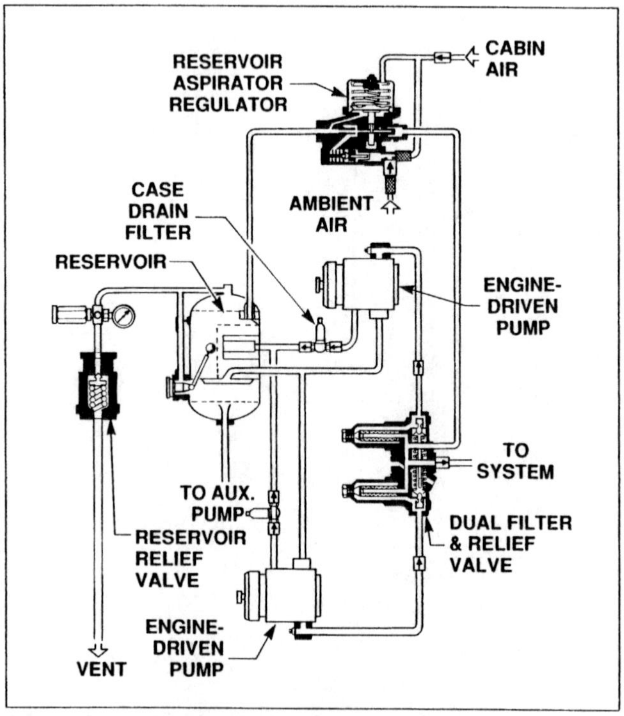

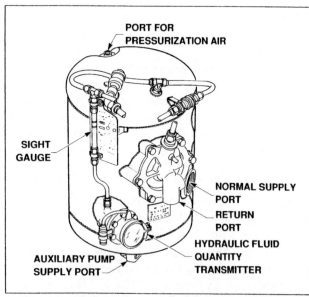

Figure 9-17. Hydraulic reservoir pressurized with an aspirator.

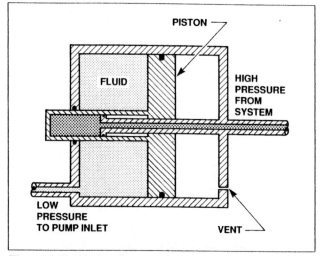

Figure 9-19. Hydraulic reservoir pressurized by hydraulic system pressure.

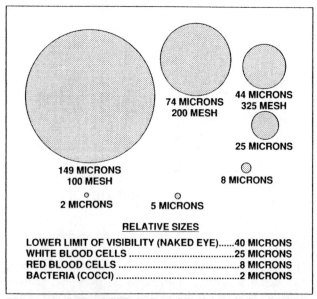

Figure 9-18. Hydraulic reservoir pressurized with bleed air.

RELATIVE SIZES

LOWER LIMIT OF VISIBILITY (NAKED EYE)	40 MICRONS
WHITE BLOOD CELLS	25 MICRONS
RED BLOOD CELLS	8 MICRONS
BACTERIA (COCCI)	2 MICRONS

Figure 99-20.The relative size of these particles may be used to help visualize the effectiveness of a hydraulic filter.

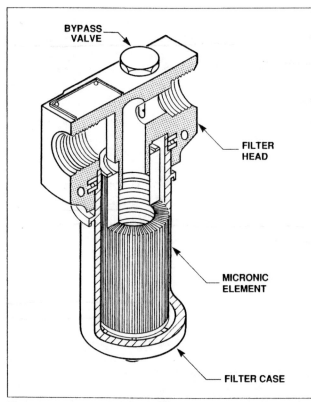

Figure 9-21. Micronic-type filter, using a paper element.

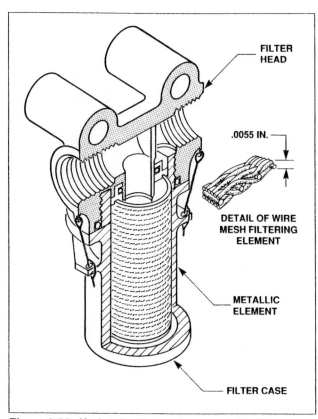

Figure 9-22. Hydraulic filter, using a metallic filter element.

c. Pumps

Hydraulic power is transmitted by the movement of fluid with a pump and pressure is produced when the flow of fluid is restricted.

In a simple hydraulic system, as a valve is closed, the flow will decrease and the pressure will increase. When the valve is fully closed, there will be no flow

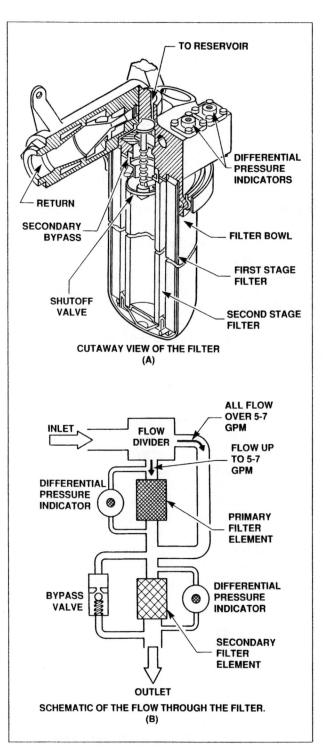

CUTAWAY VIEW OF THE FILTER
(A)

SCHEMATIC OF THE FLOW THROUGH THE FILTER.
(B)

Figure 9-23. Two-stage hydraulic filter.

133

and the pressure will increase to a value as high as the pump can produce. If the pump is of the constant displacement type, there must be some provision in the system to relieve the high pressure; otherwise, the pump will be damaged, or something in the system will be broken.

(1) Hand Pumps

Single-action pumps move fluid only on one stroke of the piston, while double-action pumps move it on both strokes. Double-action pumps are most commonly used in aircraft hydraulic systems because of their greater efficiency.

In figure 9-24, we see the operating principle of one of the more commonly used types of double-action hand pumps. This is called a piston rod displacement pump because its pumping action is caused by the difference in area between the two sides of the piston because of the piston rod.

In view A the handle is moving in the direction to pull the piston to the left, and fluid is drawn into the pump through the inlet check valve. When the piston is at the end of its stroke, chamber 1 is full of fluid, and the spring closes the check valve. As the handle is moved to the right, the piston is forced into chamber 1, and fluid flows through the outlet check valve into chamber 2. The volume of chamber 2 is smaller than that of chamber 1 because of the piston rod, and as fluid fills chamber 2 the excess leaves the pump through the outlet port. On the return stroke of the piston, the remainder of the fluid in chamber 2 is forced out, while a fresh charge is brought into chamber 1.

If we assign some values to the area of the piston, we can easily see the way this pump moves the fluid. Assume that the right side of the piston has an area of 2 sq. in. and the piston rod, an area of 1 sq. in. If the piston moves 2" with each stroke, 4 cu. in. of fluid will be pulled into chamber 1 when the piston moves its full travel. The piston rod decreases the area of the piston on the left side to 1 sq. in. so that the volume of chamber 2 is only 2 cu. in. When the piston moves to the left, 4 cu. in. of fluid flow in, and 2 cu. in. is forced out. On the next stroke, the piston moves to the right, and no fluid is taken in, but 2 cu. in. is forced out.

If a force of 500 lbs. is exerted on the piston as it moves to the left, the 1 sq. in. of area will produce a pressure of 500 PSI. But as the piston moves to the right, this same 500 lbs. of force is spread out over 2 sq. in. of piston area, and the pressure will be only 250 PSI.

(2) Powered Pumps

The function of a pump is to move fluid through the system, and in doing so converts mechanical force

into hydraulic pressure. There are two basic types of pumps: constant displacement and variable displacement. A constant displacement pump moves a specific volume of fluid each time its shaft turns. It must have some form of pressure regulator or relief valve in the system.

A variable displacement pump does not move a constant amount of fluid each revolution, but only the amount the system will accept. By varying the pump output, the system pressure can be maintained within the desired range without the use of regulators or relief valves. Variable displacement pumps can turn without fluid being forced into the system.

(a) Constant Displacement Pumps

1) Gear Pump

This is one of the most generally used types of constant displacement pumps for medium-pressure hydraulic systems. Gear pumps are rugged and dependable and are relatively inexpensive to manufacture. In figure 9-25, we have a diagram of a typical spur gear-type hydraulic pump. The upper gear is driven by the engine through a splined shaft. This gear rides in a close fitting housing and drives the lower gear, turning in the direction shown by the arrows. As the teeth of the two gears separate, the volume of the inlet chamber increases and lowers

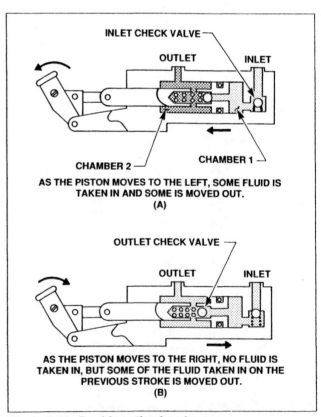

AS THE PISTON MOVES TO THE LEFT, SOME FLUID IS TAKEN IN AND SOME IS MOVED OUT.
(A)

AS THE PISTON MOVES TO THE RIGHT, NO FLUID IS TAKEN IN, BUT SOME OF THE FLUID TAKEN IN ON THE PREVIOUS STROKE IS MOVED OUT.
(B)

Figure 9-24. Double-acting hand pump.

the pressure so that fluid will flow into the pump from the reservoir. This fluid is trapped between the teeth and the wall of the pump body, and the fluid is moved around the outside of the gears to the outlet side of the pump.

A small amount of fluid leaks past the gears and around the shaft for lubrication, cooling, and sealing. This fluid drains into the hollow shafts of the gears where it is picked up by the low pressure at the inlet side of the pump. A weak relief valve holds the oil in the hollow shafts until it builds up a pressure of about 15 PSI. This is called case pressure, and is maintained so that, in the event the shaft or seal becomes scored, fluid will be forced out of the pump rather than air being drawn in. Air in the

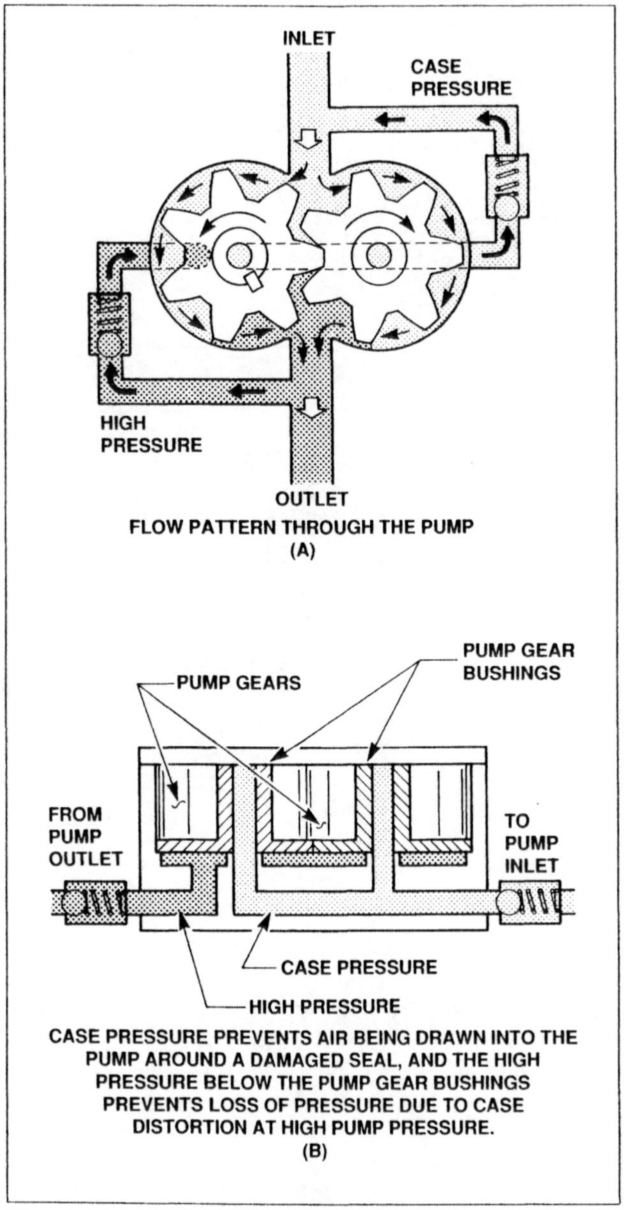

Figure 9-25. Gear-type hydraulic pump.

pump would displace some of the fluid needed for lubrication, and the pump would be damaged.

The inside of the gear cavity of some of the pumps is fitted with a bushing and flange, to minimize the problem of the case distorting when the output pressure is high. Distortion will increase the leakage and cause a loss of pressure. Fluid from the output side of the pump is fed back through a check valve into a cavity under the bushing flange, and as the output pressure rises, it forces the flange tight against the gears. This minimizes the leakage and compensates for wear.

2) Gerotor Pump

The gerotor pump is a combination internal-external gear pump. In figure 9-26, we can follow the operation of a gerotor pump. The 6-tooth spur-type drive gear is turned by an accessory drive from the engine, and as it turns, rotates the 7-tooth internal-gear rotor. If you follow the relationship between the two gears, you will see that in view A the two marked teeth are meshed, and the tooth of the spur gear almost completely fills the cavity in the rotor. As the drive gear rotates and pulls the driven gear around, the volume of the cavity increases until in view C it is maximum. During the rotation from view A to view C, the expanding cavity is under the inlet port and fluid is drawn into the pump. As the gears continue to rotate, the cavity formed by the marked teeth moves under the outlet port. As the drive gear meshes with the cavity next to the marked cavity in the rotor, its volume decreases. The fluid in this cavity is forced out of the pump through the outlet port.

3) Piston Pump

High-pressure hydraulic systems often use a fixed-angle piston-type pump (figure 9-27). These pumps usually have either 7 or 9 axially-drilled holes in a rotating bronze cylinder block. Fitted into each of these holes are close fitting pistons, attached by a ball-jointed rod to the pump drive plate, which is rotated by the engine. The housing is angled so that the pistons on one side of the cylinder block are at the bottom of their stroke, while those on the other side are at the top of theirs. As the pump rotates one-half turn, half of the pistons move from the top of their stroke to the bottom, while the pistons on the other side move from the bottom of their stroke to the top. A valve plate with two crescent-shaped openings covers the end of the cylinders. One of the openings is above the pistons moving up, and the other opening is above the pistons that are moving down. As the pistons move down, they pull fluid into the pump, and as they move up, they force the fluid out.

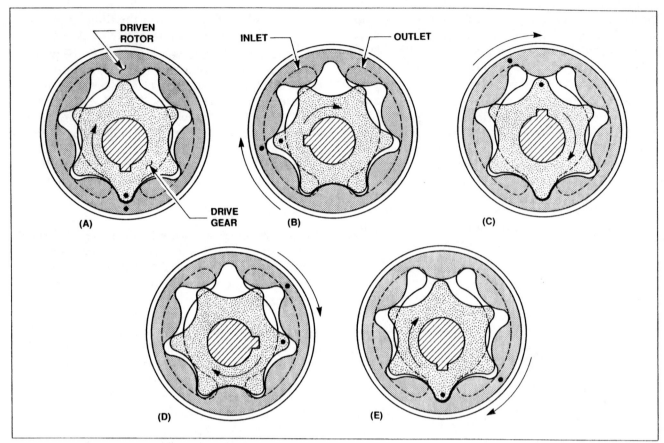

Figure 9-26. Gerotor-type hydraulic pump.

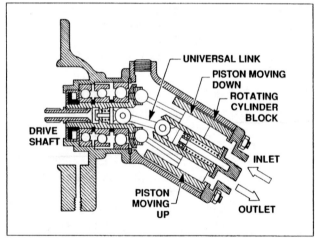

Figure 9-27. Piston-type hydraulic pump.

4) Vane Pump

Some hydraulic systems require a pump to move a relatively large volume of fluid, but do not need to produce a very high pressure. For these applications, the vane pump may be used.

The vanes in the pump shown in figure 9-28 are free-floating in the rotor and are held against the wall of the sleeve by a spacer. As the rotor turns in the direction shown by the arrow, the volume between

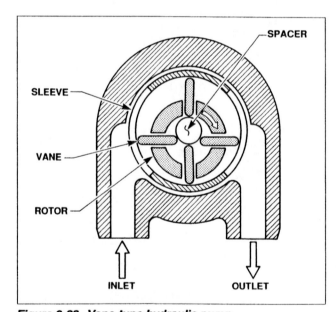

Figure 9-28. Vane-type hydraulic pump.

the vanes on the inlet side increases, while the volume between the vanes on the outlet side decreases. This change in volume draws fluid into the pump through the inlet port and forces it out through the outlet port.

Vane pumps are used more generally for moving fuel and air than they are for moving hydraulic fluid.

(b) Variable Displacement Pump

An unloading valve of some sort is needed when a constant displacement pump is used. But the same force used to control this valve may be used to control the output of a variable displacement pump. One of the more popular variable displacement pumps used for high-pressure aircraft hydraulic systems is the Stratopower demand-type pump we see in figure 9-29. This pump uses 9 axially-oriented pistons and cylinders. The pistons are driven up and down in the cylinders by a wedge-shaped cam, and the pistons bear against the surface of the cam with ball joint slippers. When the thick part of the cam is against the piston, it is at the top of the stroke; and as the cam rotates, the piston moves down the cylinder until, at the thin part of the cam, it is at the bottom. The stroke is the same, regardless of the amount of fluid demanded by the system, but the effective length of the stroke controls the amount of fluid pumped.

The balance of forces that controls the pressure the pump holds on the system is between the compensator spring and the compensator stem piston. A passage from the discharge side of the pump directs output fluid pressure around the compensator stem. This stem is cut with a shoulder that serves as a piston. As the system pressure rises, the fluid pushes the stem up, compressing the compensator spring.

The spider (figure 9-30(A)) which moves the sleeves up or down the pistons, is attached to the stem.

When the pressure is high (figure 9-30(B)) it acts on the stem piston to raise the spider against the compensator spring, and the relief holes near the bottom of the pistons are uncovered during all of the stroke. The pistons now stroke up and down, but no fluid is forced out of the pump, since it is all relieved back into the pump. Near the top of the stroke, a bypass hole in the piston aligns with a passage in the pump housing so that a small amount of fluid bypasses back into the reservoir. This amount is just enough for lubricating and cooling the pump. When the pressure is low (figure 9-30(C)), the compensator spring forces the spider and sleeves down the piston, covering the relief hole when the piston is near the bottom of its stroke. In this way, the full stroke of the piston is utilized to move the fluid. Fluid is forced out through the check valves into the pump discharge line. In any condition of intermediate pressure, the sleeve closes the relief holes at some point along the stroke of the piston. In this way, just enough fluid is pumped to maintain the system pressure at that level for which the compensator spring is set.

d. Valves

The valves used in hydraulic systems may be divided into flow control and pressure control valves. A flow control valve selects the route of flow of the fluid through the system. Pressure control valves adjust,

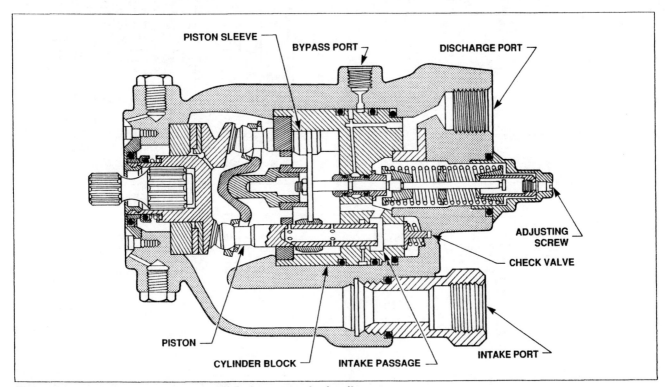

Figure 9-29. Variable-displacement, axial-piston-type hydraulic pump.

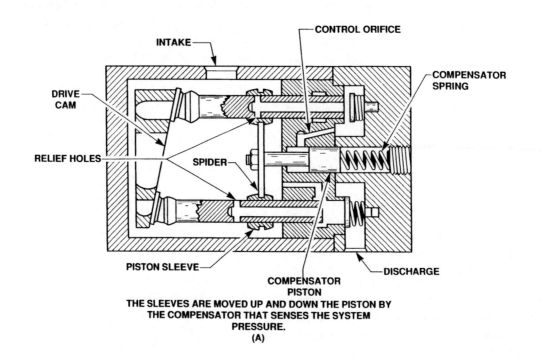

THE SLEEVES ARE MOVED UP AND DOWN THE PISTON BY
THE COMPENSATOR THAT SENSES THE SYSTEM
PRESSURE.
(A)

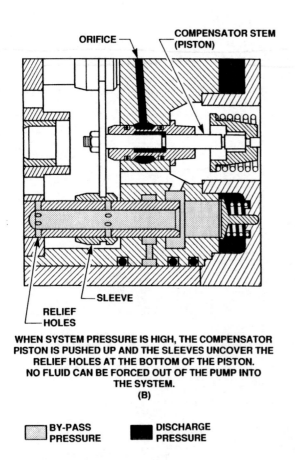

WHEN SYSTEM PRESSURE IS HIGH, THE COMPENSATOR
PISTON IS PUSHED UP AND THE SLEEVES UNCOVER THE
RELIEF HOLES AT THE BOTTOM OF THE PISTON.
NO FLUID CAN BE FORCED OUT OF THE PUMP INTO
THE SYSTEM.
(B)

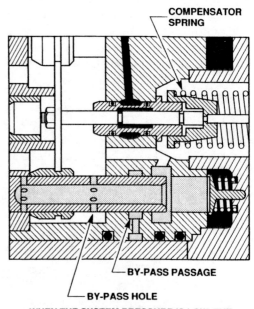

WHEN THE SYSTEM PRESSURE IS LOW, THE
COMPENSATOR SPRING FORCES THE SLEEVES DOWN
OVER THE RELIEF HOLES, SO THE FULL STROKE OF THE
PISTON WILL BE USED TO MOVE FLUID INTO THE SYSTEM.
(C)

☐ BY-PASS   ■ DISCHARGE
   PRESSURE   PRESSURE

Figure 9-30. Details of control of variable-displacement piston-type hydraulic pump.

regulate, or limit the amount of pressure in the system, or in any portion of the system.

(1) Flow Control Valves

For hydraulic components and systems to operate as intended, the flow of fluid must be rigidly controlled. Many kinds of valve units are used for exercising such control.

(a) Selector Valves

One of the most familiar flow control valves is the selector valve, which determines the direction of flow of fluid. There are two commonly used types of selector valves. The open-center valve directs fluid through the center of the valve back to the reservoir when a unit is not being actuated. The closed-center valve stops the flow of fluid when in its neutral position. Both valves direct fluid from the pump to one side of the actuator and direct fluid from the opposite side to the reservoir.

1) Open-center Valve

In figure 9-31, we see a typical open-center poppet-type selector valve. When the selector handle is in the neutral position, poppet 3 is off of its seat. Fluid flows straight through the valve from the pump to the next selector valve and on to the reservoir.

Moving the gear selector handle to the GEAR DOWN position causes the cams to open valves 1 and 4. Fluid can now flow from the pump to the actuator around poppet 4, while the return fluid from the vent side of the actuator flows around poppet 1 back to the reservoir. When the actuator reaches the end of its travel, the pump continues to produce pressure. A system relief valve (figure 9-15) must off-seat to allow a flow back to the reservoir until the selector valve is moved to its neutral position. Some open-center valves have an automatic feature which causes them to move to the neutral position when the pressure rises to a specified value.

When the gear selector is moved to the GEAR UP position, poppets 2 and 5 open, and fluid from the pump flows around poppet 2, while the return fluid flows around poppet 5.

2) Closed-center Valve

Plug-type selector valves such as the one we see in figure 9-32 are often used in aircraft hydraulic systems. In one position, the pressure port and actuator port A are connected, while actuator port B is connected to the return port. Rotating the selector handle 90° reverses the connection between the actuator ports and the pressure and return lines.

A more positive shutoff of fluid may be provided by using a poppet-type selector valve (figure 9-33).

In the GEAR UP position, poppets 2 and 3 are off of their seats, and poppets 1 and 4 are seated. Fluid flows from the pump around poppet 2 to one side of the actuator piston and raises the landing gear. The fluid from the opposite side of the actuator piston is pushed out of the cylinder, around poppet 3, and back to the reservoir.

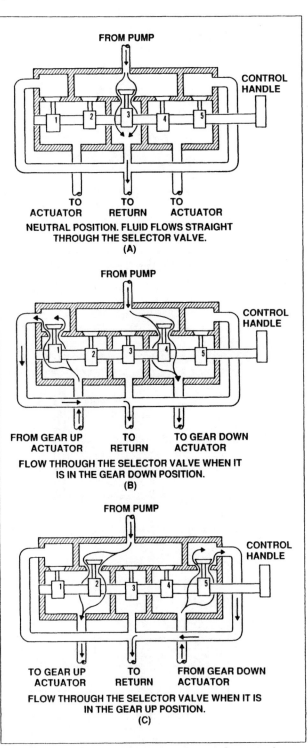

Figure 9-31. Open center, poppet-type selector valve.

When the gear selector handle is placed in the GEAR DOWN position, poppets 1 and 4 are off-seated, and poppets 2 and 3 are seated. Fluid flows

from the pump around poppet 1 into the actuator, while the displaced fluid flows around poppet 4 back into the reservoir.

In a closed-center hydraulic system, the selector valve may shut off the flow of fluid without causing any rise in the system pressure. This is because the system uses a pressure regulator to maintain the system pressure independent of the position of any selector valve.

3) Check Valves

There are many instances in an aircraft hydraulic system where it is desirable to allow fluid to flow in one direction but prevent its flow in the opposite direction. We can do this with check valves.

Check valves are made in two general designs to serve two different needs. In one, the check valve is complete within itself. It is inter-connected with other components, with which it operates, by means of tubing or hose. Check valves of this design are commonly called in-line check valves.

In the other design, the check valve is not complete within itself because it does not have a housing exclusively its own. Check valves of this design are

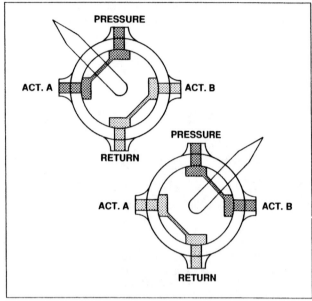

Figure 9-32. Closed center, plug-type, 4-part selector valve.

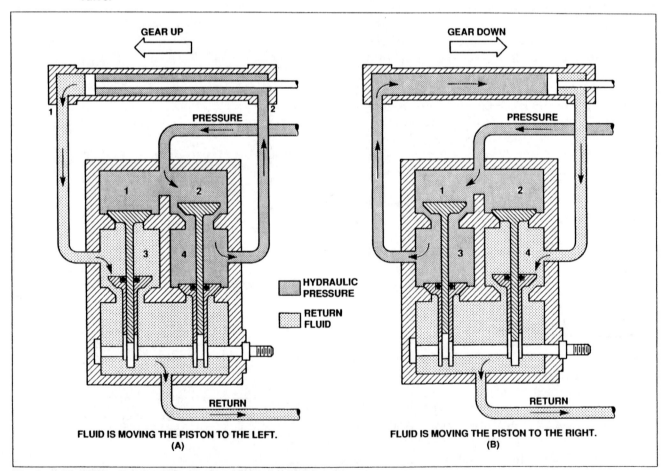

Figure 9-33. Closed center, 4-part, poppet-type selector valve.

commonly called integral check valves. This valve is actually an integral part of some major component and, as such, shares the housing of that component.

There are several types of check valves in use. The ball-type valve is perhaps the most familiar. The one we have illustrated in figure 9-34 will allow fluid to flow in the direction shown by the arrow, but it cannot flow in the opposite direction.

The cone-type check valve, also shown in figure 9-34, functions in the same way except that the seal is provided by a cone rather than by a ball. Neither of these check valves allows an entirely free flow because flow is opposed by the spring that holds the valve seated. The spring force determines the pressure needed to open the check valve.

Some applications for a check valve cannot tolerate the opposition to the flow of fluid, and if this is the case, a swing-type valve may be used. A disk is held with a very weak spring over the opening to the passage inside the check valve, and fluid flowing in the direction of the arrow can very easily force the valve open and flow through with almost no opposition. But, fluid attempting to flow in the opposite direction will force the disc over the opening and prevent any flow.

Certain applications require full flow of fluid in one direction and restricted flow in the opposite direction. An example of this is in a landing gear system where air loads and the weight of the gear cause the extension to be excessively fast, and the weight of the gear against the air loads requires every bit of pressure possible to get the gear up. An orifice check valve is installed in such a way that fluid flowing through the gear-up lines is not restricted, while fluid leaving the gear-up side of the actuator is restricted by the orifice in the check valve.

4) Sequence Valves

Modern aircraft with retractable landing gear often have doors that close in flight to cover the wheel well and make the airplane more streamlined. To be sure the landing gear does not extend while the doors are closed, sequence valves (figure 9-36) may be used. These are actually check valves which allow a flow in only one direction, but may be opened manually to allow fluid to flow in both directions.

In figure 9-37, we see the way sequence valves can be installed in a landing gear system. The wheel well doors must be fully open before the sequence valve opens, to allow fluid to flow into the main landing gear

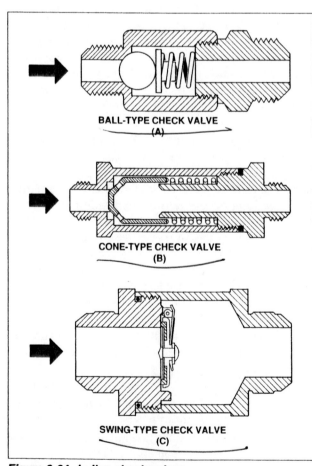

Figure 9-34. In-line check valves.

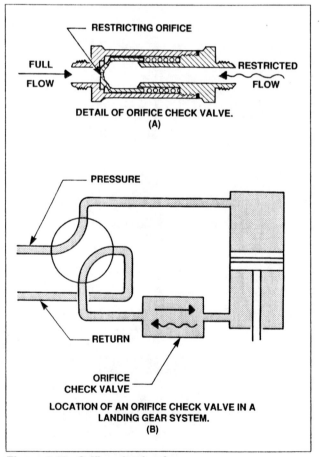

Figure 9-35. Orifice check valve.

cylinder. The return fluid flows unrestricted through the sequence valve on its way back into the reservoir.

5) Priority Valves

Priority valves (figure 9-38) are similar to sequence valves, except that they are opened by hydraulic pressure rather than by mechanical contact. They are called priority valves because such devices as wheel well doors, which must operate first, require a lower pressure than the main landing gear, and the valve will shut off all the flow to the main gear until the doors have actuated and the pressure builds up at the end of the actuator stroke. When this buildup occurs, the priority valve opens so fluid can flow to the main gear.

6) Quick Disconnect Valves

Quick-disconnect, or line-disconnect valves, are installed in hydraulic lines to prevent the loss of fluid when units are removed. Such valves may be installed in the pressure and suction lines of the system just in front, and immediately behind the power pump. These valves can also be used in ways other than just for unit replacement. A power pump can be disconnected from the system and a hydraulic test stand connected in its place.

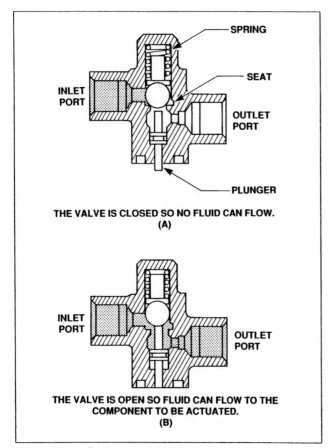

THE VALVE IS CLOSED SO NO FLUID CAN FLOW.
(A)

THE VALVE IS OPEN SO FLUID CAN FLOW TO THE COMPONENT TO BE ACTUATED.
(B)

Figure 9-36. Sequence valves.

These valve units consist of two interconnecting sections coupled by a nut when installed in the system. Each valve section has a piston and poppet assembly. These are spring loaded to the CLOSED position when the unit is disconnected.

The top illustration of figure 9-39 shows the valve in the LINE-DISCONNECTED position. The 2 springs (A and B) hold both poppets (C and F) in the CLOSED position as shown. This prevents loss of fluid through the disconnected line. The bottom illustration of figure 9-39 shows the valve in the LINE-CONNECTED position. When the valve is being connected, the coupling nut draws the two sections together. The extension (D or E) on one of the pistons forces the opposite piston back against its spring. This action moves the poppet off its seat and permits fluid to flow through that section of the valve. As the nut is drawn up tighter, one piston hits a stop; now the other piston moves back against its spring and, in turn, allows fluid to flow. Thus, fluid is allowed to continue through the valve and on through the system.

7) Hydraulic Fuses

Modern aircraft depend on their hydraulic systems not only for raising and lowering the landing gear and flaps, but for control system boosts, thrust reversers, brakes, and many auxiliary systems. For this reason, most aircraft use more than one independent hydraulic system, and provisions are made in these systems to block a line if a serious leak should occur. This blocking is done with hydraulic fuses.

There are two basic types of hydraulic fuses in use. One of these operates in such a way that it will shut off the flow of fluid if a sufficient pressure drop occurs across the fuse. Fluid flows from A to B (figure 9-40) as long as the spring holds the piston away from any of the holes. If a break should occur in a line beyond the fuse, the pressure on side B will drop, and the pressure at side A will force the piston over to cover the holes in the body and stop all flow of fluid. Only when pressure on side A is greater than it is on side B will the fuse close the line, so a reverse flow is not restricted in any way.

Another type of hydraulic fuse shuts off the flow when a specified volume of fluid passes through the fuse.

The fuse in figure 9-41(A) is in its static condition with the pressure at side A and B the same, and there is no flow through the fuse.

In figure 9-41(B), fluid is flowing normally through the fuse. Some of it passes through the metering orifice and drifts the piston to the right. The fluid has pushed the sleeve valve back and opened the passage for fluid to flow out of the fuse.

In figure 9-41(C), we see what happens when the limiting amount of fluid has passed through the fuse. Enough fluid has passed through the metering orifice to drift the piston over the holes in the housing and shut off the flow through the fuse, and this results in a pressure drop across the fuse. The piston

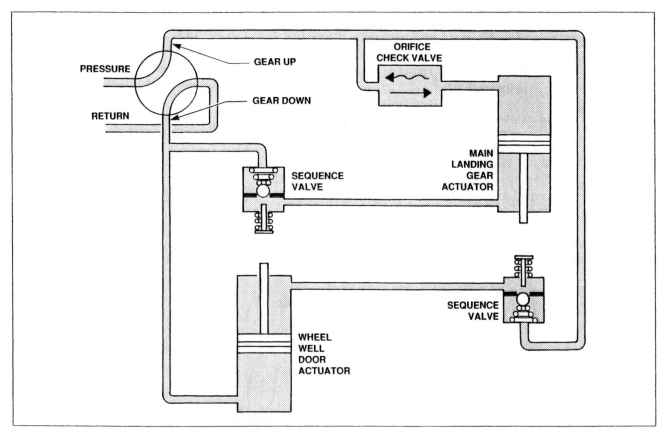

Figure 9-37. *Location of sequence valves in a landing gear system. The main landing gear actuator piston must be fully extended before the wheel well door actuator piston can retract. In the GEAR DOWN position, the wheel well door actuator piston must be fully extended before the landing gear actuator piston can retract.*

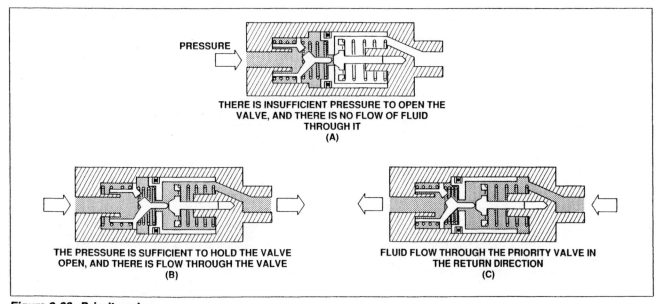

Figure 9-38. *Priority valve.*

holds the spring in the sleeve valve collapsed, and the sleeve valve holds the piston over the holes, preventing any flow of fluid.

This type of fuse has no appreciable opposition to the reverse flow of the fluid. In figure 9-41(D), we see the conditions when the flow is reversed. Both the sleeve valve and the check valve move to the left and the sleeve valve forces the piston away from the holes, allowing the fluid to follow the paths shown by the arrows.

(2) Pressure Control Valves

(a) Relief Valves

The simplest type of pressure control valve is the relief valve. It is used primarily as a backup rather than a control device because of the heat generated and the power dissipated when the valve relieves pressure. The main system pressure relief valve is set to relieve any pressure above that maintained by the system pressure regulator, and only in the event of a malfunction of the regulator will the relief valve be called into service.

In systems where fluid may be trapped in a line between the actuator and its selector valve, there is the problem of pressure buildup by heat expansion of the fluid. Thermal relief valves are installed in these lines to prevent damage by releasing a small amount of fluid back into the return line. We have a simple relief valve in figure 9-42.

(b) Pressure Regulators

A closed-center hydraulic system whose pressure is supplied by a constant delivery pump needs a regulator to maintain the pressure within a specified range and to keep the pump unloaded when no unit

is being actuated. The simplest pressure regulator is the balanced type whose principle is shown in figure 9-43.

Starting with a discharged, or flat, system, the pump forces fluid through the check valve into the system and the accumulator. When no fluid is required for actuation, the accumulator fills and pressure builds up. This pressure pushes both up on the piston and down on the ball, and a condition is soon reached where there is a balance of forces. The fluid pressure pressing down on the ball and the spring pressing down on the piston are both opposed by the fluid pressure forcing the piston up.

To see the way this system works, let's assume some values: The piston has an area of 1 sq. in., the ball has a seat area of ⅓ sq. in., and the spring exerts a force of 1,000 lbs. on the top of the piston. This system balances when the hydraulic system pressure is 1,500 PSI. There is an upward force of 1,500 lbs., and the downward force on the ball is one-third of this, or 500 lbs., and the spring exerts the other 1,000 lbs. Just as soon as the system pressure rises above 1,500 PSI, the piston will be forced up, and the

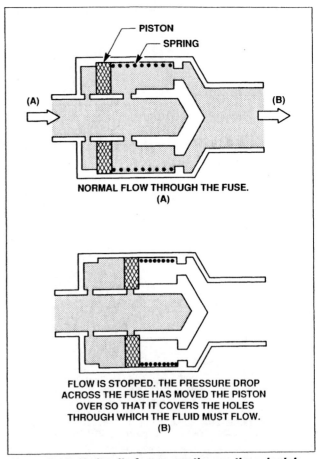

NORMAL FLOW THROUGH THE FUSE.
(A)

FLOW IS STOPPED. THE PRESSURE DROP ACROSS THE FUSE HAS MOVED THE PISTON OVER SO THAT IT COVERS THE HOLES THROUGH WHICH THE FLUID MUST FLOW.
(B)

Figure 9-40. Hydraulic fuse operating on the principle of pressure drop across the fuse.

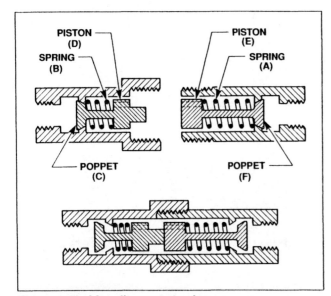

Figure 9-39. Line disconnect valve.

pin will lift the ball from its seat. As soon as the ball is unseated, we lose 500 lbs. downward force, and the piston then forces the pin up enough to raise the ball completely off its seat.

Fluid flows from the pump, around the ball, and out the return to the reservoir. Since the pressure on the inlet side of the check valve has dropped, the system pressure will close it, and the pressure will be trapped in the system and held there by the air pressure in the accumulator. This is the unloaded condition of the valve, and the pump will remain unloaded until the system pressure drops to less than 1,000 PSI. At this time, the spring will force the piston down so the ball can reseat, and with the ball seated the pressure will build back to 1,500 PSI. The pressure at which the pump is placed on the line, 1,000 PSI, is called the "kick-in" pressure, and the pressure at which the pump is unloaded (1,500 PSI) is called the "kick-out" pressure.

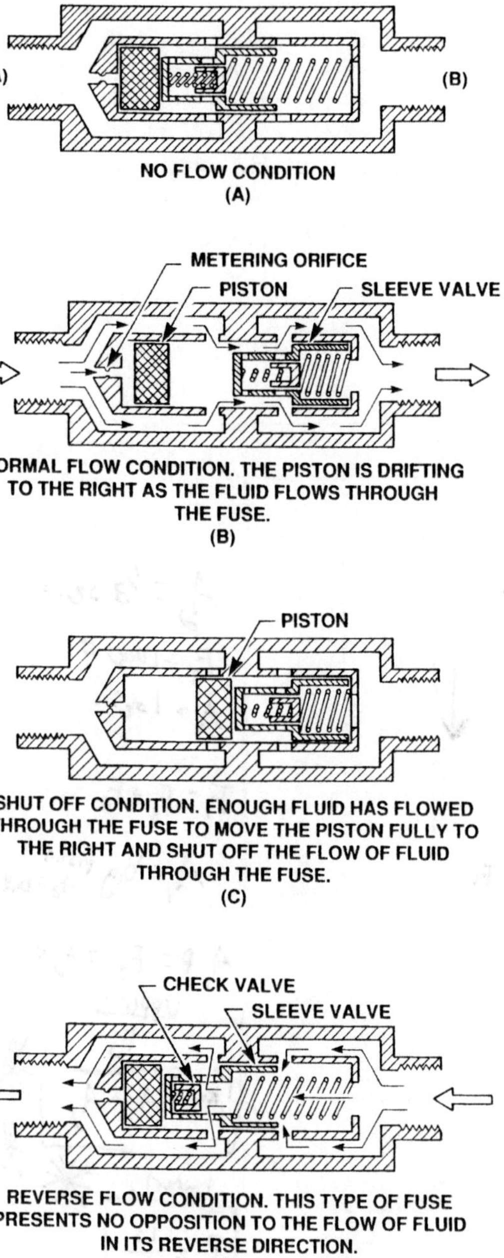

(c) Pressure Reducers

It is sometimes necessary to operate some portion of a hydraulic system at a pressure lower than the normal system pressure, and we can do this by using a pressure reducer similar to the one in figure 9-44.

We must have a balance of forces to maintain the pressure at a predetermined value below the regulated system pressure. In order to understand how this works, assume the following values: The system pressure is held constant at 1,500 PSI by the system pressure regulator, and we need a reduced pressure of 200 PSI to operate the hydraulic servos in an automatic pilot system. The relief valve in the reducer

Figure 9-41. Hydraulic fuse operating on the principle of the quantity of flow needed to isolate the line.

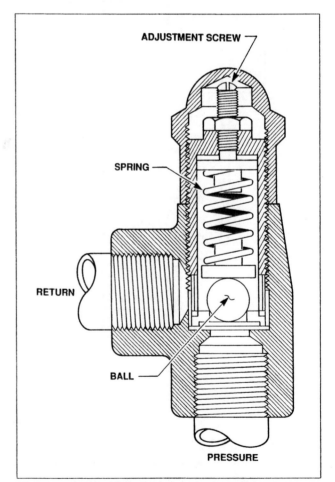

Figure 9-42. Simple ball-type pressure relief valve.

145

maintains the pressure above the piston at 750 PSI, and the spring presses down on the piston with a force of 100 lbs. The area of that portion of the piston that is exposed to system pressure is ½ sq. in., and the area of the ball seat exposed to the 200 PSI reduced pressure is ½ sq. in. Fluid from the main system bleeds through the hole in the piston, where it builds up pressure above the piston until the relief valve unseats to maintain this pressure at 750 PSI. The downward force of 750 lbs. caused by the pressure above the piston acting on the entire 1 sq. in. of area is added to the 100 lbs. of spring force, to give a total downward force of 850 lbs. This is opposed by an upward force of 850 lbs. and 750 lbs. of this force is caused by the system pressure acting on the ½ sq. in. piston shoulder area. We also have 100 lbs. of upward force caused by the reduced pressure acting on the ½ sq. in. ball seat area.

The relief valve maintains 750 PSI inside the piston cavity, by a balance of forces between the pressure inside the piston trying to move the relief valve ball off its seat, while the reduced pressure and the force of the spring acting on the opposite side holds the ball seated. When the reduced pressure drops, the seating force decreases, and the ball moves off its seat and drops the pressure above the piston. This enables the system pressure to raise the piston enough for some fluid under system pressure to enter the reduced pressure portion of the system and bring its pressure back up to 200 PSI. The very small bleed hole in the piston prevents the piston chattering as it maintains the reduced pressure. The ball end of the piston remains off of its seat, just enough to maintain the reduced pressure as fluid is used in this portion of the system.

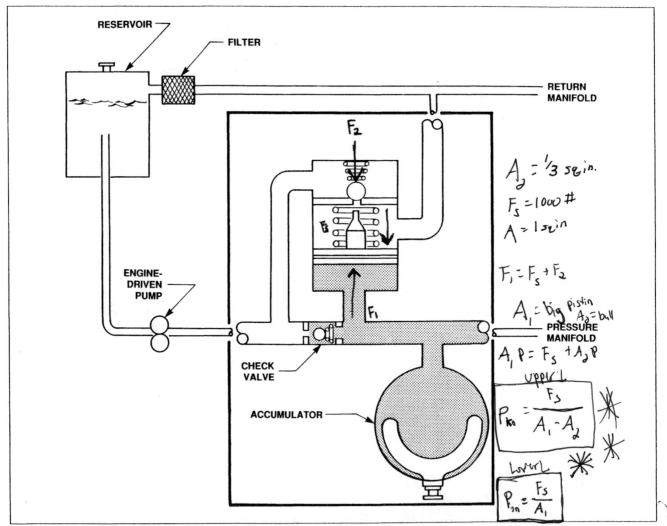

Figure 9-43. Piston-type pressure regulator. In the position shown, the system is being charged by the pump. When the pressure rises sufficiently to force the piston up, it will move the ball off its seat and the check valve will trap pressure in the system where it is held by the accumulator. The pump is unloaded and fluid flows around the ball in the regulator and back to the reservoir.

e. Accumulators

Hydraulic fluid is non-compressible, and pressure may be stored only with compressible fluids. We can gain the effect of compressibility for fluid by using an accumulator.

All accumulators consist of a high-strength container divided by some form of movable partition into two sections or compartments. One compartment is connected to the hydraulic pressure manifold, and the other compartment is filled with either compressed air or nitrogen. There are three types of accumulators commonly found in aircraft hydraulic systems: the piston type, the bladder type, and the diaphragm type.

The piston-type accumulator is cylindrical (figure 9-45) and a free-floating piston divides the cylinder into the two compartments. A high-pressure air valve allows us to charge one compartment with a preload of air or nitrogen with approximately one-half to one-third of the normal system operating pressure. When there is no system pressure, the piston is forced over until it contacts the cylinder head. As soon as fluid is moved into the pressure manifold by a pump, some fluid enters the accumulator and forces the piston over against the compressed air.

This movement increases the pressure of the air and holds this pressure of the fluid. When the system pressure rises to the kick-out pressure of the unloading valve, the pump unloads, and a check valve traps the fluid in the pressure manifold. With the pump no longer forcing fluid into the system, the pressure is maintained by the air in the accumulator forcing the piston against the fluid.

Some hydraulic systems have the pressure gauge connected to the air side of the accumulator. When there is no hydraulic pressure, the gauge will indicate the air preload. If the system pressure gauge is connected into the fluid side of the system, you may find the preload air pressure by watching the gauge as you use the hand pump. No pressure will be shown on the gauge as fluid begins to move into the accumulator, but as soon as the piston moves, the air will oppose it and create a pressure on the fluid equal to the pressure of the air.

The other two accumulators are both spherical, one having a synthetic rubber bladder and the other

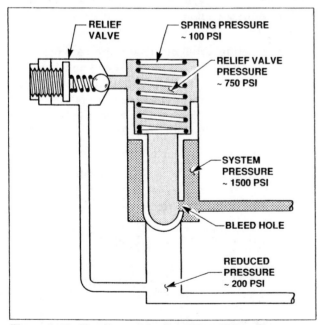

Figure 9-44. *Pressure reducing valve. This valve reduces the pressure from 1,500 PSI to a low pressure of 200 PSI for operation of automatic pilot servos.*

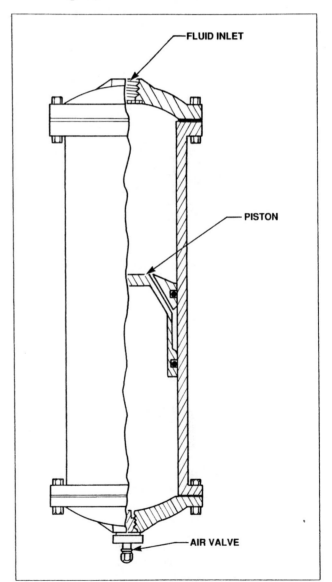

Figure 9-45. *Piston-type accumulator.*

a diaphragm. In both types of accumulators, compressed air or nitrogen fills one compartment, and hydraulic fluid, the other. The flexible partition allows the compressed air to hold pressure on the fluid.

There are three types of air valves that may be used in an accumulator. The AN812 (figure 9-47) is the simplest valve, and it screws directly into the air

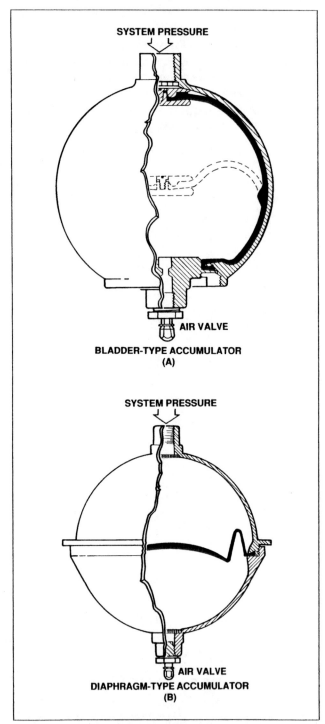

Figure 9-46. Spherical accumulators.

chamber of the accumulator and holds the air with a high-pressure valve core. This core is similar in appearance to the one used in an inner tube or with a tubeless tire, but it is definitely not interchangeable. High-pressure valve cores are identified by the letter "H" embossed on the end of their stem.

f. Actuators

(1) Linear Actuators

The ultimate function of any hydraulic or pneumatic system is to convert the pressure in the fluid into work. In order to do this, there must be some movement. Linear actuators which produce straight-line movement consist of a cylinder and piston, and the cylinder is usually attached to the aircraft structure, with the piston attached to the component being moved.

In figure 9-48, we see a typical landing gear actuator. The cylinder attaches to the wing spar and the piston to the landing gear side-brace link. To retract the landing gear, the piston is pulled into the cylinder.

There are three basic types of linear actuators: single-acting, double-acting unbalanced, and double-acting balanced. The piston in a single-acting cylinder (figure 9-49) is moved in one direction by hydraulic pressure, and it is returned by a spring. The wheel cylinders in shoe-type brakes are good examples of single-acting cylinders. Hydraulic pressure moves the pistons out to apply the brakes, but when the pedal is released, springs pull the shoes away from the drum and move the pistons back into the cylinder.

Double-acting unbalanced actuators are normally used for such applications as raising and lowering the landing gear. In figure 9-50 the fluid entering the up-port acts on the entire area of the piston, while the fluid entering the down port acts only on that portion of the piston not covered by the actuating

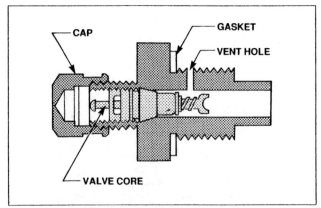

Figure 9-47. AN812 high-pressure air valve for accumulators and air-oil shock struts.

rod. Because of this difference in effective piston area, there is a much greater force produced to raise the landing gear that is used to lower it.

Some applications require the same amount of force in both directions of piston movement, and where we need this, we can use a balanced actuator. In figure 9-51, we see a balanced actuator such as would be used as an automatic pilot servo actuator.

There are many special applications for linear actuators. In figure 9-52, we have a cushioned actuator in which the piston starts its movement slowly, accelerates to full speed, and then is cushioned at the end of its movement. Fluid enters the actuator through the gear-down port, and it must flow around the metering rod to move the piston out of the

cylinder. As soon as the piston travels far enough to remove the metering rod from the orifice, the fluid flow increases and moves the piston out at its full speed. As the piston nears the end of its travel, the piston head contacts the poppet and compresses the poppet spring to bring the piston to a smooth stop at the end of its travel.

When the selector is placed in the gear-up position, fluid enters the gear-up port and moves the piston rapidly until the metering pin enters the orifice. The travel is then slowed until it reaches the full-up position.

Some actuators incorporate a means for locking the piston at the end of its travel. In figure 9-53(A), we see the piston in its retracted position which, in

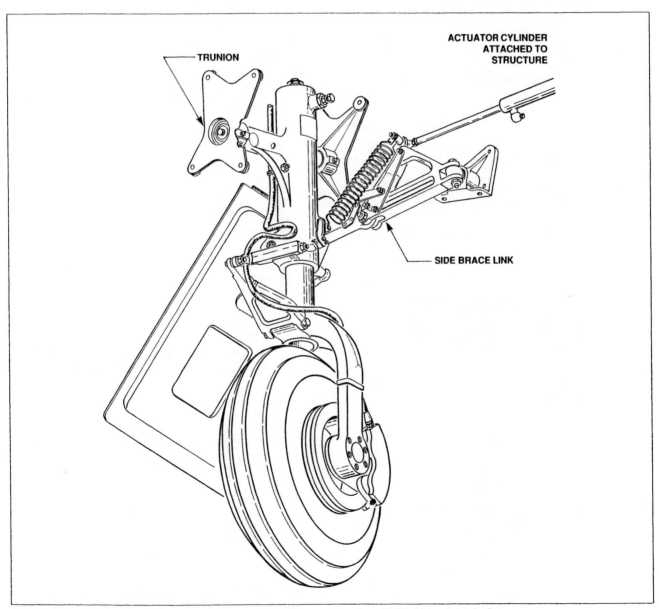

Figure 9-48. Typical retractable landing gear actuation system for a light, low-wing airplane.

this installation, has the landing gear down and locked. The locking pin is holding the locking ball in the groove in the piston so the piston cannot move out of the cylinder.

In figure 9-53(B), fluid under pressure enters the gear-up port and moves the locking pin back, which allows the ball to drop out of the groove in the piston and release it so the fluid can move the piston out of the cylinder and raise the landing gear. The collar holds the ball down in the step of the locking pin and

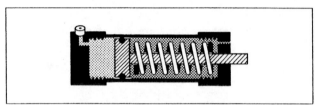

Figure 9-49. Single-acting linear hydraulic actuator. Hydraulic pressure moves the piston to the right, and a spring returns it when the pressure is released.

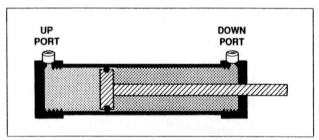

Figure 9-50. Double-acting unbalanced linear hydraulic actuator.

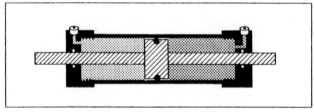

Figure 9-51. Double-acting balanced linear hydraulic actuator.

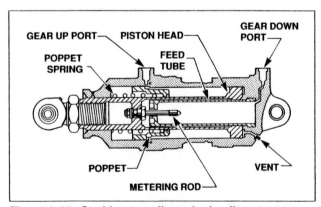

Figure 9-52. Cushion-type linear hydraulic actuator.

prevents its extending until the gear is lowered, and the piston forces the collar back, allowing the ball to release the locking pin. This in turn locks the ball into the groove in the piston.

(2) Rotary Actuators

Perhaps one of the simplest forms of a rotary actuator is the rack-and-pinion type that is used in the popular high-performance, single-engine Cessna aircraft for retracting the main landing gear. Figure 9-54 is an exploded view of this actuator. The piston has a rack of teeth cut in its shaft. These teeth mesh with those in a pinion gear that rotates as the piston moves in or out. Rotation of the pinion shaft raises or lowers the landing gear.

If a continuous rotational force is needed, a hydraulic motor may be used (figure 9-55). Fluid under pressure from the system enters the motor through the inlet port and forces the pistons to the bottom of the cylinder block. As they move down the cylinder bore, they force the driveshaft to rotate. By the time the pistons reach the bottom of the bore, the cylinder block has rotated until the cylinders whose pistons are

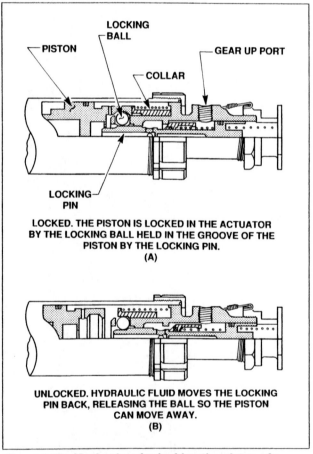

Figure 9-53. Mechanism for locking the piston of a linear hydraulic actuator at the end of its stroke.

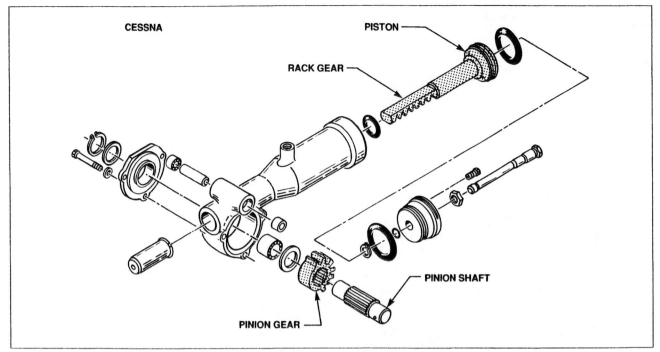

Figure 9-54. Rack-and-pinion-type linear hydraulic actuator having a rotary output.

moving upward are under the outlet port, and as they move up force fluid out into the return manifold.

Where less torque is needed, a vane-type motor may be used. The motor shown in figure 9-56 is a balanced vane-type motor, in which pressure is directed to vanes on opposite sides of the rotor to balance the load on the shaft. Fluid under pressure enters the inlet chambers of the motor and pushes the vanes around to the outlet chambers. The vanes are free to slide back and forth in the slots in the rotor, and centrifugal force holds them against the outside of the chambers.

E. Aircraft Pneumatic Systems

Modern aircraft may use compressed air (pneumatic) systems for a variety of purposes. Some use pneumatics rather than hydraulics for the operation of the landing gear, flaps, brakes, cargo doors, and other forms of mechanical actuation. Other aircraft using hydraulics for these major functions may have a cylinder of compressed air or nitrogen as a backup source of power to lower the landing gear and/or apply the brakes in the event of a failure of the hydraulic power. Still other aircraft use pneumatics only for deicing and for the operation of various flight instruments.

Some of the advantages of using compressed air over hydraulic or electrical systems are:

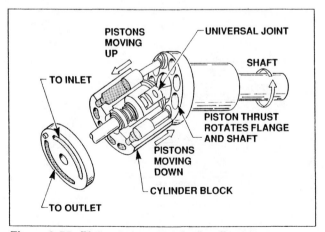

Figure 9-55. Piston-type rotary hydraulic motor.

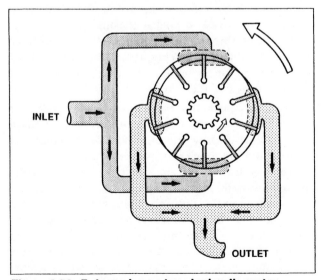

Figure 9-56. Balanced vane-type hydraulic motor.

1. Air is universally available in an inexhaustible supply.
2. The units in a pneumatic system are reasonably simple and lightweight.
3. Compressed air, as a fluid, is lightweight and, since no return system is required, weight is saved.
4. The system is relatively free from temperature problems.
5. There is no fire hazard, and the danger of explosion is minimized by careful design and operation.
6. Installation of proper filters minimizes contamination as a problem.

The type of unit used to provide pressurized air for pneumatic systems is determined by the system's air pressure requirements.

1. High Pressure Systems

For high-pressure systems, air is usually stored in metal bottles (figure 9-57) at pressures ranging from 1,000 to 3,000 PSI depending on the particular system. This type of air bottle has two valves, one of which is a charging valve. The other valve is a control or shutoff valve.

Although the high pressure storage cylinder is light in weight, it has a definite disadvantage. Since the system cannot be recharged in flight, operation is limited by the small supply of bottled air. Such an arrangement can not be used for the continuous operation of such systems as landing gear or brakes. The usefulness of this type of system is increased, however, if other air-pressurizing units are added to the aircraft.

On some aircraft, permanently installed air compressors have been added to recharge air bottles whenever pressure is used for operating a unit. Several types of compressors are used for this purpose. Some have two stages of compression, while others have three. Figure 9-58 shows a simplified schematic of a 2-stage compressor: the pressure of the incoming air is boosted first by cylinder No. 1 and again by cylinder No. 2.

The compressor has three check valves. Like the check valves in a hydraulic hand pump, they allow fluid to flow in only one direction. Some source of power, such as an electric motor or aircraft engine, operates a drive shaft. As the shaft turns, it drives the pistons in and out of their cylinders. When piston No. 1 moves to the right, the volume in cylinder No. 1 becomes larger, and outside air flows through the filter and check valve into the cylinder. As the drive shaft continues to turn, it reverses the direction of piston movement. Piston No. 1 now moves deeper into its cylinder, forcing air through the pressure line

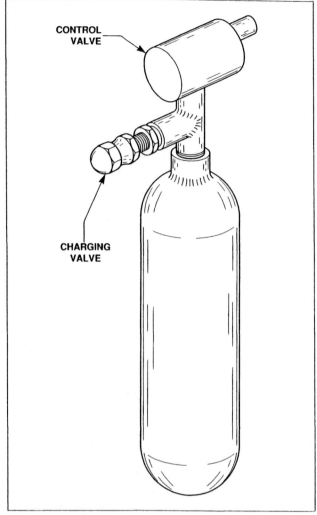

Figure 9-57. Steel cylinder for high-pressure air storage.

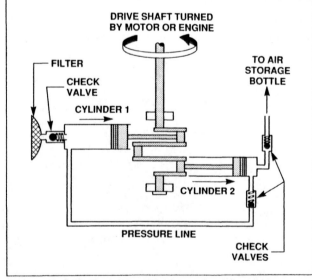

Figure 9-58. Schematic of 2-stage air compressor.

152

and into cylinder No. 2. Meanwhile piston No. 2 is moving out of cylinder No. 2 so that cylinder No. 2 can receive the incoming air. But cylinder No. 2 is smaller than cylinder No. 1; thus, the air must be highly compressed to fit into cylinder No. 2.

Because of the difference in cylinder size, piston No. 1 gives the air its first stage of compression. The second stage occurs as piston No. 2 moves deeper into its cylinder, forcing high-pressure air to flow through the pressure line and into the air storage bottle.

2. Medium Pressure Systems

A medium pressure pneumatic system (100-150 PSI) usually does not include an air bottle. Instead, it generally takes bleed air from the turbine engine compressor section. Engine bleed air will first be routed to a pressure-controlling unit and then to the operating units.

Some jet aircraft use compressor bleed air from the engines to provide a relatively large volume of compressed air at a low pressure to heat the leading edge of the wing and prevent the formation of ice, to provide air for starting the engine, and for pressurizing and controlling the temperature of the air in the aircraft cabin. A diagram of this type of system is presented in figure 9-59.

3. Low-Pressure Systems

Many aircraft use low-pressure, air-driven gyro instruments as either the primary gyro instruments or as backup instruments when the primary gyros are electrically driven.

For many years, all of the air-driven gyro instruments used an engine-driven vacuum pump to evacuate the instrument case, and filtered air was pulled into the instrument to spin the gyro. The reason for this was that it was much easier to filter air being pulled into the instrument than it was to filter the air after it had been pumped by an engine-driven pump lubricated by engine oil. The output of these pumps always contained some particles of the oil.

Pressurized aircraft created extra problems for suction-operated instruments, and the latest generations of air-driven gyros now almost all use pressure. Turbine-powered aircraft bleed some of the pressure from the engine compressor, regulate and filter it, and then direct it over the gyros. Aircraft with reciprocating engines use air pumps driven by electric motors or by the aircraft engine to provide

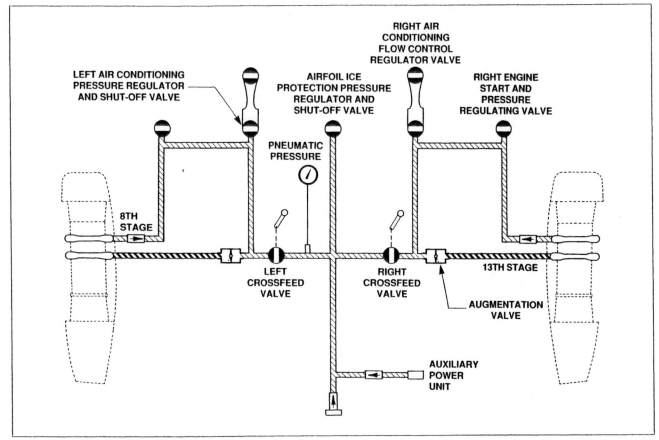

Figure 9-59. Pneumatic system of a jet transport aircraft using compressor bleed air to operate air conditioning and ice control systems.

the airflow for the gyros. This air is regulated and filtered before it is ready for the instrument.

4. Pneumatic System Components

Pneumatic systems are often compared to hydraulic systems, but such comparisons can only hold true in general terms. Pneumatic systems do not utilize reservoirs, hand pumps, or accumulators. Similarities, however, do exist in some components.

a. Relief Valves

Relief valves are used in pneumatic systems to prevent damage. They act as pressure-limiting units and prevent excessive pressures from bursting lines and blowing out seals. Figure 9-60 illustrates a cutaway of a pneumatic system relief valve.

At normal pressures, a spring holds the valve closed, and air remains in the pressure line. If pressure grows too high, the force it creates on the disk overcomes spring tension and opens the relief valve. Then, excess air flows through the valve and is exhausted as surplus air into the atmosphere. The valve remains open until the pressure drops to normal.

b. Control Valves

Control valves are also a necessary part of a typical pneumatic system. Figure 9-61 illustrates how a valve is used to control emergency air brakes. The control valve consists of a 3-port housing, two poppet valves, and a control lever with two lobes.

In figure 9-61(A), the control valve is shown in the "off" position. A spring holds the left poppet closed

so that the compressed air entering the pressure port cannot flow to the brakes. In figure 9-61(B), the control valve has been placed in the "on" position. One lobe of the lever holds the left poppet open, and a spring closes the right poppet. Compressed air now flows around the opened left poppet, through a drilled passage, and into a chamber below the right poppet. Since the right poppet is closed, the high-pressure air flows out of the brake port and into the brake line to apply the brakes.

c. Check Valves

Check valves are used in both hydraulic and pneumatic systems. Figure 9-62 illustrates a flap-type pneumatic check valve. Air enters the left port of the check valve, compresses a light spring, forcing the check valve open and allowing air to flow out the right port. But if air enters from the right, air pressure closes the valve, preventing a flow of air out the

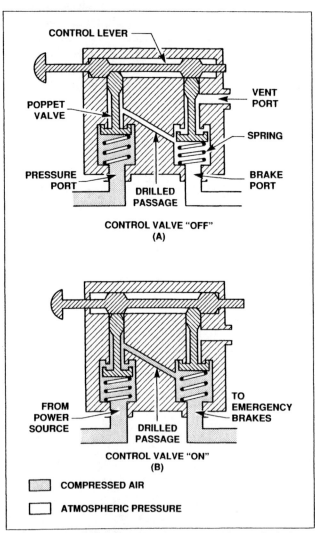

Figure 9-61. Flow diagram of a pneumatic control valve.

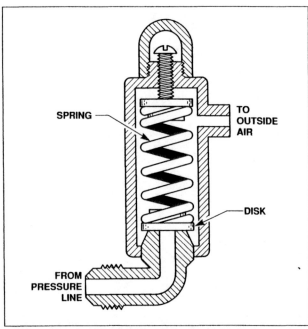

Figure 9-60. Pneumatic system relief valve.

left port. Thus, a pneumatic check valve is a 1-direction flow control valve.

d. Restrictors

Restrictors are a type of control valve used in pneumatic systems. Figure 9-63 shows an orifice type restrictor with a large inlet port and a small outlet port. The small outlet port reduces the rate of airflow and the speed of operation of an actuating unit.

e. Variable Restrictor

Another type of speed-regulating unit is the variable restrictor shown in figure 9-64. It contains an adjustable needle valve, which has threads around the top

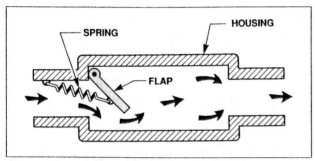

Figure 9-62. Pneumatic system check valve.

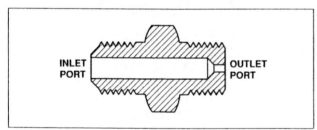

Figure 9-63. Orifice restrictor.

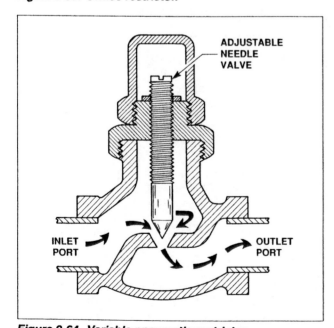

Figure 9-64. Variable pneumatic restrictor.

and a point on the lower end. Depending on the direction turned, the needle valve moves the sharp point either into or out of a small opening to decrease or increase the size of the opening. Since air entering the inlet port must pass through this opening before reaching the outlet port, this adjustment also determines the rate of airflow through the restrictor.

f. Filters

Pneumatic systems are protected against dirt by means of various types of filters. A micronic filter (figure 9-65) consists of a housing with two ports, a replaceable filter cartridge, and a relief valve. Normally, air enters the inlet, circulates around the cellulose cartridge, then flows to the center of the cartridge and out the outlet port. If the cartridge becomes clogged with dirt, pressure forces the relief valve open and allows unfiltered air to flow out the outlet port.

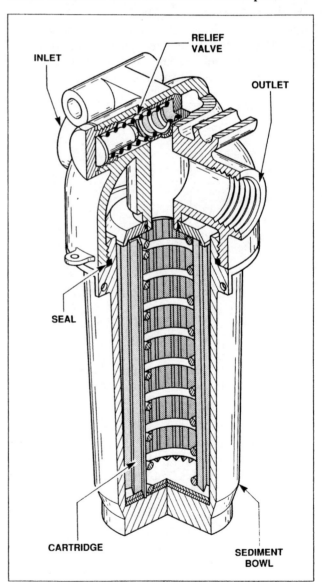

Figure 9-65. Micronic filter.

A screen-type filter (figure 9-66) is similar to the micronic filter but contains a permanent wire screen instead of a replaceable cartridge. In the screen filter, a handle extends through the top of the housing and can be used to clean the screen by rotating it against metal scrapers.

g. Desiccant/Moisture Separator

Moisture in a compressed air system will condense and freeze when the pressure of the air is dropped for actuation and, for this reason, every trace of water must be removed from the air. A moisture separator collects the water that is in the air on a baffle and holds it until the system is shut down. When the inlet pressure to the separator drops below a preset value, a drain valve opens and all of the accumulated water is blown overboard. An electric heater built into the base of the separator unit prevents the water from freezing.

After the air leaves the moisture separator with about 98% of its water removed, it must pass through a desiccant, or chemical dryer, to remove the last traces of moisture. This unit consists of a tubular housing with an inlet and outlet port and contains a desiccant cartridge. These replaceable cartridges consist of a dehydrating agent (MIL-D-3716) and incorporate a bronze filter at each end. Any moisture not removed by the separator will be absorbed by the dehydrating agent.

h. Shuttle Valves

Shuttle valves may be installed to allow a pneumatic system to operate from a ground source. When the pressure from the external source is higher than that of the compressor as it is when the engine is not running, the shuttle slides over and isolates the compressor. The pneumatic systems may then be operated from the ground source. Shuttle valves may also be used to provide an emergency pneumatic backup for hydraulically operated landing gear or brake systems.

5. Emergency Backup System

All aircraft with retractable landing gear must have some method of assuring that the gear will move down and lock in the event of failure of the main extension system. One of the simplest ways of lowering and locking a hydraulically actuated landing gear is by using compressed air or nitrogen stored in an emergency cylinder. The gear selector is placed in the gear down position to provide a path for the fluid to leave the actuator and return into the reservoir. Compressed air is then released from the emergency cylinder, and it enters the actuator through a shuttle valve (figure 9-67). This valve is moved over by air pressure to close off the hydraulic system so no air

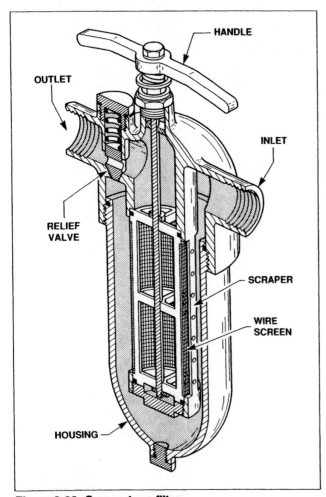

Figure 9-66. Screen-type filter.

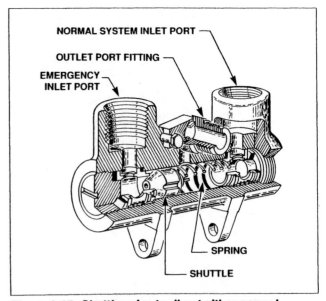

Figure 9-67. Shuttle valve to direct either normal hydraulic system pressure or emergency air pressure into a landing gear or brake actuator.

can enter it. The air pressure is sufficient to lower and lock the landing gear against the flight loads.

Emergency operation of the brakes is also achieved in many airplanes by the use of compressed air. When the pilot is sure he has no hydraulic pressure to the brakes, he can rotate the pneumatic brake handle. Clockwise rotation of this handle increases the brake pressure, and when the handle is held stationary, the pressure is constant. Nitrogen pressure released by this control handle forces hydraulic fluid in the transfer tube into the main wheel brakes through shuttle valves. When the brake handle is rotated counterclockwise, pressure is released and the nitrogen is exhausted overboard.

6. Typical Pneumatic Power System

In figure 9-69, we see a typical full pneumatic system as is used on a popular European-built, twin-engine commuter transport airplane. We can examine each of the components illustrated and see how they work together to create a reliable system.

a. Components

Each of the two compressors is a 4-stage piston-type pump driven from the accessory gearbox of the two turboprop engines. Air is taken into the first stage through an air duct and is compressed, then passed successively to the other three stages. The discharge air from the fourth stage is routed through an intercooler and a bleed valve to the unloading valve. The bleed valve is kept closed by engine oil pressure and, in the event of a loss of the engine lubricating oil, the valve will open and relieve the pump of any load.

The unloading valve maintains pressure in the system between 2,900 and 3,300 PSI. When the pressure rises to 3,300 PSI, a check valve traps it and dumps the output of the pump overboard. When the system pressure drops to 2,900 PSI, the output of the pump is directed back into the system.

A shuttle valve in the line between the compressor and the main system makes it possible to charge the system from a ground source. When the pressure from the external source is higher than that of the compressor, as it is when the engine is not running, the shuttle slides over and isolates the compressor.

A moisture separator collects the water that is in the air and holds it until the system is shut down. When the inlet pressure to the separator drops below 450 PSI, a drain valve opens and the accumulated water is blown overboard. After the air leaves the moisture separator it passes through a desiccant, or chemical dryer, to remove the last traces of moisture.

The air, before it enters the actual operating system, is filtered through a 10-micron sintered metal filter. When we realize that the lower level of visibility with the naked eye is about 40 microns, we see that this provides really clean air to the system.

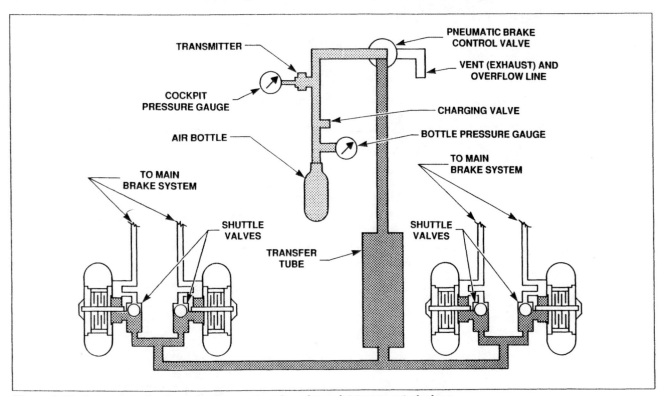

Figure 9-68. Emergency brake actuating system for a large jet transport airplane.

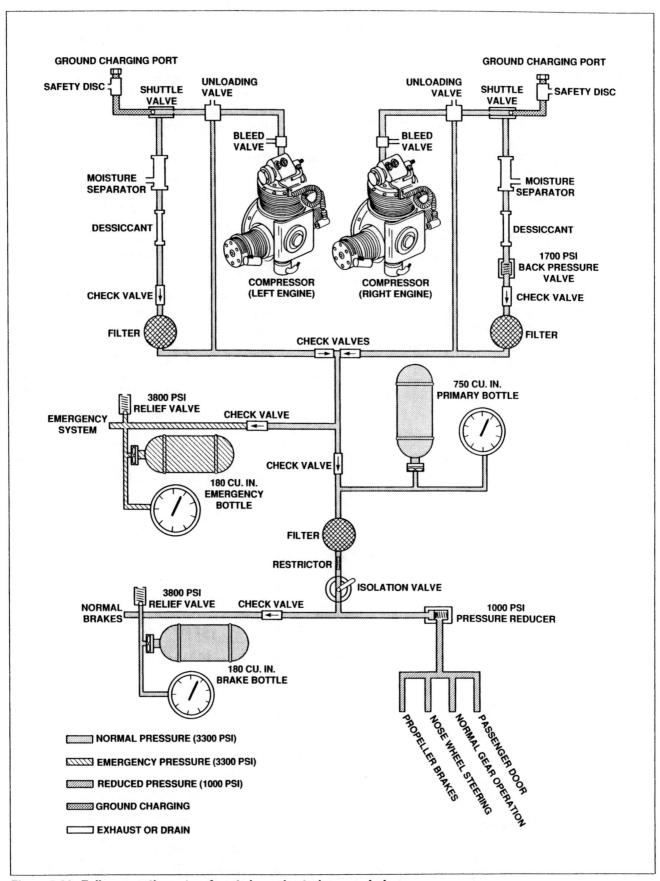

Figure 9-69. Full pneumatic system for a twin-engine turboprop airplane.

A back pressure valve is installed in the right engine nacelle. This is essentially a pressure relief valve in the supply line that does not open until the pressure from the compressor or ground charging system is above 1,700 PSI, and this assures that the moisture separator will operate most efficiently. If you should want to operate the system from an external source of less than 1,700 PSI, it can be connected into the left side where there is no back pressure valve.

There are three air storage bottles in this airplane; a 750-cu. in.bottle for the main system, a 180-cu. in. bottle for the normal brake operation, and a second 180-cu. in. bottle for emergency operation of the landing gear and brakes.

A manually operated isolation valve allows a technician to close off the air supply so he can service the system without having to discharge the storage bottle.

The majority of the components in this system operate with pressure of 1,000 PSI, so a pressure reducing valve is installed between the isolation valve and the supply manifold for normal operation of the landing gear, passenger door, drag brake, propeller brake, and nose wheel steering. This valve not only reduces the pressure to 1,000 PSI, but it also serves as a backup pressure relief valve.

The emergency system stores compressed air under the full system pressure of 3,300 PSI and supplies it for landing gear emergency extension.

Chapter X

Aircraft Hydraulic Landing Gear Systems

The landing gear was not very complex in the development of aircraft.. The Wright Flyer, for instance, took off from a rail and landed on skids. Bicycle wheels and motorcycle wheels were first used, but soon gave way to specially designed landing gears that demanded more of the designer's skill.

A. Small Aircraft Retraction Systems

When the parasite drag of the landing gear hanging in the airstream is greater than the induced drag caused by the added weight of the retracting system, retractable landing gear becomes practical. Some smaller aircraft use a simple mechanical retraction system, incorporating a roller chain and sprockets, operated by a hand crank. Many aircraft use electric motors to drive the landing gear retracting mechanism, and some European-built aircraft use pneumatic systems.

1. Hydraulic Power Pack System

Many manufacturers use an electric motor to drive the hydraulic pump. They incorporate the reservoir, control valve, and many other components, into a single unit called a power pack. In figure 10-1, we see the hydraulic system of a typical light twin-engine airplane using a power pack. In this diagram, the pump is driven by a reversible DC motor in the direction to lower the landing gear. When the gear-type pump turns in the direction indicated, the fluid comes from the reservoir down through the right check valve, around the outside of the gears, and down to the shuttle valve. This is pushed over, compressing the spring and opening the passage to the down-side of the three landing gear cylinders. This same pressure moves the gear-up check valve over and opens the valve so that fluid returning from the up-side of the cylinders can flow back through the pump and to the down-side of the cylinders.

When the selector is placed in the GEAR UP position (figure 10-2) the pump turns in the opposite direction. Fluid is drawn from the reservoir through the filter and around the gears in the pump, and through the gear-up check valve, to the up-side of the three cylinders. The return fluid passes through the shuttle valve which is now moved over by the spring, and back up into the reservoir. When all three gear cylinders are up, pressure will build up

and open the pressure switch that shuts off the electrical power to the pump motor. There are no mechanical up-locks in this system, and the gear is held up by hydraulic pressure. If the pressure bleeds off, the pressure switch will start the pump motor and restore the pressure before the gear has a chance to fall out of the wheel wells.

B. Large Aircraft Retraction Systems

The actual system for retracting and extending the landing gear on large aircraft is similar to that we have just described, but there are several additional features and components used because of the size and complexity of the system.

Normally, large aircraft have wheel-well doors that are closed at all times the landing gear is not actually moving up or down. Sequence valves are used in the system to ensure the doors are opened before the landing gear is actuated.

Almost all large aircraft use mechanical locks to hold the landing gear in its UP as well as in its DOWN position. There must be a provision in these systems for the hydraulic pressure to release the locks before fluid is directed into the actuating cylinders.

Some provision is normally made to apply the brakes when the landing-gear selector is placed in the GEAR UP position. This prevents the fire hazard that would exist if the wheels were spinning while in the wheel wells.

Most of the large aircraft landing-gear systems use some form of orifice check valve in the fluid lines to the actuators. The weight of the landing gear dropping out of the wheel wells could cause it to fall so fast that there could be damage to the structure, so the return flow from the actuator is restricted. Unrestricted flow, however, is allowed into and out of the actuator when the gear is being retracted.

In figure 10-3, we have the block diagram of a large jet transport aircraft hydraulic system. This aircraft has a utility system and an auxiliary system. The fluid for the utility system is supplied from the utility reservoir, and the pressure is produced by two engine-driven pumps. These pumps are of the variable displacement type, and therefore do not require a pressure regulator, but do have a return line back

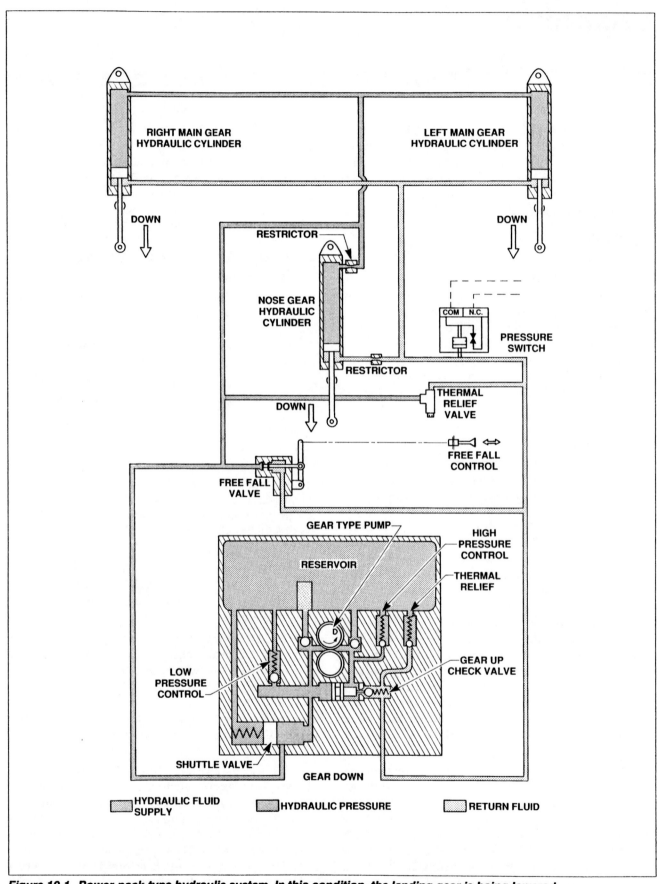

Figure 10-1. Power-pack-type hydraulic system. In this condition, the landing gear is being lowered.

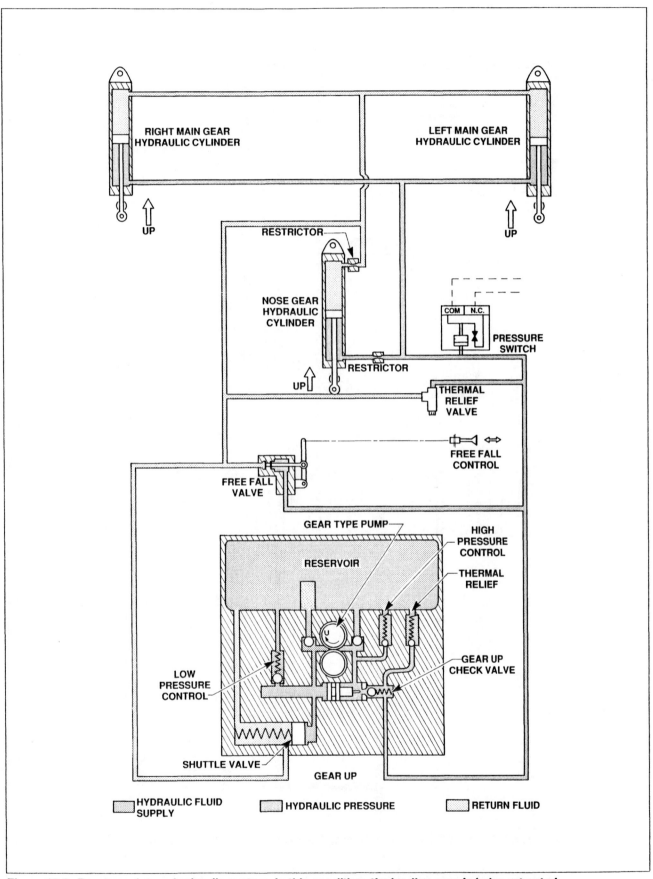

Figure 10-2. Power-pack-type hydraulic system. In this condition, the landing gear is being retracted.

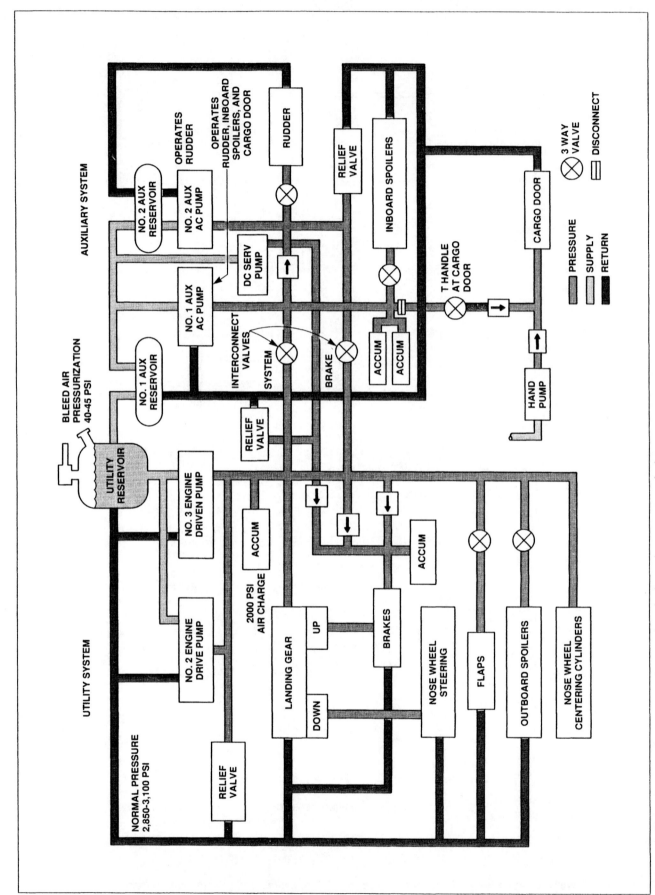

Figure 10-3. Block diagram of a hydraulic system of a large jet transport airplane.

into the reservoir. An accumulator holds pressure on the system and a relief valve is installed to bypass fluid back into the reservoir if there should be a malfunction in the pumps that would produce too much pressure in the system.

This utility system provides the pressure to raise and lower the landing gear, operate the brakes, flaps, and the outboard spoilers, and to provide for centering the nose wheel as it is being retracted. When the landing gear is down, pressure for nose wheel steering is provided by this system, and when the landing gear is retracted, the brakes are automatically applied to stop the wheels spinning before they enter the wheel wells.

The auxiliary system consists of two reservoirs, two AC electrically driven hydraulic pumps, and one DC electric motor-driven service pump. Both AC pumps can supply pressure to the rudder. Pump NO. 1 also supplies pressure to the inboard spoilers and the cargo door. And through an interconnect valve, it can supply pressure to the landing gear. Pump NO. 2 can supply the brakes through an interconnect valve.

C. Nose Wheel Steering Systems

1. Small Aircraft

Almost all airplanes with tricycle landing gear have some provisions for steering on the ground by controlling the nose wheel. Some of the smallest airplanes, however, have a castering nose wheel, and steering is done by independent use of the brakes. Other small airplanes have the nose wheel connected to the rudder pedals, some directly, and others that are steerable up through a specified angle, after which the steering disconnects and the gear is free to caster up to the limit of its travel.

2. Large Aircraft

Some large aircraft are steered on the ground by directing hydraulic pressure into the cylinders of a dual shimmy damper (figure 10-4). A control wheel operated by the pilot directs fluid under pressure into one or the other of the steering cylinders. Fluid from the opposite side of the piston in these cylinders is directed back to the system reservoir through a pressure relief valve that holds a constant pressure on the system to snub any shimmying. An accumulator in the line to the relief valve holds pressure on the system when the steering control valve is in its neutral position.

3. Shimmy Dampers

The geometry of the nose wheel makes it possible for it to shimmy, or oscillate back and forth, at certain speeds, sometimes violently. To prevent this highly undesirable condition, almost all nose wheels are equipped with some form of hydraulic shimmy damper between the piston and cylinder of the nose wheel oleo strut. A typical shimmy damper is shown in figure 10-5.

a. Piston Type

Shimmy dampers are normally small hydraulic cylinders with a controlled bleed of fluid between the two sides of the piston. The restricted flow prevents rapid movement of the piston, but has no effect on normal steering.

b. Steer Dampers

In many cases, the steering actuators serve as the steering dampeners, since they are constantly charged with hydraulic fluid under pressure. As the nose wheel attempts to vibrate or shimmy, these cylinders prevent movement of the nose gear. This type of system is used on large aircraft with a piston type shimmy dampener used on small aircraft.

D. Shock Struts

By far, the most widely used shock absorber for aircraft is the air-oil shock absorber, more commonly known as an oleo strut. The cylinder of this strut is attached to the aircraft structure, and a close fitting piston is free to move up and down inside the cylinder as seen in figure 10-6. It is kept in alignment and prevented from coming out of the cylinder by torsion links, or scissors. The upper link is hinged to the cylinder and the lower link to the piston. The wheel is mounted on the axle, which is a part of the piston.

a. Shock Strut Operation

In figure 10-7, the operation of a shock strut is illustrated. The cylinder is divided into two compartments by a piston tube and the piston itself fits into the cylinder around the tube. A tapered metering pin, which is a part of the piston, extends through the orifice in the bottom of the piston tube. To fill the strut, the piston is pushed all of the way into the cylinder, which is filled with hydraulic fluid to the level of the charging valve. Then with the weight of the aircraft on the wheel, compressed air or nitrogen is pumped through the charging valve to raise the airplane until the piston extends out of the cylinder for a specified distance.

When the weight is removed from the landing gear, the piston extends the full amount allowed by the torsion links and the fluid drains past the metering pin into the fluid compartment in the piston. Then, when the wheels contact the ground on landing, the

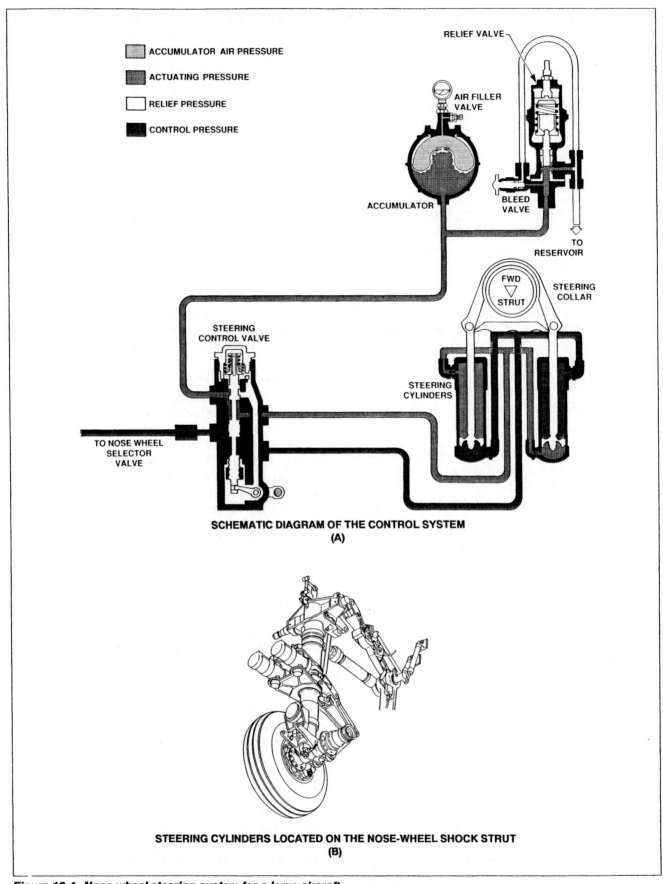

KEY:
ACCUMULATOR AIR PRESSURE
ACTUATING PRESSURE
RELIEF PRESSURE
CONTROL PRESSURE

RELIEF VALVE

AIR FILLER VALVE

ACCUMULATOR

BLEED VALVE

TO RESERVOIR

FWD STRUT

STEERING COLLAR

STEERING CYLINDERS

STEERING CONTROL VALVE

TO NOSE WHEEL SELECTOR VALVE

SCHEMATIC DIAGRAM OF THE CONTROL SYSTEM
(A)

STEERING CYLINDERS LOCATED ON THE NOSE-WHEEL SHOCK STRUT
(B)

Figure 10-4. Nose wheel steering system for a large aircraft.

piston is forced up into the cylinder. The metering pin restricts the flow of fluid into the cylinder, and much of the energy of the impact is absorbed by forcing the fluid through this restricted orifice. The taper of the metering pin provides a graduated amount of opposition to the flow and smoothly absorbs the shock. Taxi shocks are taken up by the cushion of compressed air above the oil.

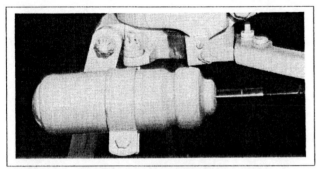

Figure 10-5. A shimmy damper snubs the rapid oscillations of a nose wheel, yet it allows the wheel to be turned by the steering system.

Figure 10-6. An oleo strut-type nose wheel shock absorber.

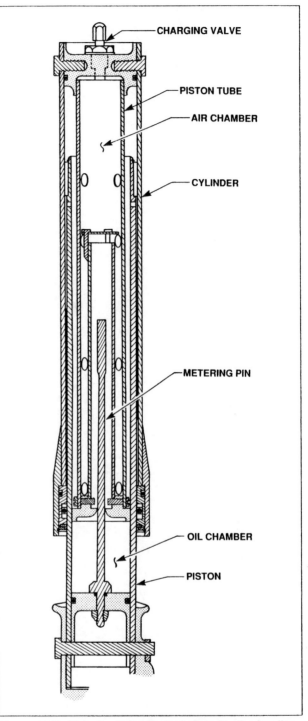

Figure 10-7. The oleo (air-oil) strut absorbs the landing impact as oil transfers from the oil chamber into the air chamber around the tapered metering pin. Taxi shocks are taken up by the compressed air in the upper chamber.

Chapter XI

Aircraft Brake Systems

There are two basic types of disk brakes in use today. For the smaller aircraft whose brakes do not require the dissipation of great amounts of kinetic energy, the single-disk brake (figure 11-1) using spot-type linings have proven very effective.

Large aircraft whose brakes must dissipate tremendous amounts of kinetic energy when they are required to stop the aircraft use multiple-disk brakes (figure 11-2). A stack of disks, of which each alternate disk is keyed to the wheel, rotate between stationary disks keyed to the torque tube attached to the landing gear strut. When the brakes are applied, hydraulic pressure forces pistons in the brake housing to clamp the stack of disks together.

A. Types of Brakes

1. Single-disk Brakes

Aircraft whose brakes must dissipate a relatively small amount of kinetic energy may use single-disk brakes with a spot-type lining made of an organic friction material.

Many of the smaller general aviation aircraft use a brake in which the disk is bolted rigidly to the wheel and rotates between two linings mounted in a caliper, which is free to move in and out, but is restrained from rotating. When the brake is applied, a hydraulic piston moves out and clamps the disk between the linings (figure 11-3).

The steel disk may also be made separate from the wheel, but keyed to rotate with it. It is free to move in and out as the fixed caliper, which is bolted to the axle, applies a clamping action to it.

The linings used in these brakes are made of an organic material which has a high coefficient of friction and good thermal characteristics. In the past, an asbestos compound was used, but because of the manufacturing hazards associated with asbestos, modern linings use other forms of friction material. When it is necessary to increase the capacity of these single-disk brakes, additional cylinders and lining pucks may be added (figure 11-4).

2. Multiple-disk Brakes

When the doughnut, or high-flotation, type of tire with its large outside dimension and small inside diameter became popular just before World War II, a non-fading brake was needed that would fit into the small diameter wheel. To gain the maximum amount of friction area, stacks of disks were keyed to a torque tube bolted to the wheel strut, and between each of these disks were thin bronze- or copper-plated steel disks keyed to rotate with the wheel. This type of disk

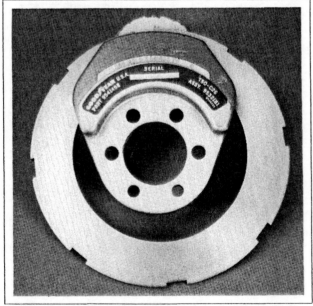

Figure 11-1. Single-disk brake used on a small general aviation aircraft.

Figure 11-2. Multiple-disk brake used in the wheel of a large jet-transport aircraft.

169

brake is shown in figure 11-5. Hydraulic fluid under pressure forced an annular piston out against a pressure plate which clamped the disks together. This type of brake had a very smooth action and provided a high torque, but the thin disks had a tendency to warp, and the brake required manual adjustment to compensate for disk wear.

Figure 11-3. Fixed-disk, single-disk brake used on light general aviation aircraft.

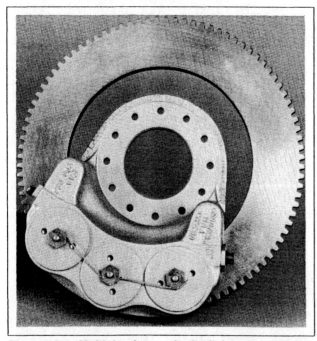

Figure 11-4. Multiple-piston, single-disk brake used on some of the medium-size general aviation aircraft.

The requirements for the dissipation of vast amounts of energy brought about the use of multiple-disk brakes which use fewer disks but disks with much greater mass. Instead of bronze or copper plating on the rotating disk, modern brakes use a sintered copper- and iron-base friction material bonded to the steel rotating disks by heat and pressure. A series of small circular pistons, rather than a singular annular piston, force the pressure plate against the disk stack to apply the clamping force. Automatic adjusters compensate for the disk wear each time the brake is applied, and this eliminates the need for the manual adjustment previously required.

3. Segmented Rotor-disk Brakes

The segmented rotor-disk brake is a multiple-disk type brake in which the rotating plates or rotors are made up of several segmented plates. The space between the rotor segments and brake linings allow

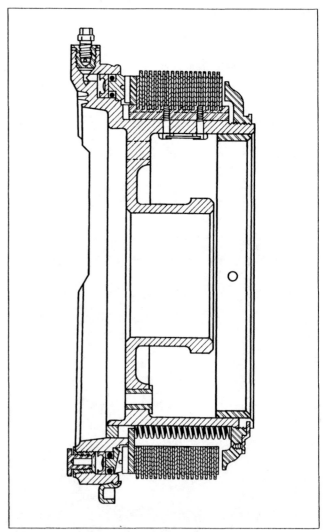

Figure 11-5. Thin-disk, annular-piston-type, multiple-disk brake.

this type of brake to provide improved brake cooling. Since the brake cools better than other types of multi-disk brakes, it can provide more efficient and longer braking action before the temperature limit of the brake is reached.

4. Carbon Brakes

One of the most recent developments in multiple-disk brakes is the carbon brake, which uses disks made of pure carbon. The weight saving of these brakes is tremendous, and the heat-absorbing properties of the relatively thick carbon disks eliminate the need for extensive cooling periods after heavy braking. At present, these brakes are used primarily on the higher-performance military aircraft and jet transport aircraft.

B. Brake Construction

1. Single-disk Brake

a. Fixed-disk Brake

The popular Cleveland brake for general aviation aircraft uses a steel disk bolted to the inside wheel half. The caliper for this brake consists of a cylinder assembly holding one or more pistons that are moved out by hydraulic pressure to squeeze the disk between two brake linings, one of which is riveted to the pressure plate and the other to the back plate.

The entire caliper is free to move back and forth on two anchor bolts that ride in holes in the torque plate that is bolted to the landing-gear axle. A sectional view of a fixed-disk, single-disk hydraulic brake can be seen in figure 11-6. In figure 11-7, the components of a fixed-disk, single-disk brake are shown. The disk itself is not shown here as it is attached to the wheel.

b. Floating-disk Brake

A forged-steel disk having a smooth ground surface is keyed by steel disk drive keys to rotate with the wheel. The disk is free to move in and out enough to prevent its binding as the brakes are applied. Anti-rattle clips apply a spring pressure to the outside of the disk to hold it centered so it will not rattle against the wheel as it rotates.

A cast-aluminum or magnesium alloy housing is bolted to a flange on the aircraft landing-gear strut, and lining cavities in the housing hold the fixed anvil lining on one side of the rotating disk and the movable piston-side lining on the opposite side.

A piston cavity (cylinder) holds a machined aluminum alloy piston, which is sealed in the cavity with an O-ring packing around its circumference. The cavity is closed with a cylinder head that is either threaded into the housing or held onto it with a

snap-ring or machine screws. An O-ring seal keeps the cylinder head from leaking.

When hydraulic fluid is forced into the cylinder, the piston pushes the movable lining over and clamps the rotating disk between the two linings.

Hydraulic fluid enters the cylinders through a passage into which a standard hydraulic fitting is screwed.

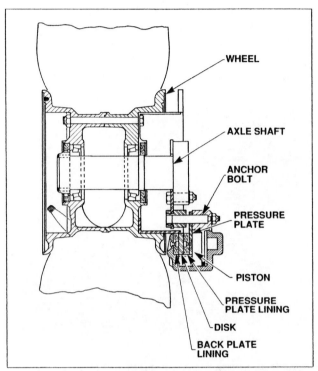

Figure 11-6. Sectional view of a fixed-disk, single-disk hydraulic brake.

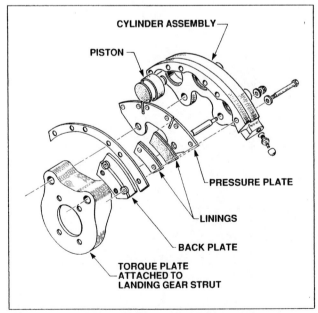

Figure 11-7. Components of a fixed-disk, single-disk brake.

171

In many of these housings, an identical passage on the opposite side is fitted with a bleeder plug. This arrangement makes it possible to use the same housing for either the right or the left side of the aircraft. All that needs to be done is to reverse the fitting.

Modern organic composition linings are made without the use of asbestos as new materials have been discovered that have the desired coefficients of friction, good wearing capability, excellent thermal characteristics, and cause no health problems in their manufacture.

Particles of brass or copper or copper wool may be embedded in the material to provide the exact friction

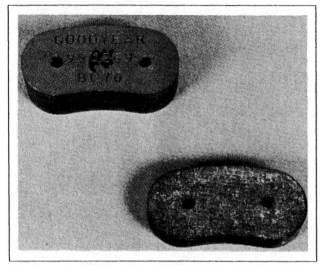

Figure 11-8. Lining pucks for a single-disk Goodyear brake.

characteristics needed. To give the lining the required strength, either a piece of steel mesh is embedded near its back side, or the lining may be bonded into a steel cup. Linings are installed with the smooth side next to the disk, and the lettering or steel cup away from the disk (figure 11-8).

Many models of single-disk brakes have automatic adjusters (figure 11-9), to maintain a constant clearance between the lining and the disk when the brake is released. Pistons on brakes having automatic adjusters have a pin with a large head held centered in the piston cavity by a return spring and a spring retainer. The end of the pin extends through the cylinder head where it is held by a friction grip collar.

When the brake is applied, hydraulic pressure forces the piston against the lining, and the two linings clamp the disk. When the piston moves over, the return spring collapses enough for the spring retainer to press against the head of the pin and pull the pin stem through the grip collar. The more the lining wears, the more the pin pulls through the collar. When the pressure is released from the brake, the return spring pushing against the head of the pin moves the piston back until the bottom of the piston cavity rests against the head of the pin. This spacing will be maintained throughout the life of the brake, automatically adjusting itself each time the brake is applied.

2. Multiple-disk Brake

A high-strength steel torque tube bolts to the aircraft landing-gear strut, concentric with the axle, and the

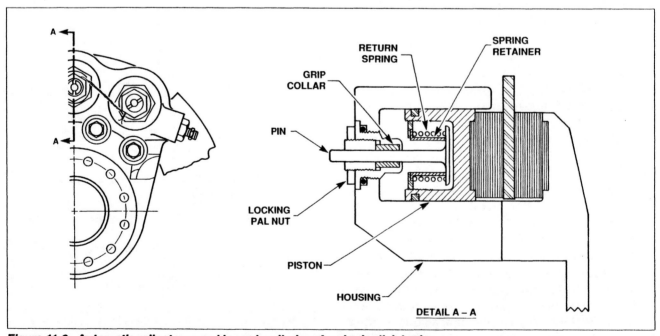

Figure 11-9. Automatic adjusters used in each cylinder of a single-disk brake.

brake housing bolts to the torque tube. Keyways on the outside circumference of the torque tube engage slots in the pressure plate and the stationary disks to prevent their rotating. The back plate bolts rigidly to the torque tube to form the clamp for the stack of disks. A multiple-disk brake used on an executive jet airplane can be seen in figure 11-10.

The housing (figure 11-11), is cast of aluminum or magnesium alloy and attaches to the strut by bolts through the torque tube. Cavities in the housing hold the pistons which provide the clamping action as they force the pressure plate against the stack of disks.

Drilled passages within the housing connect the cylinders to allow for the flow of hydraulic fluid. Some housings have each alternate cylinder connected to one hydraulic system and a backup system connected to the other cylinders. A brake with this arrangement is said to have an A and B system. This arrangement supplies adequate pressure from either the main or the backup system for brake application.

Provision is made in the housing for a series of return springs and automatic adjusters which pull the pressure plate back from the disk stack each time the brake is released. Each of the cavities, or cylinders, in the housing is fitted with a machined-aluminum alloy piston. These pistons are sealed in the cylinder with an O-ring packing, backed up with a spiraled Teflon® backup ring. A composition insulator is attached to the face of each piston, where it bears against the pressure plate. This insulator minimizes the transfer of heat from the disk stack into the piston, where it could have an adverse effect on both the fluid and the seals.

Almost all multiple-disk brakes use some form of return system to pull the pressure plate back from the disk stack when the brake is released. These return systems also serve as automatic adjusters to maintain a constant clearance between the disks as they wear in service.

A machined-steel spring housing slips through a hole in the brake housing to provide a base for the return spring. Inside the spring housing is a fairly heavy coil spring and spring holder, held in place by a retaining ring when the brake is released.

The head of the adjusting pin engages a slot in the pressure plate, and its stem passes through a hole in both the spring housing and the spring holder. A grip and tube subassembly slips over the pin and is held in place with a nut.

When the brake is applied, the pistons force the pressure plate over and clamp the disk stack against the back plate. The grip around the tube inside the spring holder forces the spring holder to compress the return spring until the holder bottoms against the spring housing. As the disks wear, the pressure plate moves further away from the bottom of the spring housing, and the tube is forced to slip through the grip.

When the brakes are released, the return spring forces the spring holder back against the retaining ring, and the grip around the tube is sufficiently tight to pull the pin back, moving the pressure plate away from the disk stack so the clearance will remain the same as the disk stack wears (figure 11-12).

The pressure plate for multiple-disk brakes is a special stationary disk made of high-strength steel, and it has steel wear pads riveted to its inner surface where it contacts the rotating disk.

The back plate is made of high-strength steel, and it also serves as a stationary disk. But instead of being keyed to the torque tube so it can move back and forth,

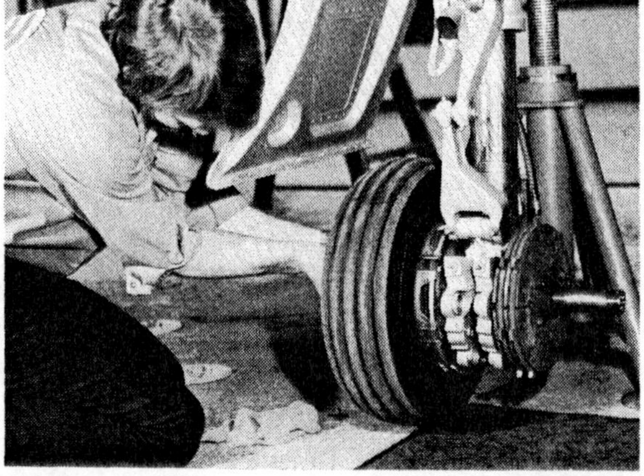

Figure 11-10. Multiple-disk brake used on an executive jet airplane.

Figure 11-11. Brake housing of a multiple-disk brake.

it is bolted to the housing through the torque tube, and it serves as the rigid member of the clamps.

When the brakes are applied, the pistons act against the pressure plate and force the disk stack over against the back plate. But since the back plate is immovable, the disk stack is clamped between the pressure plate and the back plate. Wear pads are riveted to the face of the back plate where it contacts the rotating disk.

The stationary disks are keyed to the torque tube so they are free to slide back and forth as the brakes are applied (figure 11-13), but they cannot rotate. Many brakes have steel wear pads riveted to each side of the stationary disk to extend their life. These pads may be replaced rather than having to replace the entire disk.

Narrow slots are often cut into the stationary disks to allow for expansion as they get hot. These expansion slots prevent the disk warping which could cause the brakes to drag.

A rotating disk (figure 11-14) is placed between each of the stationary disks, and these disks are driven by either a tang on the disk, which fits into a steel reinforced slot in the wheel, or by a steel key attached to the inside of the wheel engaging a slot in the outer rim of the disk.

These rotating disks are made of steel and have a special friction surface of sintered material bonded to their surface by heat and pressure. Expansion slots are cut into these disks to prevent their warping from heat.

3. Segmented Rotor-disk Brake

As previously mentioned, the segmented rotor-disk brake is a multiple-disk brake with special rotors which are constructed of pads of highly wear-resistant steel riveted to the rotors surface. These special type of rotors help cool the brake.

4. Carbon Brake

This a multiple-disk brake that uses a thick carbon disk as the brake rotor. These brakes can absorb tremendous amounts of kinetic energy and yet have relatively low weight. The thick black carbon disk absorbs heat very well along with having excellent wear properties. A typical carbon brake setup is shown in figure 11-15.

5. Expander Tube Brake

One of the early types of non-servo brakes used on airplanes as small as the Piper Cub and as large as

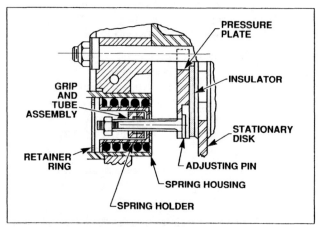

Figure 11-12. Automatic adjusters in the cylinder of a multiple-disk brake.

Figure 11-13. The torque tube of a multiple-disk brake.

Figure 11-14. Rotating disks are keyed into the wheel by the disk drive tangs.

the Boeing B-29 was the expander tube brake. In this brake, a flat synthetic rubber tube around the brake body on the axle was filled with hydraulic fluid under pressure from the brake master cylinder, or from the power brake-control valve. As the fluid filled the tube, it forced asbestos-compound blocks out against the inner surface of a rotating iron drum. When the brakes were released, flat steel springs in the brake body pressed the blocks back against the expander tube and away from the drum as can be seen in figure 11-16.

C. Brake Actuating Systems

1. Independent Master Cylinders

As the brakes themselves evolved, so have the methods for their actuation. Most of the earliest drum-and-shoe brakes were mechanically operated by a flexible steel cable pulling on a lever inside the brake. This lever actuated a cam to move the lining against the drum. The cables were pulled by a long lever which, if pulled straight back, applied both brakes; but if pulled back and to one side, applied only the brake on that side. This system gave the pilot some degree of independent braking.

In order to increase the pressure applied to the brake linings, hydraulic cylinders soon replaced the mechanical cams, and individual master cylinders were used to apply pressure to the cylinders inside the wheels.

In the quest for simplicity, the hydraulic brakes for some of the smaller aircraft used a sealed hydraulic system consisting of a diaphragm-type master cylinder (figure 11-17) connected to the actuator in the wheel with appropriate tubing and filled with hydraulic fluid. When the pedal was pushed, fluid moved from the master cylinder into the wheel cylinder to apply the brakes.

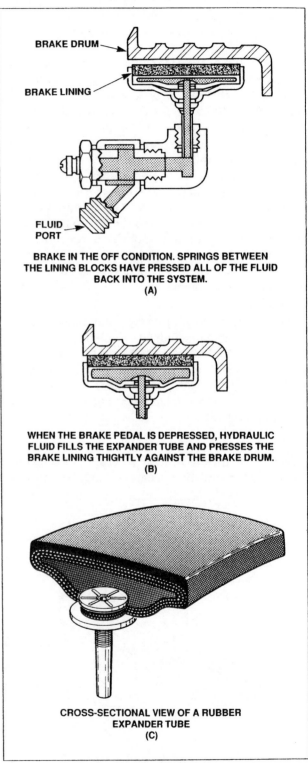

BRAKE IN THE OFF CONDITION. SPRINGS BETWEEN THE LINING BLOCKS HAVE PRESSED ALL OF THE FLUID BACK INTO THE SYSTEM.
(A)

WHEN THE BRAKE PEDAL IS DEPRESSED, HYDRAULIC FLUID FILLS THE EXPANDER TUBE AND PRESSES THE BRAKE LINING THIGHTLY AGAINST THE BRAKE DRUM.
(B)

CROSS-SECTIONAL VIEW OF A RUBBER EXPANDER TUBE
(C)

Figure 11-16. An expander tube brake.

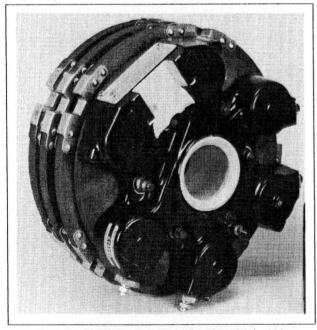

Figure 11-15. Multiple-disk brakes using thick carbon disks.

Larger aircraft require more fluid for their brakes, and a need to vent this fluid to the atmosphere when the brakes are released. This prevents the brakes dragging from thermal expansion of the fluid. There are many types of vented master cylinders, but all have the same basic components. The master cylinder (figure 11-18) is one of the more popular types that attaches to the rudder pedal. The body of the master cylinder serves as the reservoir for the fluid, and it is vented to the atmosphere through a vent hole in the filler plug. The piston is attached to the rudder pedal so when the pilot pushes on the top of the pedal, the piston is forced down into the cylinder. When the pedal is not depressed, the return spring forces the piston up so the compensator sleeve will hold the compensator port open. Fluid from the wheel unit is vented to the atmosphere through the compensator port. When the pedal is depressed, the piston is pushed away from the compensator sleeve, and a special O-ring and washer (the Lock-O-Seal) seals fluid in the line to the brake. The amount of pressure applied to the brake is proportional to the amount of force the pilot applies on the pedals. When the pedal is released, the compensator port opens and vents the brake line into the reservoir.

The parking brake for this type of master cylinder is a simple ratchet mechanism that holds the piston down in the cylinder. To apply the parking brake, the pedal is depressed and the handle pulled; this locks the piston. To release the brake, the pedal is depressed more than the initial application, and the ratchet can release.

2. Boosted Brakes

Mid-size airplanes require more braking force than can be applied with an independent master cylinder,

yet do not require the complex system of a power brake; the boosted brake fills this need.

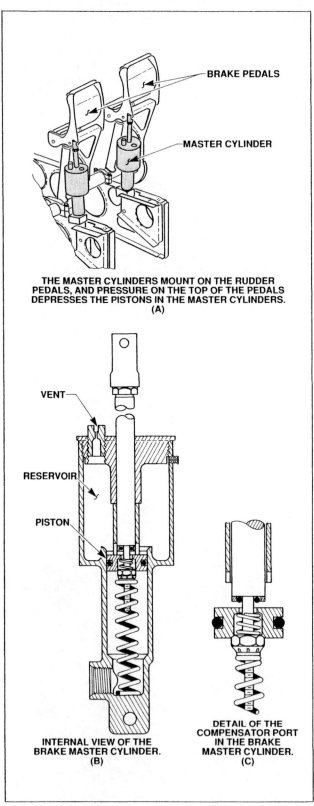

THE MASTER CYLINDERS MOUNT ON THE RUDDER PEDALS, AND PRESSURE ON THE TOP OF THE PEDALS DEPRESSES THE PISTONS IN THE MASTER CYLINDERS.
(A)

INTERNAL VIEW OF THE BRAKE MASTER CYLINDER.
(B)

DETAIL OF THE COMPENSATOR PORT IN THE BRAKE MASTER CYLINDER.
(C)

Figure 11-18. Master cylinder for individual hydraulic brakes.

Figure 11-17. A diaphragm-type master cylinder.

The boosted brake master cylinder (figure 11-19) is mounted on the rudder pedal and attached to the toe-brake pedal in such a way that depressing the pedal pulls on the rod and forces fluid out to the brake cylinder. If the pilot needs more pressure on the brakes than can be applied with the pedal, the pilot continues to push, and as the toggle mechanism straightens out, the spool valve is moved over so it will direct hydraulic system pressure behind the piston where it assists the pilot in forcing fluid out to the brake. When the pedal is released, the spool valve moves back to its original position and vents the area on top of the piston back to the system reservoir. At the same time, the compensator poppet unseats and vents the brakes to the reservoir.

3. Power Brakes

Almost all large aircraft use brakes operated by pressure from the main hydraulic system. This cannot be done by simply directing part of the system pressure into the brake actuating unit, since the brake system has special requirements that must be met. The brake application must be proportional to the force the pilot exerts on the pedals, and the pilot must be able to hold the brakes partially applied without there being a build-up of pressure in the brake lines. Since these brakes are used on airplanes so large that the pilot has no way of knowing when one of the wheels is locking up, there must also be some provision to prevent any wheel skidding. The pressure actually supplied to the wheel must be lower than the pressure of the main hydraulic system, so a pressure-reducing or deboosting device must be incorporated in the system. Since the wheels are susceptible to damage, provision should also be made to lock off the fluid from a wheel in the event a hydraulic line is broken. Finally, there must be an emergency brake system that can actuate the wheel units in the event of a failure of the hydraulic system.

In figure 11-20, a simplified schematic of the brake system of a large jet transport-type aircraft is shown. The brakes get their fluid from the main hydraulic system, through a check valve, and an accumulator holds pressure for the brakes in the event of a

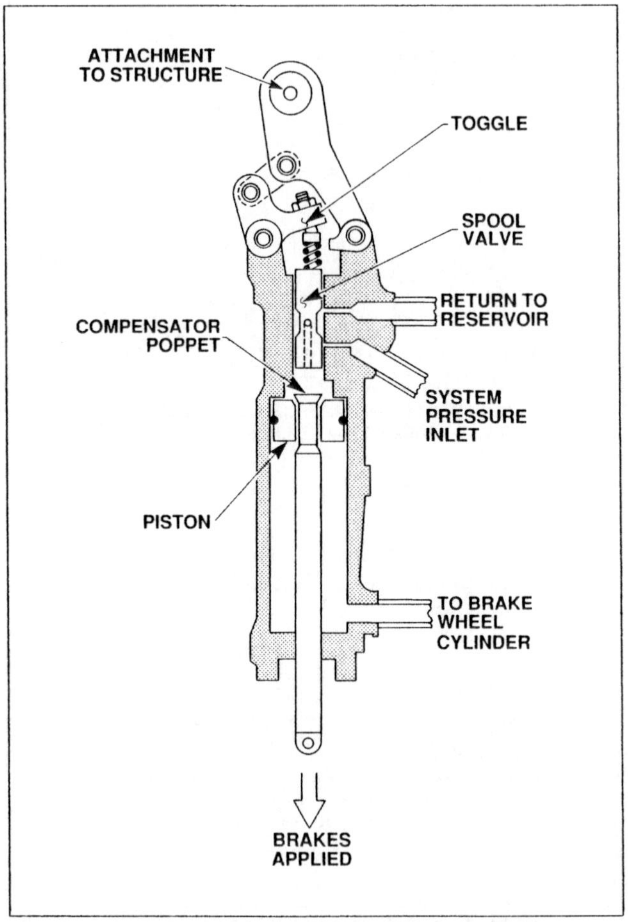

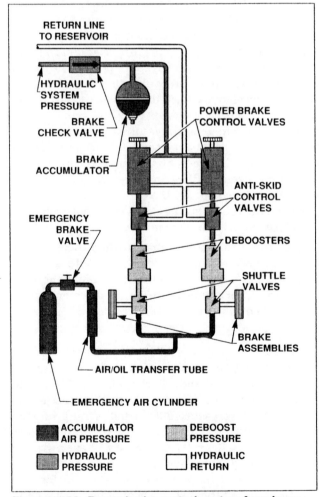

Figure 11-20. Power brake control system for a large jet aircraft.

Figure 11-19. Brake valve for a hydraulic system pressure boosted brake.

hydraulic system failure. The pilot and copilot operate power brake control valves through the appropriate linkages. These valves are actually pressure regulators that provide an amount of pressure to the brakes that is proportional to the force the pilot applies to the pedals. Once the desired pressure is reached, the valve holds it as long as that amount of force is held on the pedals. In large aircraft an antiskid system is installed to sense the rate of deceleration of each wheel and compare it with a maximum allowable rate of deceleration. If any wheel attempts to slow down too fast, as it does at the onset of a skid, the antiskid valve will release the pressure from that wheel back into the system return manifold.

The pressure applied by the brake control valve is too high for the proper brake application, so a debooster is installed in the line between the antiskid valve and the brake. This lowers the pressure and increases the volume of fluid supplied to the wheel units.

a. Power Brake Control Valves

In figure 11-21, the operation of an internal-spring-type power brake control valve, as is used on many of the large aircraft, is shown. The brake is applied when the pilot depresses the plunger and moves the spool over to connect the pressure port to the brake line. Fluid under pressure is also directed behind the spool to move it back when the pressure called for by the pilot has been reached; thus, pressure to the brake will not increase, regardless of how long the pilot holds the pedal depressed. If more pressure is required, the pilot presses on the brake pedal harder, further compressing the plunger spring and allowing more fluid to go to the brake. When the pedal is released, the return spring forces the spool back, and fluid flows from the brake into the system return line.

Optimum braking is obtained when there is just enough pressure supplied to the brake to hold the wheel on the verge of a skid, but not allow the skid to develop. This is done by the antiskid system which is discussed in the appropriate section of this text.

b. Deboosters

Hydraulic system pressure is normally too high for brake action, so deboosters are installed between the antiskid valve and the wheel cylinders. These are primarily pressure-reducing valves that operate on the basis of a pressure differential being produced by an area differential. The principle of the debooster is illustrated in figure 11-22 where we have a system pressure of 1,500 PSI applied to a piston having an area of 2 sq. in. This generates 3,000 lbs. of force. If the other end of the piston has an area of 10 sq. in., the 3,000 lbs. of force will produce a pressure of 300

PSI. The other function of the debooster is to increase the volume of fluid going to the brakes. When the 1,500 PSI system pressure moves the small piston down 1", 2 cu. in. of fluid is used, but this same travel of the larger piston moves 10 cu. in. of fluid to the brakes. The debooster has a pin-operated ball valve that allows fluid in the line to the brakes to be replenished if there should be a leak in the line. If the debooster piston should move down enough for the pin to push the ball off its seat, fluid under system pressure will flow into the lower chamber and

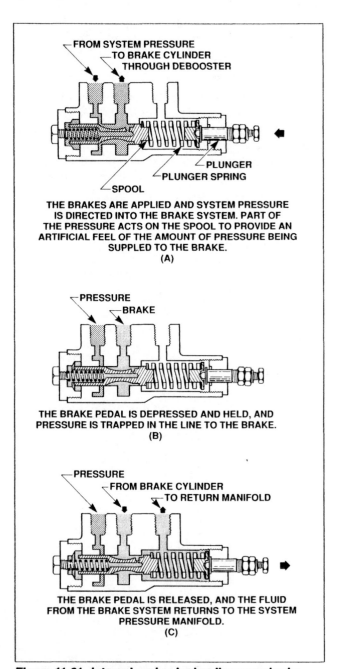

FROM SYSTEM PRESSURE
TO BRAKE CYLINDER
THROUGH DEBOOSTER

PLUNGER
PLUNGER SPRING
SPOOL

THE BRAKES ARE APPLIED AND SYSTEM PRESSURE IS DIRECTED INTO THE BRAKE SYSTEM. PART OF THE PRESSURE ACTS ON THE SPOOL TO PROVIDE AN ARTIFICIAL FEEL OF THE AMOUNT OF PRESSURE BEING SUPPLED TO THE BRAKE.
(A)

PRESSURE
BRAKE

THE BRAKE PEDAL IS DEPRESSED AND HELD, AND PRESSURE IS TRAPPED IN THE LINE TO THE BRAKE.
(B)

PRESSURE
FROM BRAKE CYLINDER
TO RETURN MANIFOLD

THE BRAKE PEDAL IS RELEASED, AND THE FLUID FROM THE BRAKE SYSTEM RETURNS TO THE SYSTEM PRESSURE MANIFOLD.
(C)

Figure 11-21. Internal-spring hydraulic power brake control valve.

replenish the lost fluid. As soon as enough fluid enters the chamber, the piston will rise and the ball will reseat.

Lockout deboosters, such as the one shown in figure 11-23, allow the piston to go all the way to the bottom. The pin pushes the ball off its seat, but the spring-loaded valve prevents fluid entering the lower chamber until the reset handle is lifted.

4. Emergency Brake System

In the case of a total failure of the hydraulic system, the pilot of most large aircraft can operate a pneumatic valve (figure 11-24) on the instrument panel and direct compressed air or nitrogen into the brake system. When the pilot turns the handle (figure 11-25), it is actually adjusting a regulator that controls air pressure to the brake. When sufficient pressure reaches the brake line, the piston moves up against the force of the control spring and shuts off the inlet valve. The compression of the spring determines the amount of pressure supplied to the brake. When the brake handle is rotated in the direction to release the brakes, the air is exhausted overboard.

Rather than allow compressed air to enter the wheel cylinders, which would require the entire brake system to be bled of this air, the emergency air may be directed into a transfer tube. The air forces hydraulic fluid from this tube into the brake system.

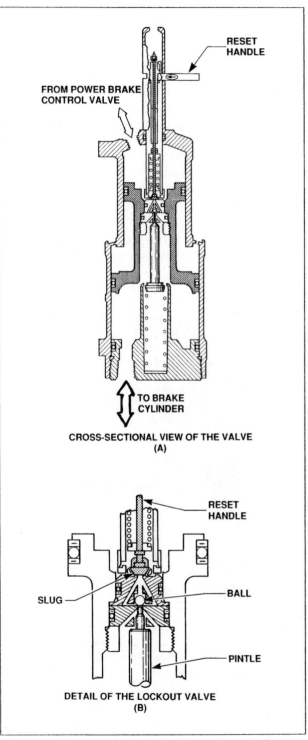

Figure 11-23. Lockout debooster for a power brake system.

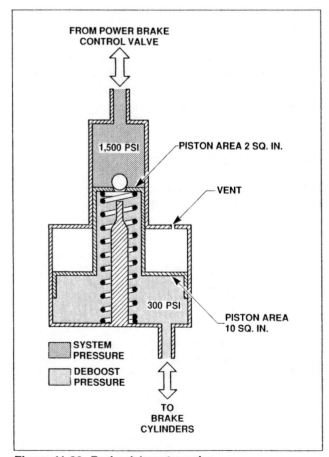

Figure 11-22. Brake debooster valve.

D. Antiskid Brake Control Systems

1. System Operation

The amount of braking the pilot uses has always been of concern. With a tailwheel-type airplane, too much braking could result in a nose-over, and with the large-diameter tires on the small wheels, there was always the possibility that too heavy braking could cause the tire to slip on the rim and pull the valve out of the tube.

The problem of brake control is still with us, but today the reason is different. Our modern high-speed jet aircraft usually have more than one wheel on each side, and all of the brakes on one side are controlled with one pedal. With this arrangement, the pilot has no way to know when one of these wheels begins to skid so that corrective action can be taken. But, if corrective action is not taken within a few seconds to release a locked-up wheel, the tire is likely to blow out and control of the aircraft can be lost.

To compound this problem, these high-speed aircraft have such restricted interior space that the wheels and tires must be very small, and generally these small tires are inflated to a high pressure. When the aircraft touches down on a water-covered runway and the pilot applies the brakes, the friction on the runway surface is so much less than that generated in the brake that the wheel locks up and the tire hydroplanes down the runway, supported on the surface of the water in much the same way a water skier is supported. All braking action and directional control is lost for a hydroplaning wheel.

For maximum brake effectiveness, the friction between the tire and the runway surfaces should closely relate to the friction in the brake so that the peripheral speed of the tire will be just slightly less than the speed of the aircraft. When this is true, the tire will grip the runway surface and slip just a little. This produces the maximum tire drag.

Maintaining this optimum friction is no easy matter, because if the brake pressure is held constant after the slip starts and the wheel begins to decelerate, the brake friction will rapidly increase to the point that the wheel will lock up. The tire will skid over the runway and produce very little effective braking.

We use a very simple form of manual antiskid control in an automobile when we drive on ice. For the most effective stopping, we pump the brakes, applying them only enough to slow the wheel, but releasing them before the wheel decelerates enough to lock up. This same on-and-off type of operation was employed in some of the early aircraft antiskid systems, but it has a major drawback if the control valves do not operate fast enough.

In figure 11-26, it can be seen how this problem comes about. When the brakes are applied, the pressure rises until the wheel starts to slip, but not skid (point A). This is the ideal condition, but the pilot, having no indication that it has been reached,

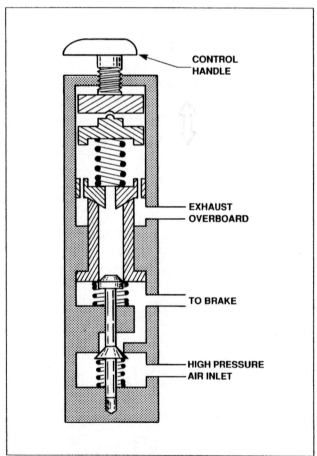

Figure 11-24. Pneumatic control valve to supply emergency air pressure to the brake.

CONTROL HANDLE

EXHAUST OVERBOARD

TO BRAKE

HIGH PRESSURE AIR INLET

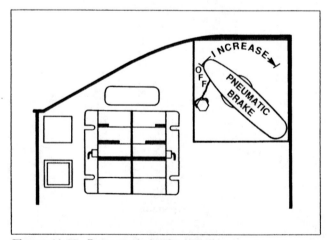

Figure 11-25. Pneumatic brake handle.

continues to increase the force on the brake pedal. A pressure is soon reached which produces enough friction in the brake to cause the tire to start to skid on the runway. The wheel now decelerates fast enough that it can be felt, so the pilot releases the pedal. But since the braking force needed becomes less as the wheel slows down, the wheel continues to decelerate even though the brake pressure is decreasing. At point C, the wheel has completely locked up, and the pressure continues to drop. At point D, the pressure is low enough for the friction between the tire and the runway surface to start the wheel rotating again, and soon after this the brake pressure drops to zero. The wheel then comes back up to speed.

A successful antiskid system requires two features these early on-and-off systems did not have. There must be some form of wheel-speed sensor that can detect a change in the rate of deceleration, and a signal for the pressure to be released before the wheel gets deep into its skid. And, the valve must act fast enough to prevent all of the pressure being released before the next application of the brake. This controlled amount of retained pressure prevents the brake-return system pulling the pressure plate all of the way back, and it allows the brakes to reapply almost immediately. The modern modulated antiskid system provides the fastest wheel speed recovery and produces the minimum stopping distance on any kind of runway surface.

When the pilot wants to stop the aircraft in the shortest distance possible, it is necessary to depress the brake pedals all the way to call for maximum braking. All of the brakes receive the maximum pressure, but if any wheel should start to decelerate at a rate which would indicate an impending skid, the pressure to that brake is dumped into the system

return manifold. Now, the control circuit measures the amount of time required for the wheel to spin back up and then applies a slightly reduced pressure to the brake, a pressure determined by the time required for the spin-up. If this reduced pressure causes a skid to begin to develop, enough of it is released to allow the wheel to spin back up. Some pressure is maintained in the wheel cylinders, however, just enough to prevent the pressure plate from moving all of the way back. This application and release process continues with progressively decreasing pressure applied until the wheel is held in the slip area, but not allowed to decelerate fast enough to produce a skid. It produces the proper amount of braking for any runway surface condition, with the pilot having only to call for maximum braking.

When the airplane is slowed down below approximately 20 MPH and there is no further danger of skidding, the antiskid system automatically deactivates to give the pilot full control of the brakes for maneuvering and parking.

As with most auxiliary systems in modern aircraft, the antiskid systems have built-in test circuits and, in the event of a malfunction, may be deactivated to give the pilot normal braking but no antiskid protection.

2. System Components

a. Wheel-speed Sensors

An antiskid system consists basically of three components: the wheel-speed sensors, the control box and the control valves (figure 11-27).

There are two types of systems in use: an AC system and a DC system. They are essentially alike except for the wheel-speed sensors and one circuit in the control box.

The AC sensor (figure 11-28) is a variable-reluctance AC generator, which uses a permanent magnet surrounded by a pickup coil in the axle of the landing

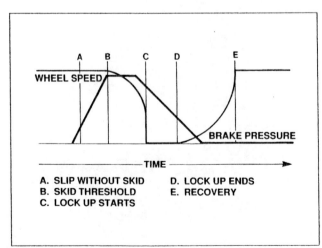

Figure 11-26. The development of a skid by on-and-off application of the brakes.

Figure 11-27. The basic components of an anitiskid brake system: the wheel speed sensor, the control box and the control valve.

gear. The outside of this sensor has four equally spaced poles with teeth cut into their periphery.

A soft iron exciter ring with internal teeth is mounted in the hubcap of the wheel so that it rotates around the sensor. The two sets of teeth pass near each other and, as the exciter ring rotates, the teeth approach each other and then separate. As the distance between the teeth changes, the reluctance of the magnetic circuit is alternately increased and decreased, and each time the distance changes, the amount of magnetic flux cutting across the coil changes and induces an alternating current in the pickup coil. The faster the wheel turns, the higher the frequency of the induced current.

The control box used with the AC sensor converts the varying frequency AC into a DC signal whose voltage is proportional to the frequency of the AC.

The DC sensor (figure 11-29), is essentially a small permanent-magnet direct-current generator whose voltage output is directly proportional to the rotational speed of its armature. When this type of sensor is used, there is no need for the converter in the control box, and there is less danger of stray voltages induced into the system causing brake interference.

The shaft of the armature is fitted with a blade driven by a bracket in the wheel hubcap and rotates with the wheel. The generator output is usually in the range of 1 volt for each 10 MPH of wheel speed.

b. Control Valves

A 3-port antiskid control valve (figure 11-30) is located in the pressure line between the brake valve and the brake cylinder, with a third line connecting the control valve to the system return manifold.

For normal operation of the brakes when no skid is being indicated, the valve allows the brake fluid to flow into and out of the brake, with the valve serving only as a passage. But, if the wheel speed sensor determines that one of the wheels is beginning to decelerate fast enough to cause a skid, its changing output voltage is measured in the control box, and a DC signal is sent to the control valve to close off the pressure port and open the passage between the brake and the system return.

This valve operates fast enough to maintain an output pressure that is directly proportional to the amount of signal current from the control box.

The DC signal from the control box flows through a coil around the armature of the flapper valve (figure 11-31). This armature is free to pivot and is centered between two permanent magnets.

When the signal from the control box indicates that no skid is impending and the braking action should be

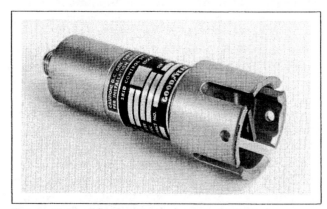

Figure 11-29. *DC wheel speed sensor used in an antiskid brake system.*

Figure 11-30. *Antiskid brake control valve.*

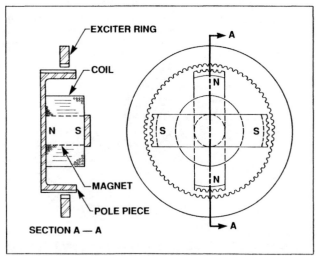

Figure 11-28. *AC wheel-speed sensor used in an antiskid brake system.*

normal, the magnetic field of the coil reacts with the fields of the permanent magnets and holds the flapper centered between the nozzle (figure 11-32).

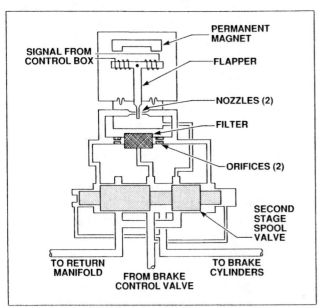

Figure 11-31. *A DC signal from the control box energizes the coil on the armature of the flapper valve, and the movement of the flapper changes the pressure drop across the fixed orifices.*

Fluid from the brake valve flows through the filter and discharges equally from each nozzle. Since the amount of flow is the same through each orifice, the pressure drop across the orifices will be the same, and the second-stage spool valve will assume a position that allows free passage between the brake valve and the brake.

But when the control box receives a signal from the wheel-speed sensor telling it that a skid is impending, it sends current through the coil of the armature to create a polarity in the armature that causes it to pivot and unbalance the flow from the nozzles. In figure 11-33, the flapper has moved over, restricting the flow from the left nozzle and opening the flow from the one on the right. There is now more flow through orifice O_2 and therefore a greater pressure drop across it, leaving P_1 greater then P_2. This imbalance of pressures moves the second stage spool over, shutting off the flow of fluid from the brake valve to the brake, and opening a passage from the brake to the return manifold.

The extremely fast reaction time for this type of valve allows it to maintain a pressure at the brake

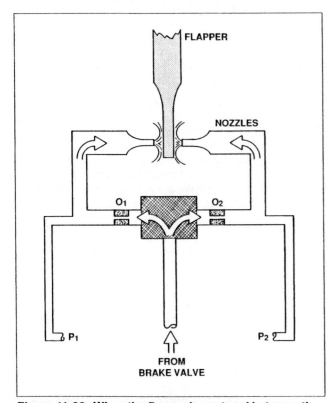

Figure 11-32. *When the flapper is centered between the nozzles, the pressure drop across the two orifices is the same and P_1 is equal to P_2.*

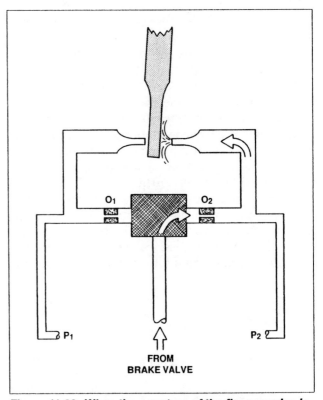

Figure 11-33. *When the armature of the flapper valve is energized, the flapper moves over and restricts the flow through the orifice O_1 while increasing it through O_2. The increased pressure drop across O_2 causes P_1 to be greater than P_2.*

183

that is directly proportional to the amount of current flowing in the armature coil.

c. Control Box

The main functions of the control box are to generate electrical signals usable by the control valve, to control brake pressure to prevent a skid during landing deceleration, and to prevent brake pressure being applied prior to touchdown. Before the airplane touches down, the locked-wheel detector sends a signal into the amplifier, which causes the control valve to open the passage between the brakes and the system return manifold (figure 11-34). This makes it impossible to land with the brakes applied.

As soon as the airplane touches down, the squat switch opens and the wheel starts to spin up. By the time it reaches a speed of about 20 MPH, the voltage generated in the wheel-speed sensor is high enough to cause the locked-wheel detector to remove the touchdown control signal from the amplifier, and the control valve will allow full pressure to be applied to the brakes (figure 11-35).

When the airplane is on the ground and the wheels are turning more than 20 MPH, almost all of the antiskid control is by the skid detector and the modulator (figure 11-36).

A deceleration threshold of around 20 ft./sec.^{2}, with a wheel speed that is at least 6 MPH below the speed of the airplane, is designed into the skid detector circuit as a reference. Any time a wheel decelerates at a rate greater than this threshold value, a signal is sent to the amplifier and then to the control valve to dump the brake pressure. At this time, the skid detector sends a signal to the modulator which, by measuring the width of the skid detector signal, automatically establishes the amount of current that will continue to flow through the valve after the wheel has recovered from the skid. When the amplifier receives its signal from the modulator, it maintains this current, which is just

enough to hold the flapper over to prevent the pressure being completely dumped, but will maintain a pressure slightly less than that which caused the skid. A timer circuit in the modulator then allows this pressure to increase slowly until another skid starts to occur and the cycle repeats itself.

When the aircraft is operated on a wet or icy runway, the antiskid system will hold the wheels in the slip area. But if one wheel begins to hydroplane or hits a patch of ice and slows down to less than 10 MPH while its mated reference wheel is still rolling more than 20 MPH, the locked-wheel detector gets into the act. The timer measures the width of the skid detector signal, and if it is more than about one-tenth of a second, it will send a "full dump" signal to the valve, and the valve will remain in the full-dump position until the wheel spins back to more than 10 MPH.

When all of the wheels are turning at less than 20 MPH, the locked-wheel arming circuit becomes inoperative, giving the pilot full braking action for low-speed taxiing and parking (figure 11-37).

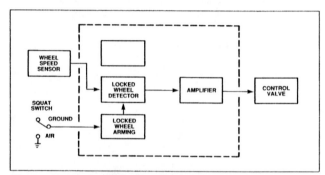

Figure 11-35. On touchdown, the squat switch removes the ground from the locked-wheel arming circuit, and the wheel-speed sensor generates a signal which allows the control valve to send full pressure to the brakes.

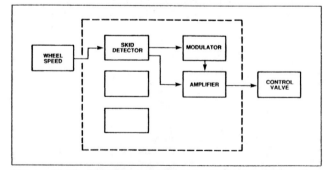

Figure 11-36. When the airplane is on the ground and all wheels are rotating more than 20 MPH, the skid detector and the modulator provide signals for the amplifier.

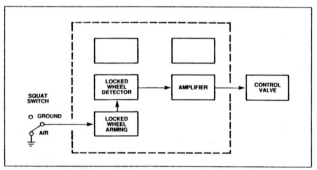

Figure 11-34. Before landing, the squat switch completes the locked-wheel arming circuit.

The control box for antiskid systems using AC sensors operates in the same way as those using DC generators, the only difference being the addition of a converter circuit. This circuit receives the varying-frequency alternating current and converts it into a varying voltage of direct current. The changes in the DC voltage follow exactly the frequency changes in the AC.

The difference between the control box of an antiskid system using an AC wheel-speed sensor and one using a DC sensor is in the converter between the sensor and the control circuit (figure 11-38).

3. System Tests

Because it is so important that the pilot know the exact condition of the brake system before it is used, antiskid systems are equipped with test circuits and control switches. These allow the pilot to test the integrity and operation of the entire system and to disable the antiskid system without affecting the normal braking action if any faults are found.

a. Ground Test

The integrity of the antiskid system can be tested on the ground before flight. With the antiskid control switch on, depress the brake pedals, and both the left and right brake lights should come on, indicating that all of the pressure from the brake valves is going to the brakes.

Now, with the brakes still applied, press the test switch and hold it for a few seconds. This sends a signal through the wheel-speed sensors into the control box to simulate a wheel speed of more than 20 MPH. The lights should remain on.

Release the test switch, and the two brake lights should go out and stay out for a couple of seconds and come back on. This simulates a wheel lockup that causes a release of pressure, and then the pressure is restored.

This test checks the continuity of all of the wiring and the operation of the locked-wheel circuits, the amplifiers and the control valves.

b. In-flight Test

A part of the pre-landing cockpit check gives an indication of the condition of the entire antiskid system. With the airplane configured for landing, depress the brake pedals and the brake lights should remain off. This indicates that the control valves are holding the brakes fully released.

Depress the test switch and the brake lights should come on. Depressing this switch sends a signal through the wheel speed sensors, simulating a wheel speed of greater than 20 MPH. If the system is operating properly, this will cause the control valve to direct normal pressure to the brake. The light should remain on as long as the test switch is held depressed.

When the switch is released, the two brake lights should go out, indicating that the antiskid system is holding all of the pressure off of the brakes. Any time a system fails either the ground test or the in-flight portion, the antiskid system may be disabled without affecting the normal braking in any way.

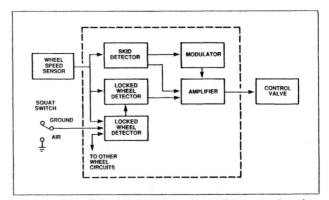

Figure 11-37. When the airplane is on the ground and all three wheels are rotating at less than 20 MPH, the locked-wheel arming circuit is inoperative and the pilot has full brake control for low-speed taxiing and parking.

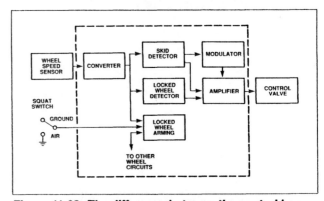

Figure 11-38. The difference between the control box of an antiskid system using an AC wheel-speed sensor and one using a DC sensor is in the converter between the sensor and the control circuit.

PART III

Aircraft Fuel/Propeller Systems

Chapter XII

Aircraft Fuel Systems

All powered aircraft, whether rotary or fixed wing, depend on the continuous flow of metered,uncontaminated fuel under all operating conditions. The weight of the fuel constitutes a good percentage of the total weight of the aircraft. This may range from about 10% of the gross weight of small personal airplanes, to more than 40% of the gross weight for some large jet aircraft.

The weight of the fuel requires that the structure be strong enough to carry it in all flight conditions. The fuel tanks must also be located so that the decreasing weight of the fuel will not cause balance problems as the fuel is being used.

There have been more aircraft accidents caused by the mis-management of the fuel system than by failures of any other single system. Engine failure may be caused by using all of the fuel in tanks, but engines will also stop if an empty tank is selected when there is fuel in the other tanks.

Contamination in the fuel may clog strainers and shut off the flow of fuel to the engines. Water that condenses in partially filled tanks will stop the engine when it flows into the metering system. Water in turbine-powered aircraft is a special problem, as the more viscous jet fuel will hold water entrained in such tiny particles that it does not easily settle out. When the fuel temperature drops at high altitude, the water may form ice crystals which can freeze on the fuel filters and shut off the flow of fuel to the engine.

The type or grade of aircraft fuel must be carefully matched to the engine. It is the responsibility of the pilot or the flight engineer to know before a flight is started that the aircraft has an adequate supply of the proper fuel on board.

A. Basic Fuel System Requirements

The requirements for the fuel system design are specified in detail in the parts of the Federal Aviation Regulations under which the aircraft was built. Since the vast majority of airplanes in the general aviation fleet are built under FAR Part 23 "Airworthiness Standards: Normal, Utility, and Acrobatic Category Airplanes", we will list a few of the more basic requirements for the fuel system of these airplanes.

1. No pump can draw fuel from more than one tank at a time, and provisions must be made to prevent air from being drawn into the fuel supply line. (FAR Part 23.951)

2. Turbine-powered aircraft must be capable of sustained operation when there is at least 0.75 cc of free water per gallon of fuel, and the fuel is cooled to its most critical condition for icing. The system must incorporate provisions to prevent the water which precipitates out of the fuel freezing on the filters and stopping fuel flow to the engine. (FAR Part 23.951)

3. Each fuel system of a multi-engine aircraft must be arranged in such a way that the failure of any one component (except the fuel tank) will not cause more than one engine to lose power. (FAR Part 23.953)

4. If multi-engine aircraft feed more than one engine from a single tank or assembly of interconnected tanks, each engine must have an independent tank outlet with a fuel shutoff valve at the tank. (FAR Part 23.953)

5. Tanks used in multi-engine fuel systems must have 2 vents arranged so that they are not likely to both become plugged at the same time. (FAR Part 23.953)

6. All filler caps must be designed so that they are not likely to be installed incorrectly or lost in-flight. (FAR Part 23.953)

7. The fuel systems must be designed to prevent the ignition of fuel vapors by lightning. (23.954)

8. A gravity feed system must be able to flow 150% of the takeoff fuel flow when the tank contains the minimum fuel allowable, and when the airplane is positioned in the attitude that is most critical for fuel flow. (FAR Part 23.955)

9. A pump feed fuel system must be able to flow 125% of the takeoff fuel flow required for a reciprocating engine. (FAR Part 23.955)

10. If the aircraft is equipped with a selector valve that allows the engine to operate from more than one fuel tank, the system must not cause a loss of power for more than 10 sec. for a single-engine or 20 sec. for a multi-engine airplane, between the time one tank is allowed to run dry and the time at which the required power is supplied by the other tank. (FAR Part 23.955)

11. Turbine-powered aircraft must have a fuel system that will supply 100% of the fuel required for its operation in all flight attitudes, and the flow must not be interrupted, as the fuel system automatically cycles through all of the tanks or fuel cells in the system. (FAR Part 23.955)

12. If a gravity feed system has interconnected tank outlets, it should not be possible for fuel feeding from one tank to flow into another tank and cause it to overflow. (FAR Part 23.957)

13. The amount of unusable fuel in an aircraft must be determined and this must be made known to the pilot. Unusable fuel is the amount of fuel in a tank when the first evidence of malfunction occurs. The aircraft must be in the attitude that is most adverse for fuel flow. (FAR Part 23.959)

14. The fuel system must be so designed that it is free from vapor lock when the fuel is at a temperature of 110°F under the most critical operating conditions. (FAR Part 23.961)

15. Each fuel tank compartment must be adequately vented and drained so no explosive vapors or liquid can accumulate. (FAR Part 23.967)

16. No fuel tank can be on the engine side of the firewall, and it must be at least one-half inch away from the firewall. (FAR Part 23.967)

17. No fuel tank can be installed inside a personnel compartment of a multi-engine aircraft. (FAR Part 23.967)

18. Each fuel tank must have a 2% expansion space that cannot be filled with fuel, and it must also have a drainable sump where water and contaminants will normally accumulate when the aircraft is in its normal ground attitude. (FAR Parts 23.969 and 23.971)

19. Provisions must be made to prevent fuel spilled during filling the tank from entering the aircraft structure. (FAR Part 23.973)

20. The filler opening of an aircraft fuel tank must be marked with the word "FUEL" and, for aircraft with reciprocating engines, with the minimum grade of fuel. For turbine-powered aircraft, the tank must be marked with the permissible fuel designation. If the filler opening is for pressure fueling, the maximum permissible fueling and defueling pressure must be specified. (FAR Part 23.1557)

21. If more than one fuel tank has interconnected outlets, the airspace above the fuel must also be interconnected. (FAR Part 23.975)

22. If the carburetor or fuel injection system has a vapor elimination system that returns fuel to one of the tanks, the returned fuel must go to the tank that is required to be used first. (FAR Part 23.975)

23. All fuel tanks are required to have a strainer at the fuel tank outlet or at the booster pump. For a reciprocating engine, the strainer should have an 8- to 16-mesh element, and for turbine engines, the strainer should prevent the passage of any object that could restrict the flow or damage any of the fuel system components. (FAR Part 23.977)

24. For engines requiring fuel pumps, there must be one engine driven fuel pump for each engine. (FAR Part 23.991)

25. There must be at least one drain that will allow safe drainage of the entire fuel system when the airplane is in its normal ground attitude. (FAR Part 23.999)

26. If the design landing weight of the aircraft is less than that permitted for takeoff, there must be provisions in the fuel system for jettisoning fuel to bring the maximum weight down to the design landing weight. (FAR Part 23.1001)

27. The fuel jettisoning valve must be designed to allow personnel to close the valve during any part of the jettisoning operation. (FAR Part 23.1001)

28. Each metal tank and nonmetallic tank with walls not supported by the aircraft structure must be able to withstand a pressure of 3.5 PSI.

B. Types of Aviation Fuel

Aviation fuel is a liquid containing chemical energy that, through combustion, is released as heat energy and then converted to mechanical energy by the engine. Gasoline and kerosene are the two most widely used aviation fuels.

1. Reciprocating Engine Fuel

Aviation fuels are distilled from crude oil by fractional distillation. This is a process in which the different boiling temperatures of the various products are used to separate them from the crude oil. Gasoline boils at a relatively low temperature, and it is taken off first; then the heavier fractions of the oil are boiled off to become turbine engine fuel, diesel fuel, and furnace oil.

Aviation gasoline consists almost entirely of compounds consisting of hydrogen and carbon. Some impurities in the form of sulphur and dissolved water will be present. This water cannot be avoided, since the gasoline is exposed to moisture in the atmosphere. A small amount of sulphur, always present in crude oil, is left in the process of manufacture.

Tetraethyl lead (TEL) is added to the gasoline to improve its performance in the engine. Organic bromides and chlorides are mixed with TEL to aid in its combustion and assure that lead oxides are not left in the cylinder.

It is necessary for the aircraft pilot to understand the characteristics and properties of aviation gasoline. This important information will govern the selection of the proper fuel and the ability to operate the engine reliably, efficiently, and without damage.

a. Volatility

Volatility is a measure of the tendency of a liquid substance to vaporize under given conditions. Gasoline is a complex blend of volatile hydrocarbon compounds that have a wide range of boiling points and vapor pressures. It is blended in such a way that a straight chain of boiling points is obtained. This is necessary to obtain the required starting, acceleration, power, and fuel mixture characteristics for the engine.

If the gasoline vaporized too readily, fuel lines may become filled with vapor and cause decreased fuel flow. If the fuel does not vaporize readily enough, it can result in hard starting, slow warm-up, poor acceleration, uneven fuel distribution to the cylinders, and excessive crankcase dilution.

b. Vapor Lock

Vaporization of gasoline in fuel lines results in a reduced supply of gasoline to the engine. In severe cases, it may result in engine stoppage. This phenomenon is referred to as vapor locking. A measure of a gasoline's tendency to vapor lock is obtained from the Reid vapor pressure test. In this test, a sample of the fuel is sealed in a "bomb" equipped with a pressure gauge. The apparatus (figure 12-1) is then immersed in a constant-temperature bath and the indicated pressure is noted. The higher the corrected vapor pressure of the sample under test, the more susceptible it is to vapor locking. Aviation gasolines are limited to a maximum of 7 PSI because of their increased tendency to vapor lock at high altitudes.

c. Carburetor Icing

Carburetor icing is also related to volatility. When the fuel changes from a liquid to vapor, it extracts heat from its surroundings to make this change. The more volatile the fuel, the more rapid the heat extraction will be. As the gasoline leaving the discharge nozzle of a float-type carburetor vaporizes, it can freeze the water vapor contained in the incoming air. This moisture may freeze on the walls of the induction system, the venturi throat, or the throttle valve. This type of ice formation restricts the fuel and air passages of the carburetor. It will cause loss of power, and if not eliminated, eventual engine stoppage.

d. Aromatic Fuels

Some fuels may contain considerable quantities of aromatic hydrocarbons, which are added to increase the rich mixture performance rating of the fuel. Such fuels, known as aromatic fuels, have a strong solvent and swelling action on some types of hose and other rubber parts of the fuel system. For this reason, aromatic-resistant hose and rubber parts have been developed for use with aromatic fuels. The use of aromatic fuels is associated with the high-horse-power reciprocating engines used on military and large transport-category aircraft.

e. Detonation

In an engine that is operating in a normal manner, the flame front traverses the charge at a steady velocity of about 100 ft./sec., until the charge is consumed. Detonation is a condition where the first portion of the charge burns normally, but the last portion burns almost instantaneously. This creates an excessive momentary pressure unbalance in the combustion chamber, and may be identified as "engine knock". The tremendous increase in the speed of combustion causes the cylinder head temperature to rise, engine efficiency is reduced, and structural damage to the piston or cylinder head may occur.

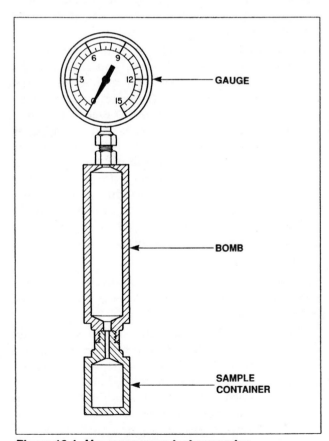

Figure 12-1. Vapor pressure test apparatus.

f. Surface Ignition

Ignition of the fuel/air mixture by hot spots or surfaces in the combustion chamber is called surface ignition. If this occurs before the normal ignition event, the phenomenon is referred to as preignition. When it is prevalent, the result is power loss and engine roughness. Preignition is generally attributed to overheating of such parts as spark plug electrodes, exhaust valves, carbon deposits, etc. Where preignition is present, an engine may continue to operate even though the ignition has been turned off.

g. Octane and Performance Number Rating

Octane and performance numbers designate the antiknock value of the fuel mixture in an engine cylinder. Aircraft engines of high power output have been made possible principally as a result of blending to produce fuel of higher octane ratings. The use of such fuels has permitted increases in compression ratio and manifold pressure, resulting in improved engine power and efficiency. However, even the high-octane fuels will detonate under severe operating conditions and when certain engine controls are improperly operated.

Antiknock qualities of aviation fuel are designated by grades. The higher the grade, the more compression the fuel can stand without detonating. There are currently three grades of aviation gasoline in general use: 80/87, 100/130, and 100LL.

The multiple numbering system used for the different grades refers to the lean and rich mixture performance numbers. The first number indicates the lean-mixture rating and the second the rich-mixture rating. Thus, grade 100/130 fuel has a lean-mixture rating of 100 and a rich-mixture rating of 130. To avoid confusion and to minimize errors in handling the different grades of aviation gasolines, it has become common practice to designate the different grades by the lean mixture performance number only. Hence, aviation gasoline is identified as Avgas 80, 100, 100LL. 100LL is a new grade indicating a low lead (TEL) content.

h. Purity

Aviation fuels must be free of impurities that would interfere with the operation of the engine or the units in the fuel and induction system.

Even though all precautions are observed in storing and handling gasoline, it is not uncommon to find a small amount of water and sediment in an aircraft fuel system. A small amount of such contamination is usually retained in the strainers in the fuel system. Generally, this is not considered a source of great danger, provided that the strainers are drained and cleaned at frequent intervals. However, the water can present a serious problem because it settles to the bottom of the fuel tank and can then be circulated through the fuel system. A small quantity of water will flow with the gasoline through the carburetor jets and will not be especially harmful. An excessive amount of water will displace the fuel passing through the jets and restrict the flow of fuel; it will cause loss of power and can result in engine stoppage.

Under certain conditions of temperature and humidity, condensation of moisture (from the air) occurs on the inner surfaces of the fuel tanks. Since this condensation occurs on the portion of the tank above the fuel level, it is obvious that the practice of servicing an airplane immediately after flight will do much to minimize this hazard.

i. Fuel Identification

Gasolines containing TEL must be colored to conform with the law. In addition, gasoline may be colored for purposes of identification. For example, Avgas 80 is red, Avgas 100 is green, and 100LL is dyed blue.

A change in color of an aviation gasoline usually indicates contamination with another product or a loss of fuel quality. A color change can also be caused by a chemical reaction that has weakened the dye component. This color change itself may not affect the quality of the fuel. If a color change has occurred, the cause should be determined before the aircraft is released for flight.

The most positive method of identifying the type and grade of fuel includes the following:

1. *Marking of Hose* — A color band not less than 1 ft. wide painted adjacent to the fitting on each end of the hose used to dispense the fuel. The bands completely encircle the hose, and the name and grade of the product is stenciled longitudinally in 1 in. letters of a contrasting color over the color band.

Examples of these markings and their locations are shown in figure 12-2.

2. Turbine Engine Fuels

The aircraft gas turbine is designed to operate on a distillate fuel, commonly called jet fuel. Jet fuels are also composed of hydrocarbons with a little more carbon and usually a higher sulphur content than gasoline. Inhibitors may be added to reduce corrosion and oxidation. Anti-icing additives are also being blended to prevent fuel icing.

a. Volatility

One of the most important characteristics of a jet fuel is its volatility. It must, of necessity, be a compromise between several opposing factors. A highly volatile fuel is desirable to aid in starting in cold weather and to make aerial restarts easier and surer. Low volatility is desirable to reduce the possibility of vapor lock and to reduce fuel losses by evaporation.

At normal temperatures, gasoline in a closed container or tank can give off so much vapor that the fuel/air mixture may be too rich to burn. Under the same conditions, the vapor given off by Jet B fuel can be in the inflammable or explosive range. Jet A fuel has such a low volatility that at normal temperatures it gives off very little vapor and does not form flammable or explosive fuel/air mixtures. Figure 12-3 shows the vaporization of aviation fuels at atmospheric temperatures.

b. Fuel Types

Because jet fuels are not dyed, there is no on-sight identification for them. They range in color from a colorless to a straw-colored (amber) liquid, depending on age or the crude petroleum source.

There are currently two types of turbine fuel in use: JET A and JET A-1 which are kerosene types, and JET B which is a blend of gasoline and kerosene fractions.

Jet A-1 specifies a freeze point of –47°C (–52.6°F) and Jet A a freeze point of –40°C (–40°F).

Jet B, similar to JP-4, is normally used by the military, particularly the Air Force. This fuel has an allowable freeze point of –50°C (–58°F).

c. Problems with Water in Turbine Fuel

Water occurs in aviation fuel in two forms, namely "dissolved" and "free."

All aviation fuels will dissolve water in varying amounts depending upon the fuel composition and temperature. This can be likened to humidity in the air. Any water in excess of that which will dissolve is called free water. Lowering the fuel temperature will cause dissolved water to come out of solution as free water somewhat like fog forms when humid air is cooled.

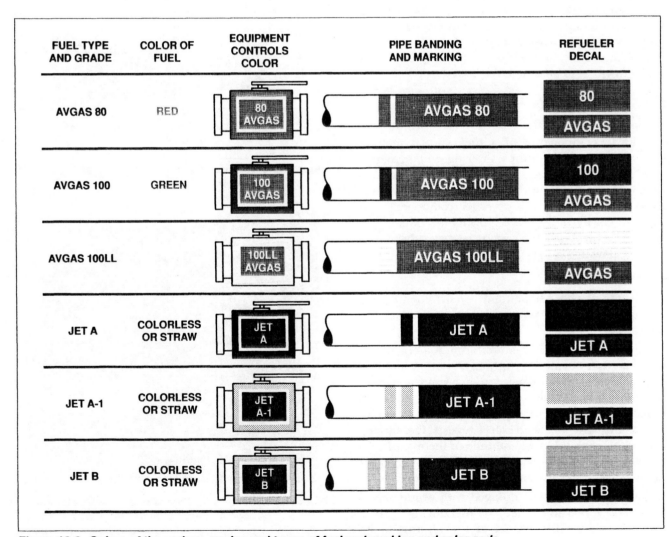

Figure 12-2. Colors of the various grades and types of fuel and marking and color code.

When the water precipitates out it may collect on the fuel filter, and freeze. This coating of ice on the filter element may shut off the flow of fuel to the engine. To warn against fuel ice, high-flying jet aircraft measure the temperature of the fuel in one of the tanks. If the fuel temperature is low, it can be heated before it flows through the filter.

The fuel filters are equipped with a differential pressure sensor across the filter element. This sensor will turn on an ice warning light on the instrument panel if the filter ices up and the pressure across the element rises to the preset value.

To further minimize the ice problem, most jet fuel is treated with an anti-icing additive that mixes with the water in the fuel and lowers its freezing point. This acts so that the water will not freeze, but will remain in its liquid state.

The other problem with water in turbine engine fuel is that it may serve as a home for microscopic-size animal and plant life. Microbial growths, or contamination with bacteria, or "bugs", has become a critical problem in some turbine fuel systems and some aircraft. Because microbes thrive in water, a simple and effective method to prevent or retard their growth is to eliminate the water.

C. Aircraft Fuel System Components

The basic components of a fuel system include tanks, lines, valves, pumps, filtering units, gauges, and primer. Some systems will include central refueling provisions, fuel dump valves, a means for transferring fuel as well as other components. In order to clarify the operating principles of complex aircraft fuel systems, the various units are discussed in the following paragraphs.

1. Fuel Tanks

The location, size, shape, and construction of fuel tanks vary with the type and intended use of the aircraft.

Fuel tanks are manufactured from materials that will not react chemically with any aviation fuel and have a number of common features. A sump and drain are provided at the lowest point in the tank, and each tank is vented to the atmosphere. All except the smallest of tanks are fitted with baffles to resist fuel surging caused by changes in the attitude of the aircraft. An expansion space is provided in fuel tanks to allow for an increase in fuel volume due to expansion.

Some fuel tanks are equipped with dump valves that make it possible to jettison fuel during flight in order to reduce the weight of the aircraft to its specified landing weight. In aircraft equipped with

dump valves, the operating control is located within reach of the pilot, copilot, or flight engineer. Dump valves are designed and installed to afford safe, rapid discharge of fuel.

a. Rigid Removeable Fuel Tanks

Many aircraft use regid removeable welded or riveted gasoline tanks to hold fuel.

The smaller fuel tanks may be made of thin sheet steel coated with an alloy of lead and tin, called terneplate. Terneplate sheets are formed into the shapes needed to construct the tank, folded, and solder sweated into the seams. This provides a good

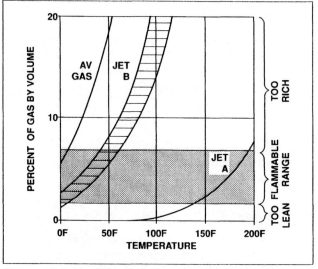

Figure 12-3. Vaporization of aviation fuels at atmospheric temperatures.

Figure 12-4. Built-up fuel tank that forms the leading edge of a light airplane wing. Sealant is placed in all of the seams before the tank is assembled.

leak-proof joint and the tanks are relatively low in cost. Most terneplate tanks are of such small capacity that they seldom require baffles.

The larger fuel tanks are generally made of either aluminum alloy 3003, or alloy 5052. Both of these metals are relatively lightweight and are easily welded. The parts of the tank are stamped out of sheet metal and formed to the required shape. The tank is often riveted together with soft aluminum rivets to hold its parts in position. Then all of the seams are torch-welded to provide a fuel-tight seal.

Many of the tanks are large enough to require baffles to prevent the fuel sloshing around in flight and either damaging the tank or causing balance problems.

All rigid fuel tanks must be supported in the aircraft structure with hold-down straps that will prevent the tank shifting during any maneuver. All tank mounts must be padded with some type of material, usually felt, to prevent the tank chafing against the structure.

Some of the more modern small airplanes use welded fuel tanks that actually form part of the leading edge of the wing. These tanks are assembled, and all of the seams are welded by electric resistance welding.

b. Integral Fuel Tanks

Rigid tanks require a large open space in the aircraft structure for their installation, and very few aircraft structures have space that is not crossed with structural members. Most wings have large empty spaces, however, and with the availability of some of the new space-age sealants, it has become standard practice for many of the aircraft manufacturers to seal off a portion of the wing to form a fuel tank. This type of tank has the advantage of using the maximum amount of space for the fuel for a minimum amount of weight. In figure 12-5, we have a drawing of a typical light aircraft integral fuel tank. This is the leading edge portion of the wing from the front spar forward, and it is sealed at both ends and all along the spar with a sealant. All of the rivets and nutplates are sealed, and sealant is used around all of the inspection openings. The sealant is spread along each seam individually.

Some airplanes have the leading edge of the wing made of formed honeycomb, with facings of sheet

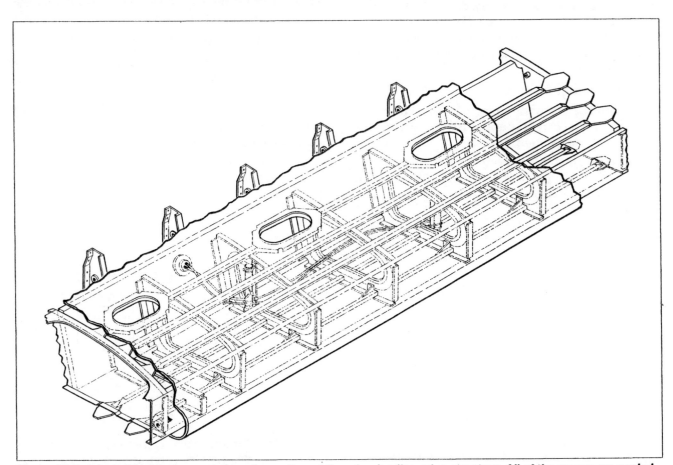

Figure 12-5. Integral fuel tank consisting of a portion of the wing leading edge structure. All of the seams are sealed with a special sealant.

aluminum or fiberglass on both the inside and outside. This makes an excellent fuel tank with a minimum of sealing.

c. Bladder Tanks

An excellent substitute for a welded fuel tank is the bladder tank that has been successfully used for both small and large aircraft. The fuel bay is prepared by covering all sharp edges of the metal structure with a chafe-resisting tape and installing a bladder made of thin fabric, impregnated with neoprene or some similar material that is impervious to the fuel.

The bladder is put into the cavity prepared for it, by rolling and inserting it through an inspection opening. Then it is snapped or clipped in place, or, laced to the structure. An opening in the bladder is then secured to the inspection opening and covered with an inspection plate.

There are a few considerations that must be observed with aircraft bladder tanks. The bladder must be secured to all of its attachment points. If it has pulled away, the amount of fuel the tank can hold will be decreased and the fuel quantity gauge will be inaccurate. Also, these tanks should never be allowed to stand empty for any extended period of time. If it is ever necessary to leave the tank empty, the inside of the bladder should be wiped very carefully with an oily rag leaving a film of engine oil on its inside surface.

d. Fuel Tank Filler Caps

Care should be taken when installing a fuel tank cap, and it should be carefully examined on each routine maintenance inspection.

Almost all fuel tank caps are located on the upper surface of the wing, and it is possible for fuel to be siphoned from the tank if the cap is leaking or is improperly installed.

Some fuel tank caps are vented, and it is important that the vent hole be clear. Some caps have a goose neck tube on the vent that extends above the tank cap. It is extremely important that these tubes point forward to provide a slight positive pressure inside the tank.

There are several types of fuel tank caps available and only the tank cap approved for a particular aircraft should be used. The cap is actually part of the fuel tank filler adapter assembly. Replacement of one type of adapter with another usually constitutes a major alteration that requires approval of the aircraft manufacturer or the FAA.

Lightning-safe fuel tank caps are often installed on aircraft. These caps have no metal exposed inside of the tank and will not conduct the lightning charge into the tank. Even the lanyard that prevents the tank cap being misplaced is made of a strong non-conductive plastic material.

Non-siphoning fuel tank cap adapters have a small spring-loaded flapper inside the adapter that is pushed open by the fuel nozzle, and when the nozzle is withdrawn from the tank, the flapper closes. Even if the cap is left off of the adapter, no fuel can siphon out of the tank.

2. Fuel Lines and Fittings

The plumbing in aircraft fuel systems must be of the very highest quality material. The metal tubing is usually made of aluminum alloy, and the flexible hose made of synthetic rubber or Teflon. The diameter of the tubing is governed by the fuel flow requirements of the engine.

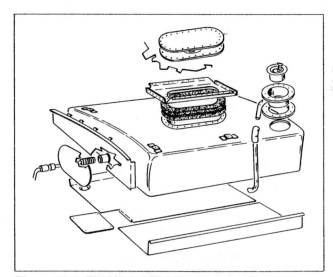

Figure 12-7. Bladder tanks are made of neoprene impregnated cloth, snapped or laced into the fuel cell cavity in the wing of the airplane.

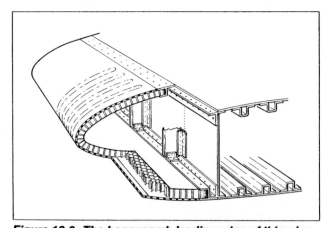

Figure 12-6. The honeycomb leading edge of this wing can easily be sealed and used as a fuel tank.

Most rigid fuel lines are made of 5052 aluminum alloy, but in some aircraft the lines installed in the wheel wells and engine compartments are made of stainless steel to avoid damage from either abrasion or heat. The fittings used may be of either the AN or MS flare or flareless type, depending upon the system installed by the aircraft manufacturer. Both the flare and flareless fittings provide a good leak-proof connection if they are properly installed, and will not usually develop a leak unless subjected to abuse or mistreatment.

When inspecting flexible hoses in a fuel system, be sure that they are not twisted. The yellow or white lay line that runs the length of the hose should be straight and show no indication of spiraling.

Many of the fuel lines in an engine compartment are encased in a fire sleeve. Be sure that the proper type of fire sleeve is used, and that it is installed in the manner specified by the aircraft manufacturer.

Routing of fuel lines should be accomplished in accordance with the manufacturer's recommendations. A few of the basic requirements for routing fuel lines in an aircraft:

1. Fuel lines should be located below electrical wire bundles. It is never permissible to clamp a wire bundle to a fuel line.
2. There should be no strain on a fitting.
3. There must always be at least one bend in rigid tubing between fittings. This allows for slight

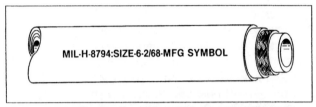

Figure 12-9. *The lay line printed along a flexible hose provides a means of identifying the type of hose and shows whether or not the hose has been twisted during installation*

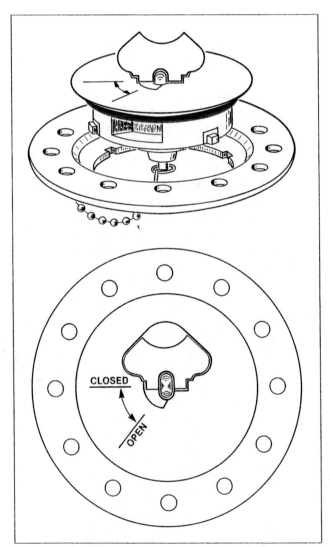

Figure 12-8. *Typical fuel tank filler cap. The tab is flush with the surface when the cap is locked in place.*

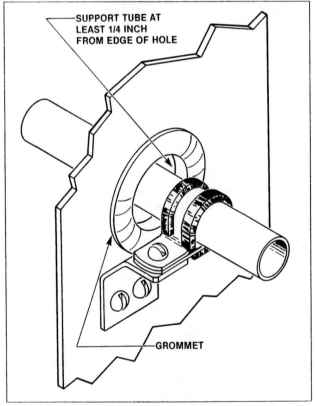

Figure 12-10. *Fuel lines in an aircraft must be supported with bonded-type cushion clamps. The edges of any hole through which the tube passes should be protected with a rubber grommet.*

misalignment of the ends and for vibration, as well as for expansion and contraction caused by temperature changes.

4. Be sure that all fuel lines are protected from being used as a handhold.

5. In order to protect fuel lines from being stepped on or from being damaged by baggage or cargo, they should be routed along the sides or top of compartments in which this type of damage could occur.

3. Fuel Valves

Selector valves are installed in the fuel system to provide a means for shutting off the fuel flow, tank and engine selection, crossfeed, and fuel transfer. The size and number of ports (openings) vary with the installation. The valve must accommodate the full flow capacity of the fuel line, not leak, and operate freely with a definite "feel" or "click" when it is in the correct position. Valves may be operated by hand, motor, or solenoid.

a. Hand-operated Valves

Hand-operated valves may be found on small and medium sized aircraft, and will likely be either the cone-type or the poppet-type selector valves.

(1) Cone-type Valves

All fuel systems have some provisions for shutting off the flow of fuel from the tanks to the engine. The simplest valve is the cone-type, in which a cone, usually made of brass, fits into a conical recess in the valve body. The cone is drilled so it will allow flow from the inlet of the valve to any one of the outlets that is selected. A detente plate is installed on the shaft that is used to turn the cone, and a spring-loaded pin slips into the detente when the hole in the cone is accurately aligned with the holes in the valve body. This allows the pilot to tell by feel when the valve is in its fully open position.

(2) Poppet-type Valve

One of the problems with cone-type valves is that they can become difficult to turn, and this can prevent the detente from providing a positive feel when the valve is in its fully open position. The poppet-type valve overcomes this problem by using a cam shaft operated by the selector valve handle to open the correct poppets and control the flow of fuel through the valve. The positive shutoff of fuel is provided by the spring on the valve, and it is easy for the pilot to tell by feel when the valve is fully open.

b. Motor-operated Valves

Larger aircraft must use remotely operated valves in the fuel system. There are two basic types of remotely operated valves in popular use today: those driven by an electric motor, and those operated by a solenoid.

There are two types of motor-operated valves. In one, the motor drives a drum through which holes are cut so fuel can flow through the drum when in one position, and the flow is shut off when the drum is rotated 90°.

The other valve uses a motor-driven sliding gate. To open the valve, the gate is drawn back from the opening so fuel can flow through. When the gate is over the opening, no fuel can flow.

c. Solenoid-operated Valves

A solenoid valve has the advantage of being much quicker to open or close. The valve in figure 12-14 is a solenoid operated poppet-type valve. When electrical current momentarily flows through the opening solenoid coil, a magnetic pull is exerted on the valve stem that opens the valve. When the stem rises high enough, the spring-loaded locking plunger of the

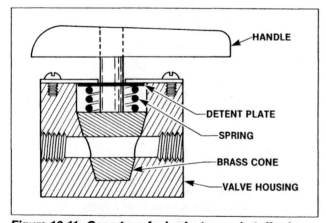

Figure 12-11. Cone-type fuel selector or shutoff valve.

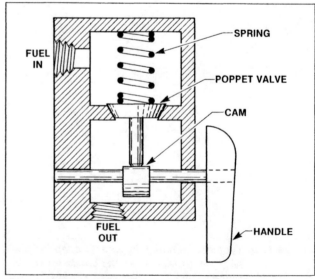

Figure 12-12. Poppet-type fuel selector shutoff valve.

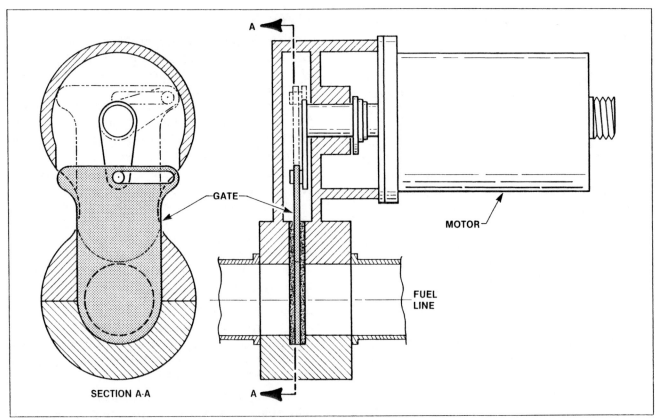

Figure 12-13. Motor-driven, gate-type fuel shutoff valve.

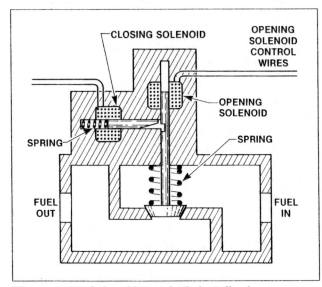

Figure 12-14. Solenoid-type fuel shutoff valve.

closing solenoid is forced into the notch in the valve stem. This holds the valve locked open until current is momentarily directed into the closing solenoid coil. The magnetic pull of this coil pulls the locking plunger out of the notch in the valve stem and the spring closes the valve and shuts off the flow of fuel.

4. Fuel Pumps

The purpose of the engine-driven fuel pump is to deliver a continuous supply of fuel at the proper pressure at all times during engine operation. Auxiliary fuel pumps may be installed in the system to aid in engine starting and to assure a positive pressure to the inlet of the engine driven fuel pump.

a. Hand-operated Pumps

Hand-operated fuel pumps are often called wobble pumps because of the means of operation of one of the early types of hand fuel pumps. The pump in figure 12-15 is of the type commonly used.

When the handle is moved up and down, the vane inside the pump rocks back and forth. When the handle is pulled down, the left side of the vane moves up and fuel is pulled into chambers A and D through the flapper-type check valve and the drilled passage between the chambers. Fuel that is in chamber B is forced through the passage drilled through the center of the vane into chamber C, and out the pump discharge line through the check valve. When the handle is moved up, the vane moves in the opposite direction and fuel is pulled into chambers B and C. The fuel that is in chamber A is forced out of the pump through chamber D. You can see that this is

199

a double-acting pump, that is, it moves fuel on each stroke of the handle.

b. Centrifugal Boost Pump

A popular type of auxiliary fuel pump in use is the centrifugal boost pump. These pumps are normally installed either inside the fuel tank or attached to the outside of the tank (figure 12-16).

A centrifugal pump is driven by an electric motor with a small impeller to sling fuel out into the discharge line. These pumps are not affected by restricting their outlet. Most are the 2-speed type which uses an electrical resistor in series with the motor to vary speed.

Some centrifugal boost pumps have a small agitator on the pump shaft to agitate the fuel being drawn into the impeller. Vapor bubbles that form in the fuel are forced to coalesce into larger bubbles and rise to the top of the tank rather than enter the fuel line.

This boost pump is used for starting the engine and as a backup for the engine-driven pump during takeoff and landing. It is also used in its high-speed position for major purging of fuel vapors. Some installations are quite sensitive with regard to the pressure delivered by the boost pump to the engine, and these systems have resistors in the boost pump circuit that are controlled by a precision switch on the throttle. When the throttle is opened and the boost pump switch is on, the pump operates at its high speed, but when the throttle is retarded the pump speed will automatically decrease and lower its output pressure enough that the boost pump will not flood the engine.

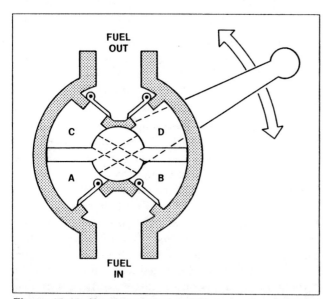

Figure 12-15. Hand-operated wobble pump for moving aircraft fuel.

c. Fuel Ejectors

To assure an adequate supply of fuel available to the boost pumps, they are sometimes located in a fuel collector can. This is an area of the fuel tank that has been partitioned off and equipped with a flapper-type valve to allow fuel to flow into the collector from the tank. A fuel ejector system uses the venturi principle to supply additional fuel to the collector can, regardless of aircraft attitude.

The submerged motor-driven boost pumps supply fuel from each tank to their respective engines. During operation of the boost pumps, a portion of their output is routed to the fuel ejectors. The flow of this fuel through a venturi supplies the low pressure which draws additional fuel from the ejector location. This fuel is then routed to the fuel collector cans.

d. Pulsating Electric Pumps

Rather than using the more expensive centrifugal boost pump, many of the smaller low-wing airplanes use a pulsating pump that is similar in its operation to the electric pumps that have been used in automobiles and trucks for many years.

This simple type of pump consists of a solenoid coil installed around a brass tube that connects the two fuel chambers. In the core of the coil, riding up and down inside the brass tube is a steel plunger. A calibrated spring forces the plunger upward, and it is pulled down by the magnetism of the solenoid. One check valve is installed inside the plunger and another check valve is in the extension of the brass tube in the fuel inlet chamber.

When the pump is not on, the calibrated spring forces the plunger up in the brass tube where it attracts the magnet through the tube and pulls the points closed. When the pump is turned on, current flows through the contact points and energizes the solenoid coil. This pulls the plunger down into the coil. The fuel in chamber B passes up through the check valve into the plunger. When the plunger is centered in the coil, it no longer has any effect on the magnet attached to the contact points and these points spring open, stopping the current flow into the coil. The calibrated spring forces the plunger up and the fuel out through chamber C and the discharge line to the engine. As the plunger moves up, fuel flows from the inlet through chamber A and the lower check valve into chamber B, and the cycle is ready to start over. This type of pump will pulsate rapidly when the engine is accepting all of the fuel it delivers, but when the needle valve on the carburetor is closed, the pressure will build up in the line between the carburetor and the pump and it will pulse slowly.

Plunger type pumps are normally installed in parallel with a diaphragm-type engine driven pump so either or both pumps can supply fuel pressure to the engine.

e. Vane-type Fuel Pumps

The pump illustrated in figure 12-18 is typical of the vane-type fuel pump. The rotor is driven from an accessory drive on the engine or by an electric motor. There are four steel vanes that slide back and forth in slots cut in the rotor. A hard steel pin floats in the hollow center of the rotor and holds the vanes against the wall of the pump cavity in which the rotor fits eccentrically. As the rotor turns, fuel is drawn into the pump through the inlet, and into the space between the vanes. It is then forced out of the pump on the discharge side. This is a constant displacement type of pump, and for each revolution, it delivers a given amount of fuel. Fuel systems are not designed to accept all of the fuel this type of pump can deliver. A provision must be made to relieve the excess pressure and fuel back to the pump inlet. This is done with a relief valve in which the discharge pressure acts on the valve face and lifts the valve off its seat when the pressure reaches the value for which the relief valve spring is set. When the valve lifts off its seat, the fuel flows back to the inlet side of the vane assembly and the discharge pressure is maintained at the value for which the relief valve is set.

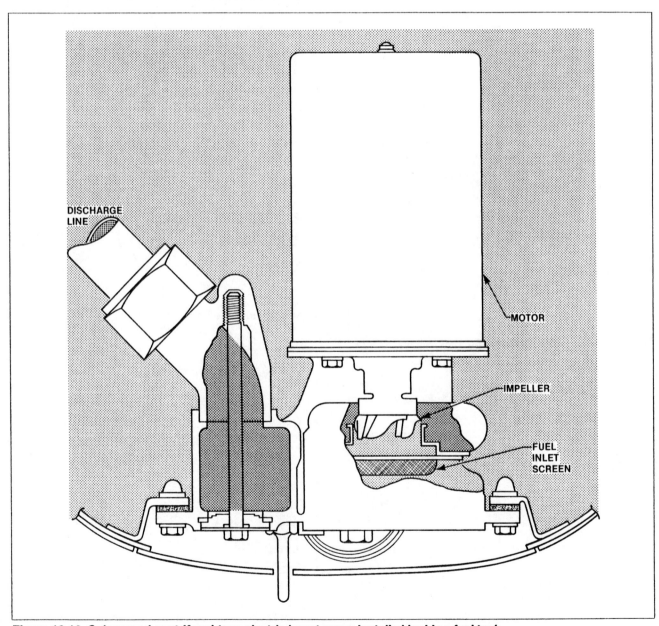

Figure 12-16. Submerged centrifugal-type electric boost pump installed inside a fuel tank.

These pumps are installed in series with the boost pump, and must be capable of bypassing all of the fuel when the engine is being started and in the event the engine-driven pump should fail. The bypass valve is usually a spring-loaded disk on the lower face of the relief valve. If the pressure at the pump inlet is greater than its outlet pressure, the fuel will force the disk away from the relief valve and fuel will flow through this opening to the engine. The bypass valve spring is so weak that there is negligible opposition to the flow of the fuel.

5. Fuel Filters

It is extremely important that the fuel supplied to an aircraft engine be free from contamination. Because

of this, a series of strainers and filters are required in every aircraft fuel system. In addition to the strainers, there must be provision for draining a sample of fuel from all of the tanks and from the main strainer to physically examine the fuel for the presence of water.

Almost all fuel tanks used in the smaller aircraft have a rather coarse mesh finger strainer at the tank outlet. This strainer increases the area of the discharge port of the tank and helps prevent contaminants shutting off the flow of fuel from the tank. If a boost pump is installed in the tank, the screen is around the inlet to the pump. Here it serves the same function, to prevent the fuel flow being stopped by an excessive amount of contamination.

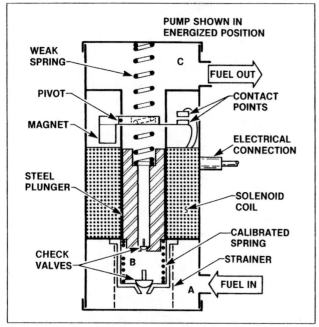

Figure 12-17. Plunger-type electric auxiliary fuel pump.

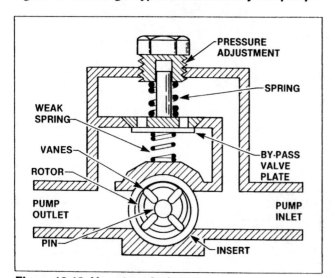

Figure 12-18. Vane-type fuel pump.

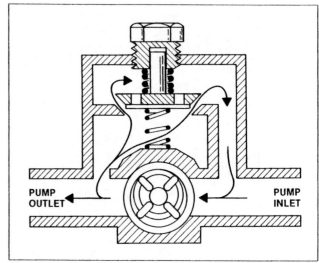

Figure 12-19. Vane-type fuel pump showing the flow of fuel through the relief valve.

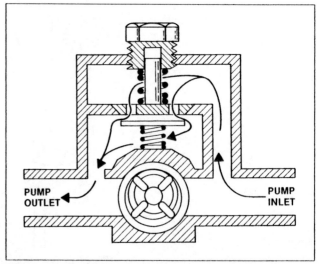

Figure 12-20. Vane-type fuel pump showing the flow of fuel through the bypass valve.

All fuel tanks have a drain valve or drain plug at their lowest point. A sample of fuel should be drained from this point before the first flight of the day, and after refueling. Any water or solid contaminants in the fuel will settle around this valve where it can be drained out.

The main fuel strainer is normally located at the lowest point in the fuel system where it can collect water or solid contaminants and hold it until it can be disposed of.

The filtering element of many smaller fuel strainers use a simple disk of relatively fine mesh screen wire at the top of the strainer bowl. Fuel from the tank enters the bowl through the center of the screen, and in order to flow to the carburetor, must flow upward through the screen. Water and solid contaminants cannot pass through the screen, and collects in the bowl. Most bowls are equipped with a

Figure 12-21. Typical fuel tank sump drain.

Figure 12-22. Drain valve installed in the main fuel strainer of a light airplane.

quick-drain valve to drain a sample of the fuel to check for water.

Many of the larger fuel strainers use a cylindrical screen wrapped around a coarse mesh screen that gives the strainer its shape and physical strength. Inside the cylinder is a cone, also made of screen wire, to provide additional surface area for the strainer. Fuel flows into the strainer around the outside of the screen and up through the inside of the cone. Contaminants and water collect in the bottom of the strainer housing that can be drained on a routine maintenance inspection or during a preflight walkaround.

6. Fuel Heaters and Ice Prevention Systems

Turbine-powered aircraft that operate at high altitudes and low temperatures for extended periods of time have the problem of water condensing out of the fuel and freezing. These ice crystals may collect on the fuel filters and shut off the flow of fuel to the engine. To prevent this, these aircraft have a fuel temperature gauge to indicate a danger of ice formation.

The fuel filters have a pressure switch connected across the filter element that will close if the element clogs enough with ice to obstruct the flow of fuel. If a fuel icing light comes on indicating that one of the fuel filters is clogging, the fuel heat valve is opened allowing compressor bleed air to flow through the fuel-air heat exchanger. This will raise the temperature of the fuel enough to melt the ice and prevent further ice formation. When the ice has melted and full flow is restored, the fuel ice light will go out. If the filter is clogged with dirt that prevents the flow of fuel, a bypass valve will open and the fuel will bypass the filtering element.

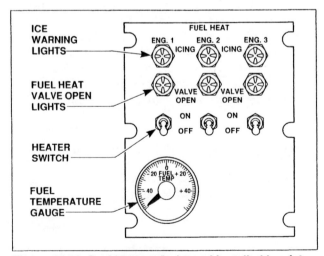

Figure 12-23. Fuel heat control panel installed in a jet transport airplane.

7. Fuel System Indicators

The complexity of fuel system indicators may vary to some degree but their purpose and operating principles remain the same.

a. Fuel Quantity Indicating Systems

This is a required instrument for all powered aircraft, and may be as simple as a cork floating on the fuel in the tank, projecting a wire out through the filler cap. There is no requirement for these simple systems to be calibrated in discreet amounts. They may show only the relative amount of fuel in the tank. Some indicators have a float drive and pointer that shows the level of fuel as is ¼, ½, ¾, or Full.

Electrical ratiometer-type fuel quantity gauges are used in many of the reciprocating engine aircraft. These gauges show the fuel level in the tanks by converting the position of the float into an analogy of resistance in a fuel tank transmitter unit. The indicator is calibrated in gallons of fuel in the tank.

When it is necessary to know the mass of the fuel in the tank, rather than just its level, the capacitance-type fuel quantity system most frequently used.

Concentric metal tubes serve as capacitors and extend across the fuel tanks from top to bottom. When the tank is empty, air serves as the dielectric, and when the tank is full, fuel is between the tubes, or plates. The change in dielectric changes the electrical capacity of the probes, and this capacity is measured on a capacitance bridge.

The density of the fuel affects its dielectric constant and thus the capacity of the probe, and because of this, the system will show on the fuel quantity indicator the number of pounds of fuel remaining.

Most large jet transport aircraft have a means for the ground servicing personnel to gauge the amount of fuel in a tank manually. One method uses a magnetically locked fuel measuring stick. A latching cam on the bottom surface of the wing tank is turned a quarter of a turn, and the measuring stick is pulled down from the tank until the magnet on the measuring stick is inside the magnet in the float. The fuel

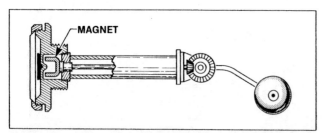

Figure 12-24. Float-type fuel quantity indicator used in light airplanes.

service technician can feel when the magnets grip together and can read the number on the measuring stick that relates to the fuel level in the tank.

Another type of measuring stick shows the fuel level by fuel dripping from the hollow measuring stick when it is pulled down to the top of the fuel in the tank. Still another type uses a measuring stick made of transparent acrylic that has a wedge-shaped top. The technician can look up through the transparent rod as it is lowered, and when the end of the rod appears as a sharply defined line, the end is at the top of the fuel in the tank, and the quantity of fuel can be determined by the amount the rod extends from the bottom of the tank.

b. Fuel Flowmeters

Small reciprocating-engine aircraft using carburetors seldom have fuel flowmeters. The pilot assumes a flow rate based on the engine RPM and manifold pressure and checks it against the amount of fuel used in a given period of time.

Larger reciprocating engines use a fuel flowmeter in the fuel system between the fuel pump and the carburetor. A spring-loaded vane is moved by the fuel flowing to the carburetor. The greater the flow, the further the vane will move over, and the movement of the vane is transmitted to the indicator, which is calibrated in gallons per hour. This is only an approximation since it assumes that the fuel is at a standard temperature and has a standard density.

Turbine-powered aircraft are concerned with the mass of the fuel flow rather than just its volume, and flowmeters for these engines actually compensate for the density of the fuel so they can indicate the number of pounds of fuel flowing per hour.

Reciprocating engines that are equipped with fuel injection systems have a flowmeter indicator that is actually a fuel pressure gauge. This is, for normally aspirated engines, a bourdon tube instrument that measures the pressure drop across the fuel injector nozzles. The greater the flow, the greater the pressure drop will be. Turbocharged engines use a differential pressure gauge to measure the flow. They measure the pressure at the distributor, or manifold valve, and compare it with the upper deck air pressure (the air pressure as it enters the fuel metering system). One major problem with this type of flow indicator is the fact that a clogged injector nozzle will decrease the fuel flow, but the pressure drop across the nozzle will increase, and it will indicate an increased fuel flow.

The latest development in fuel flow instruments is the digital-type system that uses a small turbine wheel in the fuel line to the fuel control unit. As fuel flows through this line, it spins the turbine and a digital circuit reads the number of revolutions in a specified period of time and converts this into a fuel flow rate. This flow rate may be electronically compensated for any idiosyncrasies of the specific system.

When the electronic fuel flowmeters are connected to some other electronic equipment in the aircraft, they can be made to present a running total of the fuel on board the aircraft during the flight, and to predict the amount of time the fuel will last at the present rate of consumption. When this equipment is linked to the distance measuring equipment (DME), it can even show the range of the aircraft at the present power setting.

c. Fuel Temperature Gauges

High flying jet aircraft are equipped with a ratiometer-type fuel temperature measuring system. This unit measures the temperature of the fuel in one of the tanks and displays it on the flight engineer's instrument panel. The flight engineer can direct compressor bleed air from one of the engines into a fuel-air heat exchanger to warm the fuel.

d. Fuel Pressure Gauges

It is necessary to know that a pump fed fuel system is delivering the proper amount of fuel to the carburetor,

and to do this, a bourdon tube pressure gauge connected to the fuel inlet of the carburetor to measure the fuel pressure at this point. The pressure read here before the engine is started shows the output of the boost pump, and when the engine is running and the boost pump is turned off, the gauge shows the pressure of the engine-driven pump.

Large reciprocating engines equipped with pressure carburetors are not concerned with the actual pressure produced by the pump, but with the difference between the inlet fuel pressure and the inlet air pressure. This pressure is measured at the carburetor inlet, but instead of using a simple bourdon tube indicator, it uses a differential bellows-type instrument.

e. Valve-in-transit Indicator Lights

On large multi-engine aircraft, each of the fuel crossfeed and line valves may be provided with a valve-in-transit indicator light. This light is on only during the time the valve is in motion and is off when movement is complete.

D. Aircraft Fuel Systems

The function of the aircraft fuel system is to deliver the proper amount of clean fuel at the right pressure

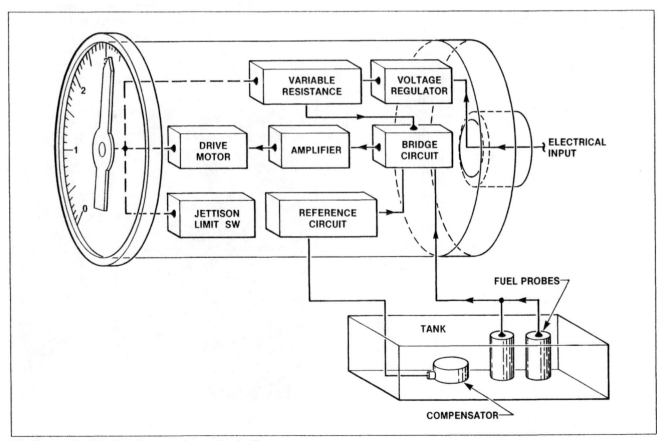

Figure 12-25. Totalizer-type fuel quantity indicator.

to meet the demands of the engine and ensure a positive, reliable fuel flow during all phases of flight. Furthermore, the system must be reasonably free from tendency to vapor lock. Such indicators as fuel pressure gauges, warning signals, and tank quantity gauges are provided to give continuous indications of how the system is functioning.

Fuel systems very with different types of aircraft and will range from the simple to the complex.

1. Small Single-Engine Aircraft Fuel Systems

Single-engine aircraft may utilize any of several types of fuel systems, depending upon the fuel metering unit (carburetor or fuel injector) used, and whether a high-wing or low-wing design.

a. Gravity-feed Systems

The most simple aircraft fuel system is that found on the small high-wing, single-engine, training-type airplane. This type of system is illustrated in figure 12-29 and normally use two fuel tanks, one in each

wing. The two tank outlets are connected to a selector valve that can draw from either tank individually, or both tanks at the same time. A fourth position on the selector valve turns off all fuel to the engine. Since both tanks can feed the engine at the same time, the space above the fuel in both tanks must be interconnected, and vented outside. The vent line

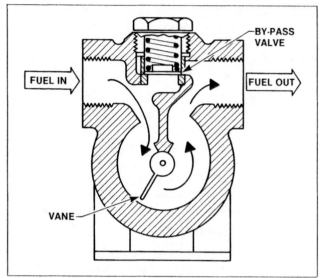

Figure 12-27. Typical fuel flowmeter transmitter for a larger piston-engine airplane. The vane which is moved by the fuel is connected to the rotor of an Autosyn transmitter. The indicator on the; flight engineer's panel shows the rate of fuel flow.

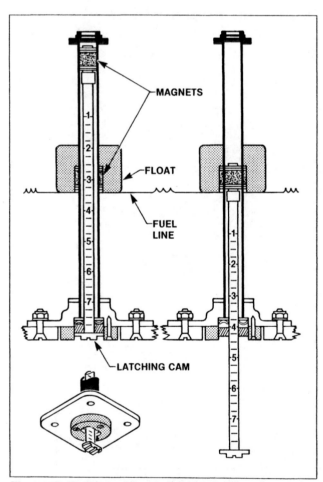

Figure 12-26. Under-wing fuel quantity indicating stick used to manually determine the quantity of fuel in a tank.

Figure 12-28. This fuel flow indicator shows not only the rate of flow, but also the amount of fuel and the time of fuel remaining.

normally terminates on the underside of the wing where the possibility of fuel siphoning is minimized.

After the fuel leaves the selector valve, it passes through the main strainer and on to the carburetor inlet. Fuel for the primer is taken from the main strainer.

b. Pump-feed Systems

Low-wing airplanes cannot use gravity to deliver fuel to the carburetor, and use a fuel system similar to that in figure 12-30. The selector valve used in these systems can normally select either tank individually, or shut off all flow to the engine. They do NOT have a "Both" position, because the pump would draw air from an empty tank rather than fuel from a full tank. After leaving the fuel selector valve, the fuel flows through the main strainer and into the electric fuel pump. If the engine-driven pump is in parallel with the electric pump, the fuel can be moved by either pump, and there is no need for a bypass feature to allow one pump to force fuel through the other. In order to assure that both pumps are functioning, the

fuel pressure produced by the electric pump should be noted before starting the engine. With the engine running and the electric pump off, the pressure indicated is that produced by the engine driven pump.

The electric pump is used to supply fuel pressure for starting the engine and as a backup in case the engine-driven pump fails and to assure fuel flow when switching from one tank to the other.

c. High-wing Airplane Using a Fuel Injection System

The fuel injection system requires an engine driven fuel pump. The system in figure 12-31 uses a Teledyne-Continental system that returns part of the fuel from the pump back to the fuel tank. This fuel may contain vapor that could block the system. By purging these vapors from the pump and returning them to the tank they cannot cause problems with the fuel metering device.

Fuel flows by gravity from the wing tanks through two feed lines, one at the front and one at the rear

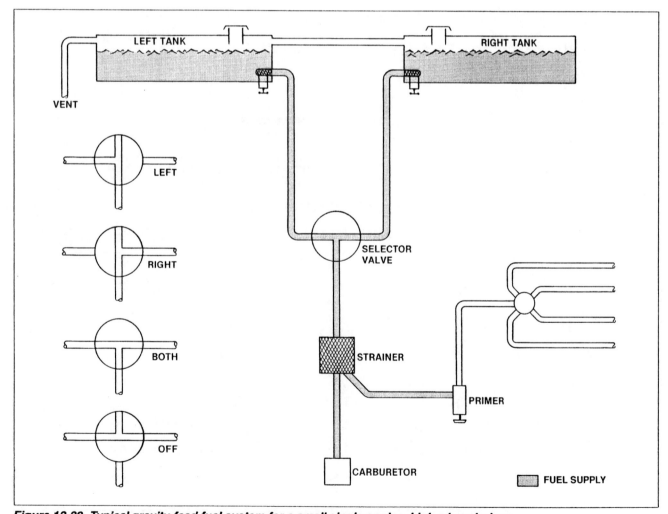

Figure 12-29. Typical gravity-feed fuel system for a small single-engine, high-wing airplane.

of the inboard end of each tank, into two small accumulator (reservoir) tanks, and from the bottom of these tanks to the selector valve.

The selector valve directs fuel from the desired reservoir tank to the engine, and at the same time directs the fuel vapor from the engine-driven pump back to the selected reservoir tank. This vapor then returns to the wing tank that supplies the reservoir tank.

The electric auxiliary fuel pump picks up the fuel at the discharge of the selector valve and forces it through the strainer and on to the inlet of the engine-driven fuel pump. From the engine driven fuel pump, the fuel flows to the fuel-air control unit where the fuel that is needed for engine operation goes to the cylinders, and all of the excess fuel returns to the inlet side of the pump. Some of the fuel that is taken into the engine driven pump has vapor in it, and this fuel is returned to the selector valve through the fuel return check valve.

2. Small Multi-Engine Aircraft Fuel Systems

The diagram in figure 12-32 shows a typical fuel system for a twin-engine airplane using an RSA fuel injection system. This fuel injection system does not return fuel to the tank like the system we have just discussed.

Each wing has two fuel tanks that are connected together and serve as a single tank, and the selector valves allow either engine to operate from the tanks in either wing. From the selector valve, the fuel flows to the fuel filter and then to the electric fuel pump, on to the engine-driven pump, into the fuel injection system, and to the cylinders.

The instrumentation for this system consists of the fuel quantity, fuel pressure, and fuel flow gauges. The fuel quantity gauges show the total amount of fuel in the two tanks in each wing. The two fuel pressure gauges show the pressure produced by the fuel pumps and is measured at the inlet of the fuel

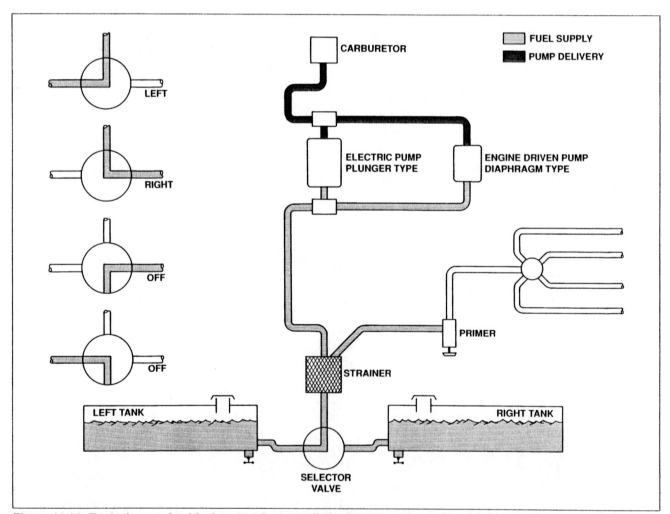

Figure 12-30. Typical pump-feed fuel system for a small single-engine, low-wing airplane.

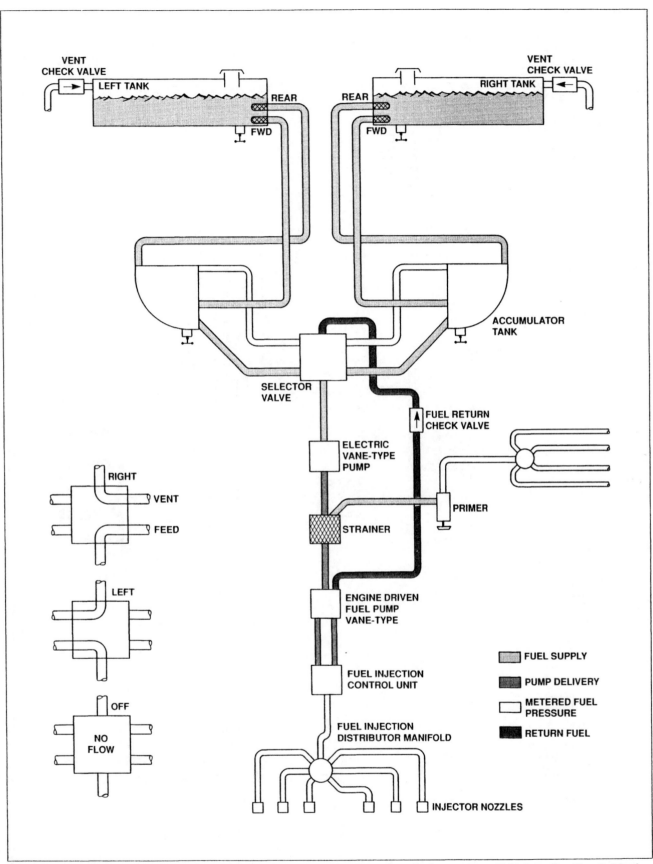

Figure 12-31. Typical fuel system for a high- performance, single-engine airplane using a Teledyne-Continental fuel injection system.

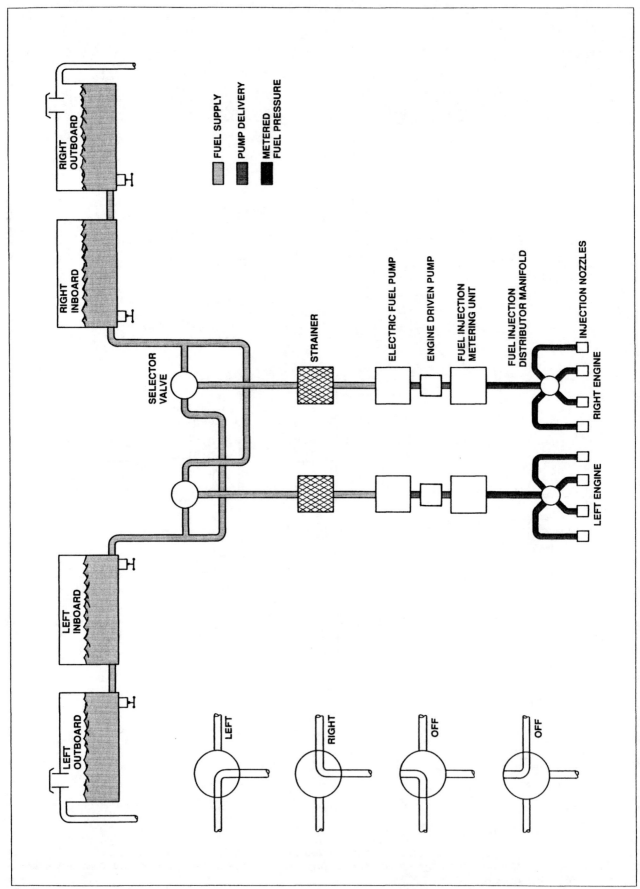

Figure 12-32. Typical fuel system for a twin-engine airplane using an RSA fuel injection system.

metering unit. The fuel flow indicator is a pressure gauge that reads the pressure drop across the fuel injector nozzles and is calibrated in either gallons per hour or in pounds per hour of fuel burned.

3. Large Reciprocating Aircraft Fuel Systems

Transport-category aircraft powered by reciprocating engines are rapidly disappearing from the active fleet. One exception seems to be the venerable Douglas DC-3. This aircraft has seen a working life of more than 50 years and is still being used for passenger and cargo applications. The fuel system installed on the DC-3 (figure 12-33) is typical for aircraft using large radial-type engines.

Fuel is supplied from two main tanks and two auxiliary tanks mounted in the center wing section of the airplane. The capacity of each main tanks is 202 gal., and the auxiliary tank hold 200 gal. each. Provisions are made for the installation of from two to eight long-range tanks, each holding 100 gal. This makes it possible to carry a fuel load of 1,604 gal. in a total of twelve tanks.

The fuel quantity is measured by the liquidometer system which consists of a float assembly and a liquidometer tank unit in each tank. These are connected electrically to the fuel gauge on the right instrument panel in the pilots' compartment. There are two tank selector valves, operated by dial and handle controls in the pilots' compartment. Ordinarily, the left hand engine draws fuel from the left tanks, and the right engine draws fuel from the right tanks, but, by using the selector valves, fuel may be supplied from any tank to either engine.

Two hand-operated wobble pumps are used to raise the fuel pressure when starting the engines, or before the engine-driven pumps are in operation. The fuel flows from the wobble pumps through lines to the strainers located in each nacelle, through the engine-driven pumps, and from there, under pressure, into the carburetors. A cross-feed line is connected on the pressure side of each engine-driven pump, and the two cross-feed valves in this line are operated by a single control in the pilots' compartment. The cross-feed system enables both engines to receive fuel from one engine-driven pump in case either pump fails.

On later model airplanes the wobble pumps are replaced by two electric booster pumps. Each fuel strainer is located in the center wing near each selector valve. The fuel, therefore, flows from the selector valves, through the strainers, through the booster pumps, through the engine driven fuel pumps into the carburetor. On airplanes equipped with electric booster pumps, there is no crossfeed system. The booster pumps will furnish ample pressure and supply for operation of the airplane in case either engine-driven pump fails.

A vapor overflow line connects from the top chamber of the carburetor to the main tanks, and a fuel line from the back of each carburetor operates the fuel pressure gauge in the pilots' compartment. This pressure gauge normally shows 14-16 lbs. pressure. On some airplanes, a pressure warning switch is installed in the fuel pressure gauge line. When the fuel pressure drops below 12 lbs., the switch illuminates a warning light on the instrument panel.

A restricted fitting on the fuel pressure gauge line connects to the oil-dilution solenoid. This unit releases fuel into the engine oil system and the propeller feathering oil, to aid in cold weather starting. Another solenoid valve in the fuel pressure gauge line releases fuel into the eight upper cylinders of the engines for priming.

Vent lines from each tank vent overboard, and a vapor line connects each main tank with its corresponding auxiliary tank.

4. Jet Transport Aircraft Fuel Systems

A large jet transport aircraft such as the Boeing 727 has a relatively simple fuel system that supplies its three engines from three fuel tanks.

Tanks No. 1 and No. 3 are integral tanks, that is, part of the wing is sealed off and fuel is carried in the wing structure itself. Each of these tanks holds about 12,000 lbs. of fuel. A fuselage tank consisting of either two or three bladder-type fuel cells holds another 30,000 lbs. of fuel.

Each of the wing tanks has two 115-volt AC electric boost pumps and the fuselage tank (tank No. 2) has four such pumps.

Each of the three engines may be fed directly from one of the three fuel tanks, or all of the tanks and engines may be opened into a cross-feed manifold.

Fueling is accomplished by connecting the fuel supply to a single-point fueling receptacle located under the leading edge of the right wing. Fuel flows from this receptacle through the fueling and dump manifold into all three tanks through the appropriate fueling valves. When the tanks are completely filled, pressure shutoff valves sense the amount of fuel and shut off the fueling valve. This prevents the tank being overfilled or damaged. If only a partial fuel load is required, the person fueling the aircraft can monitor a set of fuel quantity gauges at the fueling station and can shut off the flow of fuel to any tank when the desired level is reached.

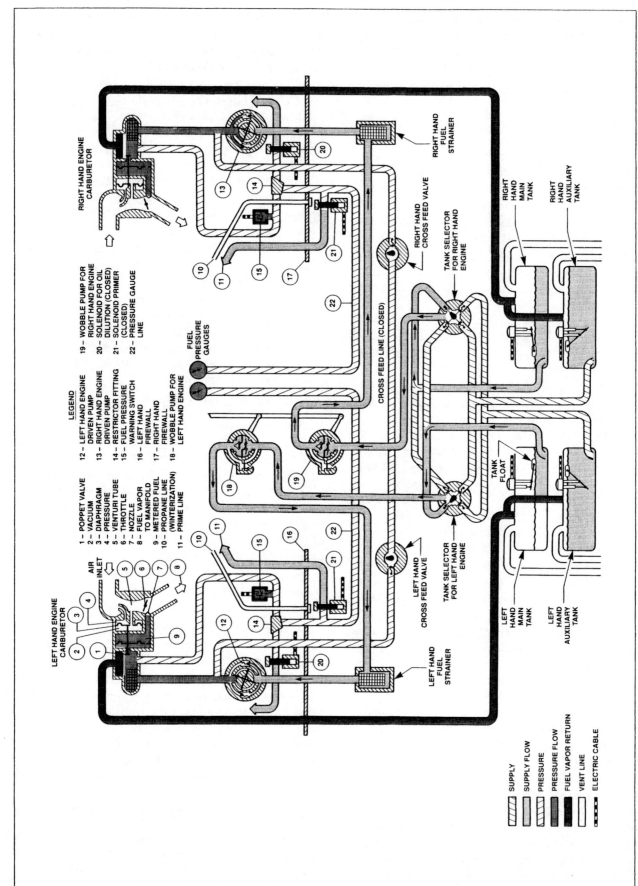

Figure 12-33. DC-3 fuel system schematic diagram.

LEGEND

1 – POPPET VALVE
2 – VACUUM
3 – DIAPHRAGM
4 – PRESSURE
5 – VENTURI TUBE
6 – THROTTLE
7 – NOZZLE
8 – FUEL VAPOR TO MANIFOLD
9 – METERED FUEL
10 – PROPANE LINE (WINTERIZATION)
11 – PRIME LINE
12 – LEFT HAND ENGINE DRIVEN PUMP
13 – RIGHT HAND ENGINE DRIVEN PUMP
14 – RESTRICTOR FITTING
15 – FUEL PRESSURE WARNING SWITCH
16 – LEFT HAND FIREWALL
17 – RIGHT HAND FIREWALL
18 – WOBBLE PUMP FOR LEFT HAND ENGINE
19 – WOBBLE PUMP FOR RIGHT HAND ENGINE
20 – SOLENOID FOR OIL DILUTION (CLOSED)
21 – SOLENOID PRIMER (CLOSED)
22 – PRESSURE GAUGE LINE

SUPPLY
SUPPLY FLOW
PRESSURE
PRESSURE FLOW
FUEL VAPOR RETURN
VENT LINE
ELECTRIC CABLE

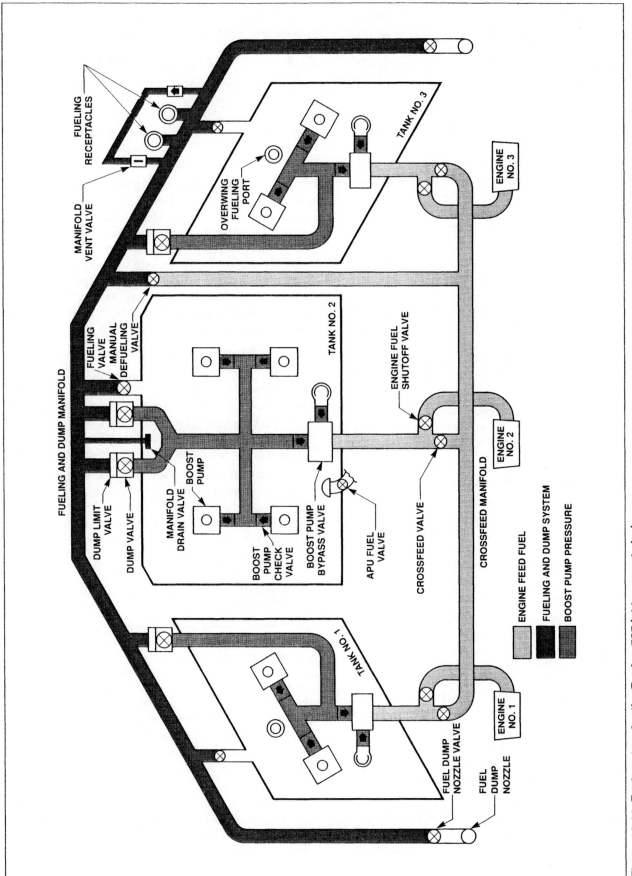

Figure 12-34. Fuel system for the Boeing 727 jet transport airplane.

213

The airplane tanks may be defueled by connecting the fuel receiving truck to the manual defueling valve, closing the engine shutoff valves, and opening the cross-feed valve from the tank to be emptied. The fuel may be either pumped out of the tank with the boost pumps, or it may be pulled from the tank by suction from the receiving truck. If it is pulled out by suction, it leaves the tank through the boost pump bypass valve.

Fuel may be dumped in-flight by opening the fuel dump valve for the tanks to be dumped and then opening the fuel dump nozzle valve in the wing tip through which the fuel is to leave the airplane. Fuel can be dumped from either wing tip or from both tips at the same time.

There is a fuel dump limit valve in each of the three systems that will shut off the flow if the pressure drops below that needed to supply the engine with adequate fuel. It will also shut off the dump valve when the level in the tank gets down to the preset dump shutoff level. This dump system is capable of dumping about 2,300 lbs. of fuel per minute when all of the dump valves are open and all of the boost pumps are operating.

This fuel system has provisions for heating the fuel before it enters the fuel filter if its temperature is low enough for there to be danger of ice forming on the filter.

5. Helicopter Fuel Systems

Figure 12-35 illustrates a typical fuel system found in a light turbine powered helicopter. This system incorporates a single bladder type fuel cell, located below and aft of the rear passenger seat. Installed in the fuel cell are two submersible centrifugal-type boost pumps, an upper and lower fuel quantity indicating probe, and a solenoid operated sump drain.

The boost pumps are connected so that their outlet ports join to form a single line to the engine. Either pump is capable of supplying sufficient fuel to operate the engine. Check valves are installed at the outlet of each pump, and a pressure switch located in the outlet port of each pump will illuminate the FUEL BOOST CAUTION LIGHT in case of a pump failure.

An electrically operated shut-off valve is installed in the fuel line running from the tank to the engine. A fuel selector valve is not necessary because only one tank is used in this system.

Fuel is filtered twice before entering the engine, and each filter is equipped with a warning light to indicate filter clogging. Additional provisions are

made in the system for a fuel pressure gauge, vent system and a fuel quantity indication.

E. Fuel System Servicing

Everyone concerned with the handling and dispensing of aviation fuels should realize that the safety of an aircraft may depend upon their skill, knowledge and ability to deliver the correct grade of clean dry fuel into the aircraft. It is one of the prime factors contributing to flight safety.

Fuels, fueling methods, and equipment are continually being developed and improved to meet the ever-increasing demands of modern aircraft and the aviation industry. However, one thing never changes — the vital importance of supplying the correct grade of uncontaminated fuel to the aircraft. The possibility of human error can never be eliminated, but it can be minimized through careful design of fueling facilities, good operating procedure, and adequate training of personnel.

1. Checking for Fuel System Contaminants

Draining a sample of fuel from the main strainers of an aircraft has, in the past, been considered an acceptable method of assuring that the fuel in the system is clean. This practice is, in most cases, no longer considered adequate.

Quality control of aviation fuel has always been of particular concern, since the failure of an aircraft powerplant during flight can be disastrous. Despite this, effective equipment and techniques for handling aviation gasoline have been relatively simple. The introduction of turbine-powered aircraft has made the need for fuel cleanliness much more important, and at the same time more difficult to maintain.

The combustion process in the jet engine is one which must be carefully controlled. This requires complicated precision fuel control systems which are much more sensitive to fuel quality, and in particular, cleanliness, than those for piston engines. Besides this, the quantity of fuel which passes through these systems for each hour of flight is considerably greater than with the piston engines; hence, any slight contamination in the fuel accumulates at a much faster rate.

Along with the introduction of the more critical jet engine has come the utilization of a fuel which is harder to keep free of contamination. For example, a particle of dirt or rust, or a drop of water, settles out of aviation gasoline four times faster than it does in turbine fuels.

To better understand what is required to maintain fuel quality, it is first necessary to have a basic knowledge of aviation fuels, the common forms of fuel contaminants, how they get into the fuel, and how they can be detected and removed.

a. Types of Contaminants

The more common forms of aviation fuel contaminants are solids, water, surfactants, micro-organisms, and miscellaneous ones including the intermixing of grades or types of fuel. Surfactants

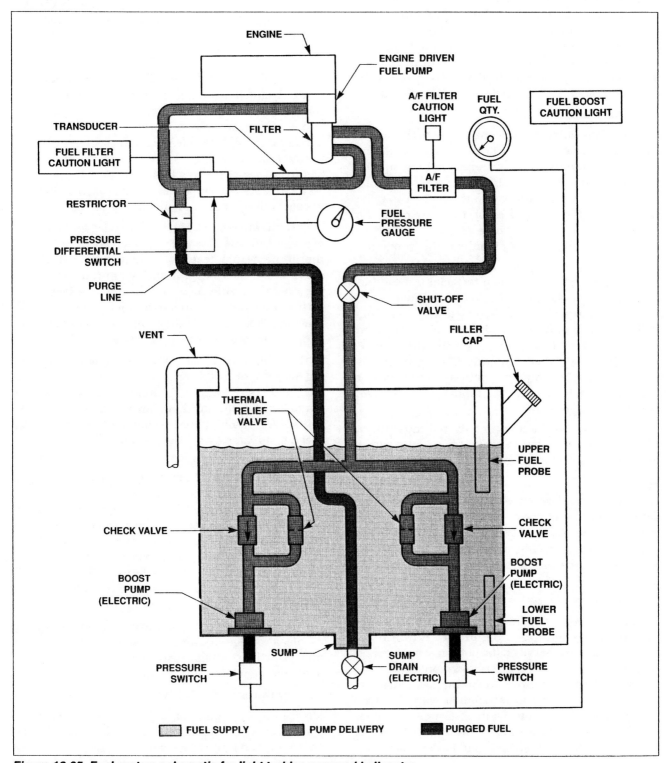

Figure 12-35. Fuel system schematic for light turbine powered helicopter.

and micro-organisms, contaminants which are virtually unknown in aviation gasolines, have become critical with the advent of turbine fuels.

(1) Solid Particles

Solid contaminants may be thought of as being those which will not dissolve in fuel. Most common are iron rust and scale, sand, and dirt. Also included, however, are such items as metal particles, dust, lint, particles of filter media, rubber, valve lubricants and even sludge produced by bacterial action. Solid contaminants can be collected by the fuel at every stage of its movement from the refinery to the aircraft.

(2) Surfactants

The term "surfactants" is a contraction of the words SURFace ACTive AgeNTS. These are soap or detergent like materials that occur naturally in fuel or may be introduced by refining processes, by inclusion of certain additives into the fuel, or may be washed off internal surfaces by the passing of the fuel through pipelines or by storage in a tank or vessel which had previously handled other products.

Surfactants are usually more soluble in water than in fuel and reduce the interfacial tension between water and fuel, thereby stabilizing suspended water droplets and contaminants in the fuel. This ability to suspend water and dirt in fuel may disarm filter/separator action and permit these contaminants to get into the aircraft. This property has resulted in surfactants becoming one of the major contaminants in aviation turbine fuels, and can cause fuel gauge problems.

Surfactants, in large concentrated quantities, usually appear as a tan to dark brown liquid with a sudsy-like water/fuel interface.

(3) Water

Although it has always been present in aviation fuel, water is now considered to be a major source of contamination. The ability of turbine fuel to entrain water, and the possibility of ice crystals interrupting fuel flow makes water in the fuel a major hazard to flight safety.

(4) Micro-organisms

There are over 100 different species of micro-organisms which can live in the free water which accumulates in sumps and on the bottom of storage and aircraft tanks. Many of these micro-organisms are airborne, while others are found in the soil. Thus, fuel is constantly exposed to inoculation with this type contaminant. The conditions most favorable to their growth are warm temperatures and the presence of iron oxides (rust) and mineral salts in the water.

The principle effects of micro-organisms are: formation of a sludge or slime which can foul filter/separators and aircraft fueling mechanisms; emulsification of the fuel; creation of corrosive compounds and offensive odors. Severe corrosion of aircraft tanks has been attributed to micro-organisms and considerable expense has been incurred removing microbial growths and repairing or replacing corroded aluminum panels in wing tanks.

b. Detection of Contaminants

Because solid contaminants generally appear in relatively small numbers and sizes in relation to the volume of fuel, their detection can be difficult. Aviation gasoline is generally considered "clean" if a one-quart sample is clear of any sediment when viewed in a clean and dry glass container. It may be helpful to swirl the container so that a vortex is created. The solid contaminants, if present, will tend to collect at the bottom beneath the vortex.

Turbine fuels must of necessity be several orders of magnitude cleaner than aviation gasoline. While the above visual test is adequate for operational checks, it is necessary, from time to time, to check the operation efficiency and cleanliness level of a turbine fuel system with a tool which is more critical than a clear bottle. The aviation industry has adopted the Millipore test for this purpose.

The Millipore is a filter-type test capable of detecting microscopic solid contaminants down to 0.8 of a micron in size, which is approximately $1/120$ the diameter of a human hair. An evaluation guide is provided, containing the instructions for conducting these tests, along with the means of evaluating the results.

The "white bucket" test is particularly helpful in detecting the presence of concentrations of surfactants in turbine fuel. All that is required is a clean white porcelain bucket and water which has been in contact with the fuel in tank bottoms, filter/separators or other points where surfactants are likely to accumulate. Surfactants, if present, will appear as a brown sudsy water layer on the bottom of the bucket or at the fuel-water interface.

Evidence of microbial growth or debris may appear as black sludge or slime, or even a vegetative-like mat growth. Growths also appear as dark brown spots on some filter/separator socks.

c. Contamination Control

Miscellaneous contaminants can include either soluble or insoluble materials or both. Fuel can be contaminated by mixing it with other grades or types of fuels, by picking up compounds from concentrations in rust and sludge deposits, by additives, or by any other of a number of soluble materials.

The greatest single danger to aircraft safety from contaminated fuels cannot be attributed to solids, exotic micro-organisms, surfactants, or even water. It is contamination resulting from human error. It is the placing of the wrong grade or type of fuel into an aircraft, the mixing of grades, or any other type of human error that allows off specification fuels to be placed aboard the aircraft.

Any fuel which is suspected to be off-specification because of contaminants or mixing with other fuels, should not be placed aboard an aircraft. If in doubt, immediately arrange for laboratory and other tests to definitely establish whether the fuel may be used for aviation purposes.

2. Fire Hazards when Fueling or Defueling

Aviation fuels are both highly flammable and volatile, and special care must be exercised when transferring them into or out of an aircraft. Be sure that the proper type of fire extinguisher is available at the aircraft and that it has been properly serviced and has not been used, even partially, since it was last serviced.

Never service an aircraft with fuel inside a hangar or in any other closed area. If fuel is stored in containers other than the fuel service truck or the aircraft fuel tanks, be sure that the containers are closed, not only to prevent the entry of contaminants, but also to prevent the release of fuel vapors.

In any fuel is spilled, wipe it up immediately. If too much has been spilled to wipe up, use an approved procedure and materials for dealing with fuel spills. There are new absorbent materials available to contain and clean up hazardous materials.

Matches, cigarette lighters, smoking, open flames, and even backfires from malfunctioning vehicles are obvious sources of ignition that need no further mention. One source of ignition, however, is not so visible or obvious. It is the sparks created by static electricity.

Static electrical charges are generated in various degrees whenever one body passes through or against another. A greater generation of static electricity may be expected when handling turbine fuels than when handling aviation gasoline. A basic reason for this is related to the higher viscosity of this class fuel. The high-speed fueling rates and the flow through the ultrafine filter/separators required can create extremely high static electrical charges.

To minimize this hazard, it is necessary to "bleed off" static electrical charges before they build up to a high enough potential to create a static spark. This can be accomplished by bonding and grounding all components of the fueling system together with static wires and allowing sufficient time for the charge to dissipate before performing any act which may draw a spark. The bleeding off of an electrical charge is not always an instantaneous act as is commonly believed. It may take several seconds to bleed off all the charge from some fuels.

3. Fueling Procedures

From time to time the aircraft mechanic may be called upon to fuel or defuel aircraft or, because of their expertise, to assist in the training of ground service personnel. The steps outlined below represent general procedures which should be carried out when fueling any aircraft (specific instructions from the pilot may at times supersede these instructions; however, they will generally only supplement them):

1. Make sure of the grade and quantity required.
2. Make sure the fueler or system contains the correct grade and quantity required.
3. Check the fueler tank sumps for water before fueling. Drain if necessary.
4. Approach the aircraft carefully. Try to position the fueler so that it can be quickly driven or pulled away in case of emergency. Avoid backing up to the aircraft; if absolutely necessary, have someone guide you from a position near the rear of the fueler. Set the brake.
5. Bond and ground the aircraft and equipment in the proper sequence: fueler to ground, then fueler to aircraft. Before opening aircraft overwing fuel filler cap, connect the nozzle ground to the aircraft. Keep a constant contact between an overwing nozzle and the filler neck spout while filling. Grounding of underwing nozzles is not required. After fueling, reverse the steps above.
6. Do not drag hoses across deicer boots or edge of wings. Drop-deck ladders should always be placed so that the pads rest squarely on the leading edge of the wings. When on the wings, walk only where designated. Clean off all greasy marks and dirt before leaving the wing.
7. Nozzles should never be propped open while fueling aircraft or otherwise left unattended. Nozzles must never be dropped or dragged across the pavement. Nozzle dust caps should be replaced immediately after fueling.
8. Leaving a filler cap off an aircraft fuel tank can be very dangerous. Never open a cap until you

are actually ready to fuel that specific tank, then lock it and close the flap immediately after fueling. Before leaving the wing, recheck each filler cap. Notify maintenance or the pilot if filler cap or flap is not working properly.

9. Check the fueler or other fueling equipment filter/separator sumps for water after fueling is complete. If more than a trace of water or other contaminants are found, the pilot should be notified and arrangements made to sample the fuel in the aircraft tanks.

10. Never pull away from an aircraft without first checking to make sure that there is no one left on the top deck and that all hoses and ground wires are properly stowed.

4. Defueling

At times, it is necessary to remove fuel from an aircraft to adjust it for changes in loading or flight plan, or to permit certain repair or overhaul operations. Normally, this will be accomplished by withdrawing fuel from the aircraft tank into a fueler. If only a small quantity is off-loaded, such as due to load changes, and there is no reason to suspect contamination, the fuel may be taken back into stock. If there is any reason to suspect the quality of the off-loaded fuel, such as a large amount defueled following an engine failure, it should be segregated, preferably held in a fueler, and quarantined until its quality is assured.

In no event should suspected fuel be returned to storage or placed aboard another aircraft. If acceptable fuel is returned to storage, make sure it is taken back into a tank containing the same grade of fuel, and that complete quality control procedures are followed — exactly as if it were a transport truck delivery.

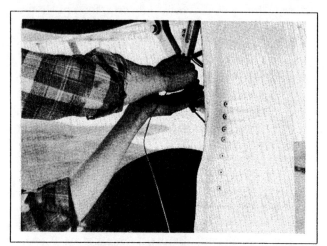

Figure 12-36. Before opening a fuel tank cap or connecting the fuel hose, be sure the aircraft and the fuel truck are connected together with an electrical bonding cable.

Figure 12-37. An aircraft fuel tank being fueled at its filler neck. This is called over-wing fueling.

Chapter XIII

Propellers

A. Basic Propeller Principles

Throughout the development of controlled flight every aircraft required some kind of device to convert engine power into thrust. With few exceptions, nearly all of the early aircraft designs used propellers to create this thrust.

By the time the Wright brothers began their first powered flights, propeller design had evolved into the standard 2-bladed style similar in appearance to those used on today's light aircraft.

As aircraft designs improved, propellers were developed which used thinner airfoil sections and had greater strength. Because of its structural strength, the aluminum alloy propeller came into wide usage. The advantage of being able to change the propeller blade angle in flight led to wide acceptance of the 2-position propeller and, later, the constant-speed propeller system.

The Federal Aviation Administration has furnished guidelines regarding propeller system design, and the maintenance required for propeller systems.

FAR Part 23, "Airworthiness Standards: Normal, Utility, and Acrobatic Aircraft", and FAR Part 25, "Airworthiness Standards, Transport Category Aircraft", outline the requirements for propellers and their control systems for aircraft certification. Part 43 of the FARs defines the different classes of maintenance for the propeller system and the minimum requirements for 100-hour and annual inspections.

1. Nomenclature

Before any discussion about propellers, it is necessary to define some basic terms to avoid confusion and misunderstanding.

A *propeller* is a rotating airfoil that consists of two or more blades attached to a central hub which is mounted on the engine crankshaft. The function of the propeller is to convert engine horsepower to useful thrust. Propeller blades have a leading edge, trailing edge, a tip, a shank, a face, and a back as shown in figures 13-1 and 13-2.

Blade angle is the angle between the propeller's plane of rotation, and the chord line of the propeller airfoil.

Blade station is a reference position on a blade that is a specified distance from the center of the hub.

Pitch is the distance, in inches, that a propeller section will move forward in one revolution.

Pitch distribution is the gradual twist in the propeller blade from shank to tip.

2. Propeller Theory

As a propeller rotates, it produces lift and causes an aircraft to move forward. The amount of lift produced depends on variables such as engine RPM, propeller airfoil shape, and aircraft speed.

a. Propeller Lift and Angle of Attack

Because a propeller blade is a rotating airfoil, it produces lift by aerodynamic action and pulls an aircraft forward. The amount of lift produced depends on the airfoil shape, RPM, and angle of attack of the propeller blade sections. Before discussing ways of varying the amount of lift produced by a propeller blade, we must understand some of the propeller design characteristics.

Starting from the centerline of the hub of a propeller, each blade can be marked off in 1 in. segments known as blade stations. If the blade angle is measured at each of these stations, the blade

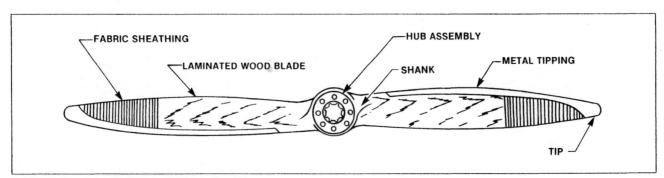

Figure 13-1. Typical wood aircraft propeller.

angle nearest the center of the propeller will be highest, with the blade angle decreasing toward the tip. This decrease in blade angle from the hub to the tip is called pitch distribution. A cross section of each blade station will show that low-speed airfoils are used near the hub and high speed airfoils toward the tip. The pitch distribution and the change in airfoil shape along the length of the blade are necessary, because each section moves through the air at a different velocity, with the slowest speeds near the hub and the highest speeds near the tip.

To illustrate the difference in the speed of airfoil sections at a fixed RPM, consider the three blade stations indicated on the propeller seen in figure 13-5. If the propeller is rotating at 1800 RPM, the 18″ station will travel 9.42 ft./revolution (192.7 MPH), while the 36″ station will travel 18.84 ft./revolution or 385.4 MPH. And the 48″ station will move 25.13 ft/revolution or 514 MPH. The airfoil that gives the best lift at 193 MPH is inefficient at 514 MPH. Thus, the airfoil is changed gradually throughout the length of the blade as we see in figure 13-4.

A look at one blade section will illustrate how the angle of attack on the blade of a fixed-pitch propeller changes with different flight conditions. The angle of attack is the angle between the airfoil chord line and the relative wind, and the direction of the relative wind is the resultant of the combined velocities of rotational speed (RPM) and airspeed.

If the aircraft is stationary with no wind flowing past it, and the engine is turning at 1,200 RPM, the propeller blade angle of 20° at the 20″ station will have an angle of attack of 20°. This is because the direction of the relative wind is opposite to the movement of the propeller.

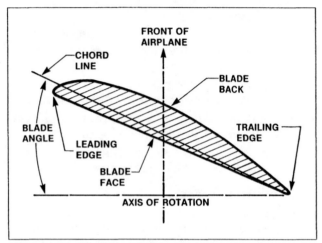

Figure 13-2. Typical airfoil section of a propeller.

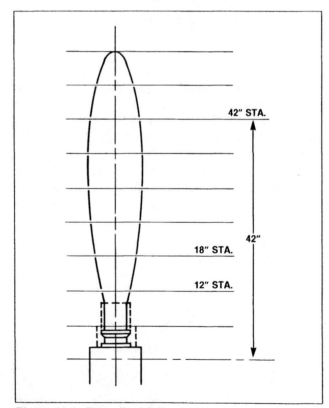

Figure 13-3. Propeller blade stations.

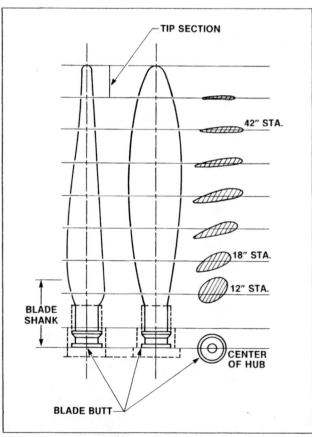

Figure 13-4. Pitch distribution in a typical aircraft propeller.

When this airplane is moving forward at 50 MPH, the relative wind now causes an angle of attack of 0.8°.

If we increase the propeller speed to 1,500 RPM, the relative wind will cause the angle of attack to be 4.4°.

The most effective angle of attack is between 2-4°, and any angle above 15° is ineffective because of the possibility of a stall. Fixed-pitch propellers may be selected to give this 2-4° angle of attack at either climb or cruise airspeeds and RPM, depending upon the desired flight characteristics.

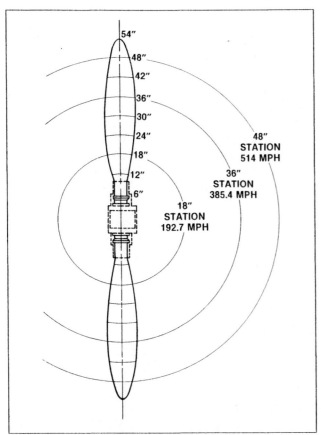

Figure 13-5. Comparative velocities at three blade stations of a typical propeller.

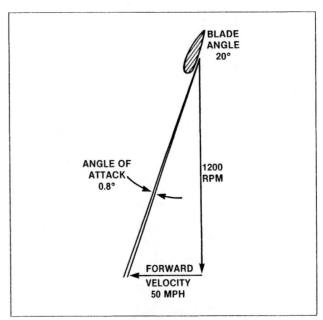

Figure 13-7. As the forward velocity of the aircraft increases, the angle of attack of the propeller blade decreases.

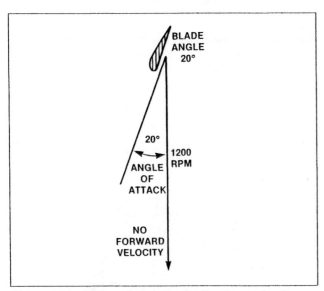

Figure 13-6. With no forward velocity, the angle of attack of a propeller blade is the same as the blade angle.

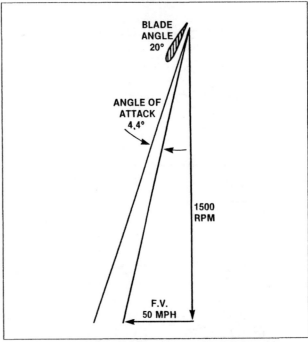

Figure 13-8. As the engine RPM increases for a given forward velocity, the angle of attack increases.

221

b. Forces Acting on the Propeller

When a propeller rotates, many forces interact and cause tension, twisting, and bending stresses within the propeller.

(1) Centrifugal Force

The force which causes the greatest stress on a propeller is centrifugal force. Centrifugal force can best be described as the force which tries to pull the blades out of the hub. The amount of stress created by centrifugal force may be far greater than the weight of the propeller blade.

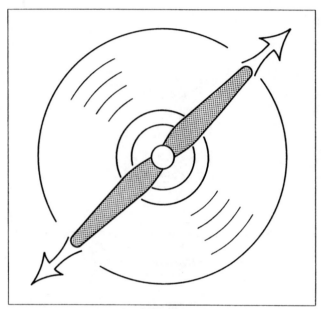

Figure 13-9. Centrifugal force tries to pull the propeller blades out of the hub.

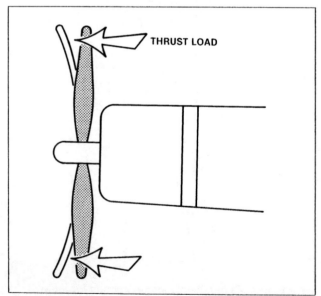

Figure 13-10. Thrust bending forces try to bend the propeller blade tips forward.

(2) Thrust Bending Force

Thrust bending force tends to bend the propeller blades forward at the tips. Lift toward the tip of the blade flexes the thin blade sections forward. Thrust bending force opposes centrifugal force to some degree.

(3) Torque Bending Force

Torque bending forces tend to bend the propeller blade back in the direction opposite the direction of rotation.

(4) Aerodynamic Twisting Moment

Aerodynamic twisting moment tends to twist a blade to a higher angle. This force is produced because the axis of rotation of the blade is at the midpoint of the chord line, while the center of the lift of the blade is forward of this axis. This force tries to increase the blade angle. Aerodynamic twisting moment is used in some designs to help feather the propeller.

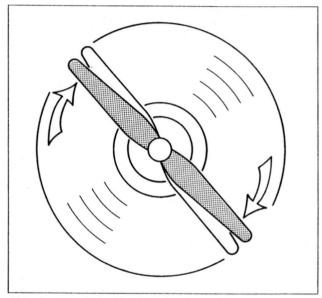

Figure 13-11. Torque bending forces try to bend the blade in the plane of rotation opposite the direction of rotation.

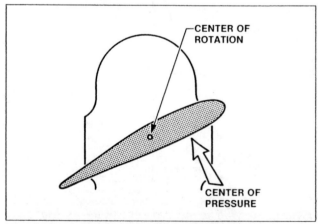

Figure 13-12. The aerodynamic twisting moment tries to increase the blade angle.

222

(5) Centrifugal Twisting Moment

Centrifugal twisting moment tends to decrease the blade angle, and opposes aerodynamic twisting moment. This tendency to decrease the blade angle is produced since all parts of a rotating propeller try to move in the same plane of rotation as the blade centerline. This force is greater than the aerodynamic twisting moment and is used in some designs to decrease the blade angle.

(6) Vibrational Force and Critical Range

When a propeller produces thrust, aerodynamic and mechanical forces are present which cause the blade to vibrate. If this is not compensated for in the design, this vibration may cause excessive flexing and work-hardening of the metal and may even result in sections of the propeller blade breaking off in flight.

Aerodynamic forces cause vibrations at the tip of a blade where the effects of transonic speeds cause buffeting and vibration.

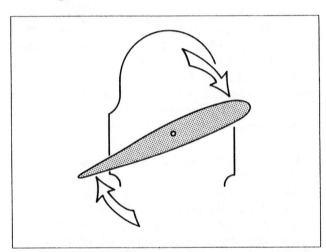

Figure 13-13. The centrifugal twisting moment tries to decrease the blade angle.

Mechanical vibrations are caused by the power pulses in a piston engine and are considered to be more destructive in their effect than aerodynamic vibration. These power pulses cause a propeller blade to vibrate and set up standing wave patterns that cause metal fatigue and failure. The location and number of stress points change with different RPM settings, but the most critical location for these stress concentrations is about 6″ in from the tip of the blade.

Most airframe-engine-propeller combinations have eliminated the detrimental effects of vibrational stresses, but some combinations are sensitive to certain engine speeds. This critical range is indicated on the tachometer by a red arc. The engine should not be operated in the critical range except as necessary to pass through it to a higher or lower RPM. If the engine is operated in the critical range, there is a possibility of structural failure because of vibrational stresses.

c. Propeller Pitch

The *geometric pitch* of a propeller is defined as the distance, in inches, that a propeller will move forward in one revolution, and is based on the propeller blade angle at the 75% blade station. Geometric pitch is theoretical because it does not take into account any losses due to inefficiency.

Effective pitch is the distance the aircraft actually moves forward in one revolution of the propeller. It may vary from zero, when the aircraft is stationary on the ground, to about 90% of the geometric pitch during the most efficient flight conditions.

The difference between geometric pitch and effective pitch is called *slip*.

If a propeller has a pitch of 50″, in theory, it should move forward 50″ in one revolution. But, if the

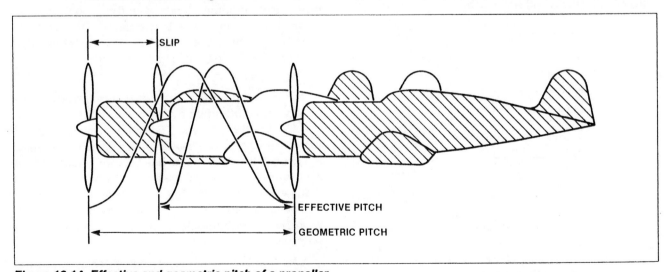

Figure 13-14. Effective and geometric pitch of a propeller.

aircraft actually moves forward only 35" in one revolution, the effective pitch is 35" and the propeller is 70% efficient.

3. Types of Propellers

There are various types or classes of propellers, the simplest of which are the fixed-pitch and ground-adjustable propellers. The complexity of propeller systems increases from these simpler types to the feathering and reversing propeller systems used on turboprop aircraft. The brief descriptions presented here are only to acquaint you with the basic types. No attempt has been made to include all propeller systems that may be encountered.

a. Fixed Pitch

Fixed-pitch propellers are simple propellers whose blade angle cannot be changed in normal operation. They are usually made of wood or aluminum alloy and are usually found on light, single-engine airplanes.

Fixed-pitch propellers are designed for best efficiency at one rotational and forward speed. They are designed to fit a set of conditions of both airplane and engine speeds. Any change in these conditions will reduced the efficiency of both the propeller and the engine.

b. Ground Adjustable

Ground-adjustable propellers are similar to fixed-pitch propellers in that their blade angles cannot be changed in flight, but the propeller is made so that the blade angles can be changed on the ground. The pitch, or blade angle, can be adjusted to give the desired flight characteristics, that is, low blade angle if the airplane is used for operation from short airstrips or high blade angle if high-speed cruise flight is of most importance. This type of propeller was widely used on aircraft built between the 1920s and the 1940s.

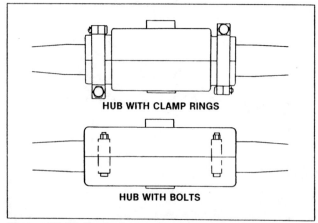

HUB WITH CLAMP RINGS

HUB WITH BOLTS

Figure 13-15. Typical propeller hubs for ground adjustable propellers.

A ground-adjustable propeller is designed so that its blades can be rotated in the hub to change the blade angles. The hub is made in two halves that must be separated slightly to loosen the blades so they can be rotated. And the hub is held together with clamps or bolts to prevent the blades from rotating during operation.

The propeller blades may be of wood, aluminum, or steel with shoulders machined on to the root to hold the blades in the hub against the centrifugal operating loads.

The hub of the propeller is made of aluminum or steel, with the two halves machined as a matching pair. Grooves in the hub mate with the shoulders on the blades. When steel blades are used, the hub is usually held together with bolts. When wood or aluminum alloy blades are used, the hub halves are held together with bolts or clamp rings.

c. Controllable Pitch

The *controllable pitch propeller* permits a change in blade pitch, while the propeller is rotating. This permits the propeller to assume a blade angle that will give the best performance for the particular flight conditions. The number of pitch positions may be limited, as with a 2-position controllable propeller; or the pitch may be adjusted to any angle between the minimum and maximum pitch settings of a given propeller.

The use of a controllable pitch propeller makes it possible to attain the desired engine RPM for a particular flight condition. As an airfoil is moved through the air, it produces two forces, lift and drag. Increasing propeller blade angle increases the angle of attack and produces more lift and drag; this action increases the horsepower required to turn the propeller at a given RPM. Since the engine is still producing the same horsepower, the propeller slows down. If the blade angle is decreased, the propeller speeds up. Thus, the engine RPM can be controlled by increasing or decreasing blade angle.

d. Automatic

In automatic propeller systems, the control adjusts pitch without attention by the operator, to maintain a specific preset engine RPM. For example, if engine speed increases, the controls automatically increase blade angle until the desired RPM has been re-established. A good automatic control system will respond to such small variations of RPM that, for all practical purposes, a constant RPM will be maintained. Automatic propellers are usually termed *constant speed propellers*.

Additional refinements, such as pitch reversal and feathering features, are included on some propeller systems to improve still further their operational characteristics.

e. Reverse-pitch

Reversing propeller systems are refinements of the constant-speed feathering systems. The propeller blades can be rotated to a negative angle to produce reverse thrust. This forces air forward instead of backwards, and permits a shorter landing roll and improved ground maneuvering.

f. Feathering Propellers

Multi-engine aircraft are equipped with *feathering propellers*. These are constant-speed propeller systems which also have the capability of being feathered. When a propeller is feathered, its blades are rotated so they present their leading edge to the wind, eliminating the drag associated with a windmilling propeller. Feathering propellers must be used on multi-engine aircraft to reduce propeller drag during engine out operations.

4. Classifications of Propellers

a. Tractor

Tractor propellers are those mounted on the upstream end of a drive shaft in front of the supporting structure. Most aircraft are equipped with this type of propeller. A major advantage of the tractor prop is that lower stresses are induced in the propeller as it rotates in relatively undisturbed air.

b. Pusher

Pusher propellers are those mounted on the downstream end of a drive shaft behind the supporting structure. As with tractor-type installations, pusher props may be constructed as either fixed- or variable-pitch propellers. Seaplanes and amphibious aircraft have used pusher propellers more than other types of aircraft.

On land planes, where propeller-to-ground clearance usually is less than propeller-to-water clearance of seaplanes, pusher propellers are subject to more damage than tractor propellers. Rocks, gravel, and small objects, dislodged by wheels, quite often may be thrown or drawn into a pusher propeller. Similarly, planes with pusher propellers are apt to encounter prop damage from water spray thrown up by the hull during landing or takeoff from water. Consequently, the pusher propeller quite often is mounted above and behind the wings to prevent such damage.

B. Propellers Used on Light Aircraft

Light aircraft may use either fixed-pitch or constant speed propellers, with design and materials depending upon the age of the aircraft, and its normal operating speed range.

1. Fixed Pitch

Fixed pitch propellers are found on small training and utility type aircraft, and may be either of wooden construction on older aircraft, or aluminum on the newer planes.

a. Wooden

Wooden propellers are often found on older single-engine airplanes. Most have a natural wood finish, although some may be found having a black or gray plastic coating. These coated blades are referred to as "armor coated".

These propellers are made of several layers of wood bonded together with a waterproof resin glue. Except for very few instances, they are nowadays made of birch. Each layer of a propeller is normally of the same thickness and type of wood, with a minimum of five layers of wood being used. When the planks of wood are glued together, they form what is called a propeller blank.

During fabrication, the blank is roughed to shape and is allowed to set for a week or so to allow the moisture to be distributed equally through all of the layers.

The white, as the rough-shaped blank is called, is finished to the exact airfoil and pitch dimensions required for the desired performance characteristics, and during this process, the center bore and bolt holes are drilled.

At this stage of its manufacture, the tip fabric, if used, is applied to the propeller. Cotton fabric is glued to the last 12-15″ of the propeller blade, where it reinforces the thin sections of the tip. The fabric is doped to prevent deterioration by weather and by the rays of the sun. The propeller is then finished with clear varnish to protect the wood surface.

Monel, brass, or stainless steel tipping is applied to the leading edge of the propeller to prevent damage from small stones during ground operations. The metal is shaped to the leading edge contour and is attached to the blade with countersunk screws in the thick blade sections and with copper rivets in the thin sections near the tip. The screws and rivets are safetied into place with solder.

Three No. 60 holes are drilled 3/16″ deep into the tip of each blade to release moisture from the propeller and allow the wood to breathe.

Wooden blades for controllable-pitch propellers are constructed in the same manner as fixed-pitch propellers, except that the shank of the blade is held in a metal sleeve with lag screws.

b. Aluminum Alloy

Aluminum propellers are the most widely used type of propellers in aviation. They are more desirable than wood propellers because thinner, more efficient airfoils may be used without sacrificing structural strength. Better engine cooling is also achieved by carrying the airfoil sections close to the hub and directing more air over the engine. These propellers require much less maintenance than wood propellers, thereby reducing the operating cost.

High strength aluminum alloy forgings are used in the manufacture of propellers, and they are finished to the desired airfoil shape by machine and manual grinding. The final pitch is set by twisting the blades to the desired angles. As the propeller is being finished by grinding, its balance is checked and adjusted by removing metal from the tip of the blade to adjust horizontal balance and from the boss or leading and trailing edges of the blades to adjust vertical balance. Some propeller designs have their horizontal balance adjusted by placing lead wool in balance holes near the boss, and their vertical balance corrected by attaching balance weights to the side of the boss.

Once the propeller is ground to the desired contours and the balance is adjusted, the surfaces are finished by anodizing and painting.

Two propeller designation systems are discussed here so the technician will be able to recognize the systems and understand the difference in propeller designs by their designation. The McCauley and Sensenich systems are representative of those presently in use.

(1) McCauley Designation System

A McCauley propeller designated as 1B90/CM7246 has a basic design designation of 1B90. The CM component of the designation indicates the type of crankshaft the propeller will fit, its blade tip contour, and the adapter used, and provides other information pertaining to a specific aircraft installation. The "72" indicates the diameter of the propeller in inches, and the "46" indicates the pitch of the propeller at the 75% station.

(2) Sensenich Designation System

The Sensenich designation 76DM6S5-2-54 indicates a propeller with a designed diameter of 76". The "D" designates the blade design, and the "M6"

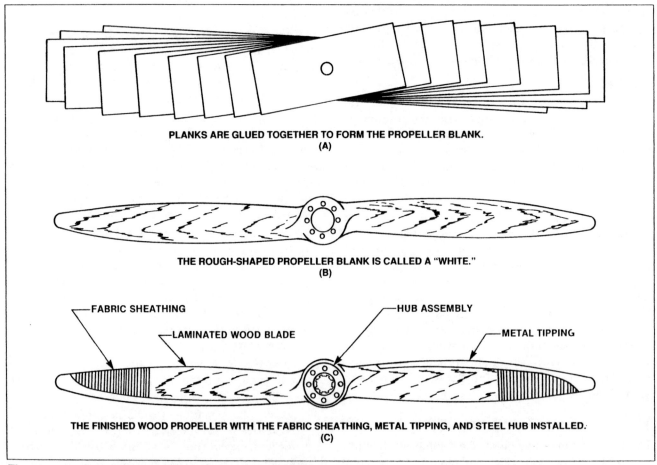

PLANKS ARE GLUED TOGETHER TO FORM THE PROPELLER BLANK.
(A)

THE ROUGH-SHAPED PROPELLER BLANK IS CALLED A "WHITE."
(B)

FABRIC SHEATHING

LAMINATED WOOD BLADE

HUB ASSEMBLY

METAL TIPPING

THE FINISHED WOOD PROPELLER WITH THE FABRIC SHEATHING, METAL TIPPING, AND STEEL HUB INSTALLED.
(C)

Figure 13-16. States in the production of a wood propeller.

indicates the hub design and mounting information, such as bolt hole size, dowel pin location, etc. The "S5" designates the thickness of the spacer to be used when the propeller is installed. The "2" indicates that the diameter has been reduced 2″ from the designed diameter, meaning that the propeller has an actual diameter of 74″. The "54" designates the pitch in inches at the 75% station.

In either designation system, a change in pitch will be indicated by the pitch stamping on the hub being restamped to indicate the new pitch setting.

Other propeller manufacturers use designation systems that are similar to the McCauley or the Sensenich system.

2. Constant Speed

Because of the long service life of aircraft and their related systems, a variety of constant speed propeller systems may be encountered in the field. The two presented here are representative of those in common use today.

a. McCauley

The McCauley constant-speed propeller system is one of the more popular constant-speed systems for light and medium size general aviation airplanes. This is the system used on most of the Cessna aircraft that require constant-speed propellers. It is also used on many other aircraft designs.

(1) The Propellers

Two series of propellers are currently being produced by McCauley, the threaded series and the threadless series. The threaded series propellers use a retention nut which screws into the propeller hub and holds the blades in the hub. The threadless design is the more modern of the two, and has the advantages of simplified manufacture and decreased overhaul time.

McCauley propellers use oil pressure on an internal piston to increase the blade angle, and this opposes a spring inside the hub which is used to decrease the blade angle. The movement of the piston is transmitted by blade actuating links to the blade actuating pins that are located on the butt of the blades. All of the pitch changing mechanism is enclosed inside the hub.

The propeller blades, hub, and piston are made of aluminum. The propeller cylinder, blade actuating pins, piston rod, and spring are all made of steel, plated with chrome or cadmium. The actuating links are made of a phenolic material.

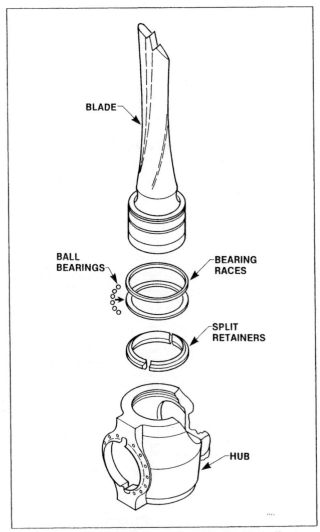

Figure 13-18. McCauley propeller with the threadless blades.

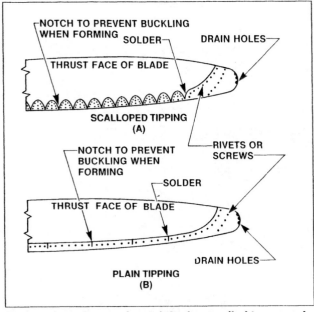

Figure 13-17. Types of metal tipping applied to a wood propeller.

The hollow piston rod through the center of the hub is used as an oil passage to direct oil from the engine crankshaft to the propeller piston. The pitch return spring is located around the piston rod and is compressed between the piston and the rear inside surface of the hub. O-ring seals are used to seal between the piston and the cylinder, the piston and the piston rod, and the piston rod and the hub.

All operating components of the propeller are lubricated at overhaul and receive no additional lubrication during operation.

Certain models of McCauley propellers have been modified to allow for an ongoing dye-penetrant type of inspection. The hub breather holes are sealed and the hub is partially filled with engine oil colored with a red dye. The red dye in the oil makes the location of cracks readily apparent and indicates that the propeller should be removed from service.

The McCauley propeller designation system is broken down as we see in figure 13-22. The most important parts of the designation are the dowel pin location, the C-number, and the modification or change letter after the C-number. The modification and change designation indicates the compliance with required or recommended alterations.

The blade designation is included with the propeller designation when determining which propeller will fit a specific aircraft. For example, a C203 propeller will fit a Cessna 180J aircraft, but the land plane version requires a 90DCA-8 blade of 82″ diameter, while the seaplane version requires a 90DCA-2 blade of 88″ diameter.

McCauley serial numbers on the propeller hub indicate the year in which the hub was manufactured.

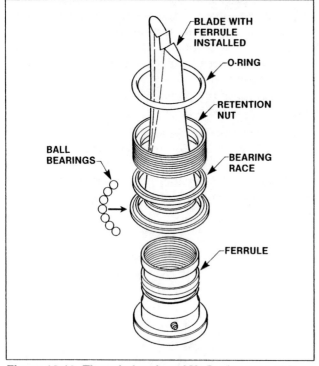

Figure 13-19. Threaded series of McCauley propeller blades.

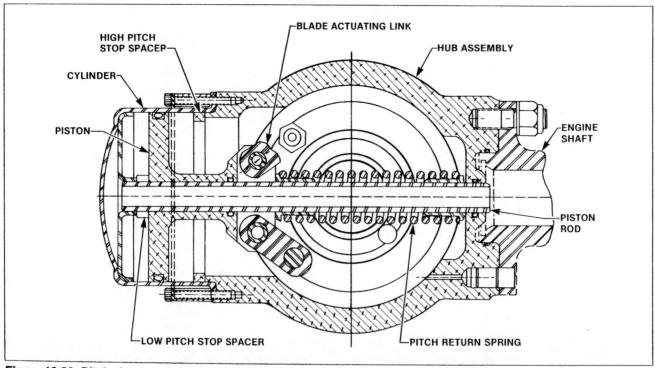

Figure 13-20. Pitch change mechanism in a McCauley propeller.

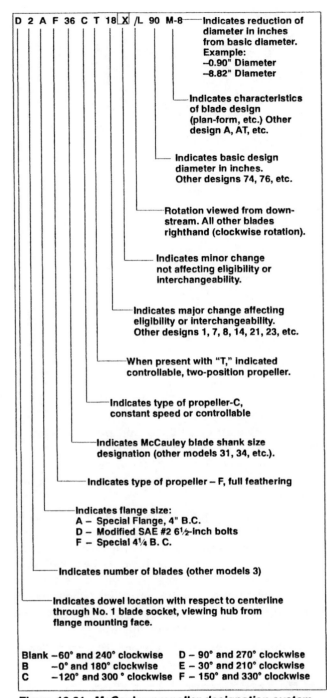

Figure 13-21. McCauley propeller designation system.

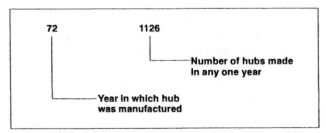

Figure 13-22. McCauley propeller and governor serial numbering system.

b. Hartzell

The Hartzell constant-speed propeller systems are used in modern general aviation airplanes and share the market with McCauley. Hartzell systems are used extensively on Piper aircraft and on many other designs.

(1) The Propellers

Hartzell produces two styles of constant-speed propellers: a steel hub propeller and a "Compact" model. Steel hub propellers are identified by their exposed operating mechanism, while Compact models have the pitch changing mechanism inside the hub assembly.

Some models of the steel hub propellers use oil pressure to decrease blade angle and the centrifugal force on the counterweights to increase blade angle. Other models of the steel hub propellers have no counterweights and use centrifugal twisting moment to decrease the blade angle and oil pressure to increase blade angle.

Hartzell steel hub propellers (figure 13-25) use a steel spider as the central component. Bearing assemblies and aluminum blades are placed on the spider arms and are held in place by 2-piece steel clamps. A steel cylinder is screwed onto the front of the spider and an aluminum piston is placed over the cylinder. The piston is connected to the blade clamps by steel link rods.

During operation, oil pressure is directed to the propeller piston through the engine crankshaft where it causes a change in blade angle. Counterweight models use oil pressure to decrease the blade angle, and centrifugal force on the counterweights increases the angle. Non-counterweighted models use oil pressure to increase the blade angle and centrifugal twisting moment to decrease the angle.

Some steel hub propellers are made so they will mount on flanged crankshafts, and others mount on splined shafts. Compact designs are normally used only with flanged crankshafts.

Hartzell Compact propellers use aluminum blades mounted in an aluminum hub. This propeller is illustrated in figure 13-26. The hub is held together with bolts and contains the pitch changing mechanism of the propeller. This mechanism consists of a piston, piston rod, and actuating links.

The Compact propeller uses governor oil pressure to increase blade angle and the centrifugal twisting moment acting on the propeller blades to decrease blade angle.

The Hartzell propeller designation system is the same for steel hub and Compact propeller models, as we see in the sample designations in figure 13-27.

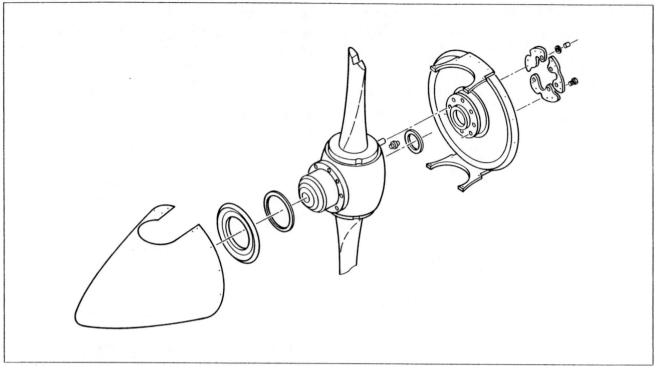

Figure 13-23. McCauley constant-speed propeller installation.

C. Feathering Type Propellers

Feathering propellers are used on most modern multi-engine airplanes. The primary purpose of a feathering propeller is to eliminate the drag created by a windmilling propeller when an engine fails.

Feathering propeller systems are constant-speed systems with the additional capability of being able to feather the blades. This means that the blades can be rotated to an approximate 90° blade angle. The constant-speed controls and operations we have discussed in previous sections apply to the feathering

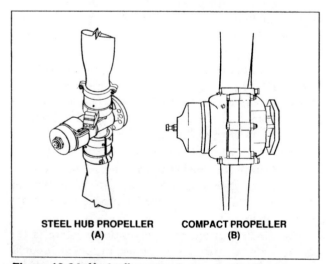

STEEL HUB PROPELLER   **COMPACT PROPELLER**
(A)   (B)

Figure 13-24. Hartzell constant-speed propellers.

propeller system, but the cockpit propeller control lever incorporates an additional range of movement to allow the propeller to feather. A separate cockpit control may be used to operate the feathering mechanism.

Feathering functions are independent of the constant-speed operation and can override the constant-speed operation to feather the propeller at any time. The engine does not have to be developing power, and in some systems the engine does not even have to be rotating for the propeller to feather. In short, propellers are feathered by forces which are totally independent of engine operation.

It should be noted that when the propeller is feathered, the engine stops rotating.

1. Hartzell Compact Propellers

Hartzell feathering systems are used on twin-engine aircraft manufactured by several different companies.

a. Propellers

Both Compact and steel hub propeller designs are used for Hartzell feathering propellers.

Compact designs use governor oil pressure to decrease the blade angle. Air pressure in the propeller cylinder and counterweights and springs on some models are used to feather the propeller. A latch stop (called the automatic high pitch stop by Hartzell) is located inside the cylinder to hold the blades in a low blade angle when the engine is stopped on the ground. The latch mechanism is composed of springs and locking pins.

b. Governors

Hartzell feathering systems may use either Hartzell or Woodward governors for operation. The governors may incorporate an internal mechanism with a lift rod and accumulator oil passages as well as valves. Or, they may have an external adapter which contains a shutoff valve linked to the governor control arm to control the accumulator operation.

c. System Operation

The constant-speed operation of the Hartzell feathering propellers is the same as for the constant-speed models, except for the change in direction of oil flow in some models.

The feathering propellers utilize oil pressure from the governor to move the blades into low pitch (high RPM). The centrifugal twisting moment of the blades also tends to move the blades into low pitch. Opposing these two forces is a force produced by compressed air trapped between the cylinder head and the piston, which tends to move the blades into high pitch in the absence of governor oil pressure.

Feathering is accomplished by moving the cockpit control full aft. The governor pilot valve is raised by the lift rod and releases oil from the propeller. With the oil pressure released, the Compact models will go to feather by the force of the air pressure in the cylinder. The time necessary to feather depends upon the size of the oil passages back through the engine and governor, and the air pressure carried in the cylinder. The blades are held in feather by air pressure.

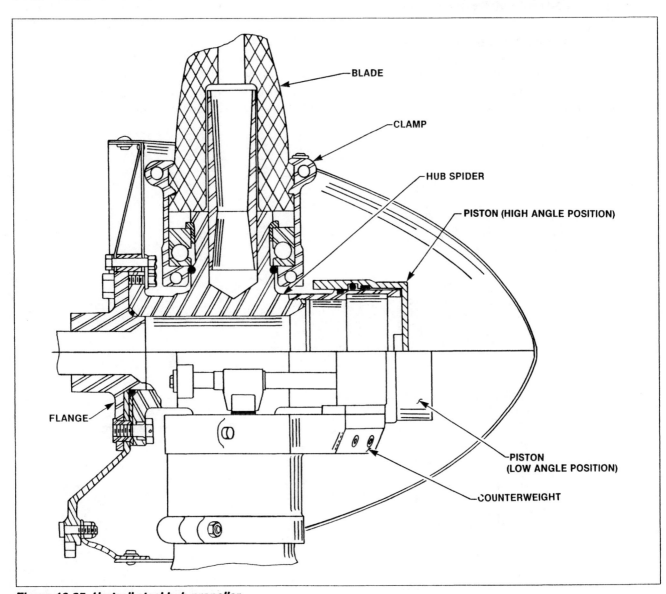

Figure 13-25. Hartzell steel hub propeller.

When unfeathering the propeller in flight, the system relies on engine rotation by the starter to initiate the unfeathering operation unless an accumulator is used. If an accumulator is installed in the system and the cockpit control is moved forward (out of the "feather" position) a check valve will be opened in the governor and allow the oil pressure from the accumulator to flow to the propeller cylinder and force the blades to a lower angle.

When shutting the engine down after flight, the propeller cockpit control should be placed in full forward position while the engine is idling. This causes the spring in the latch mechanism to force the lock pin into a low-pitch lock position and to engage when the engine is shut down and the blades attempt to rotate toward feather.

2. Hamilton-Standard Hydromatic Propellers

The Hamilton-Standard feathering system is used on many medium and large reciprocating engine transports. The Hamilton-Standard design has the trade name of "Hydromatic", indicating that the principal operating forces are oil pressure.

a. Propellers

The Hamilton-Standard Hydromatic propeller has three major assemblies: the hub or barrel assembly, the dome assembly, and the distributor valve.

The barrel assembly contains the spider, blades, blade gear segments, barrel halves, necessary support blocks, spacers, and bearings. Front and rear cones, a retaining nut, and a lock ring are used to install the barrel assembly on the splined crankshaft.

The dome assembly contains the pitch changing mechanism of the propeller and includes the dome shell, piston, rotating cam, stationary cam, and two blade angle stop rings. The dome shell acts as the cylinder for the propeller piston.

The distributor valve is used to direct oil from the crankshaft to the inboard and outboard side of the piston and is shifted during unfeathering to reverse the oil passages to the piston.

b. Governors

The feathering Hydromatic governor includes all of the basic governor components discussed for constant-speed governors. And, in addition, the Hydromatic

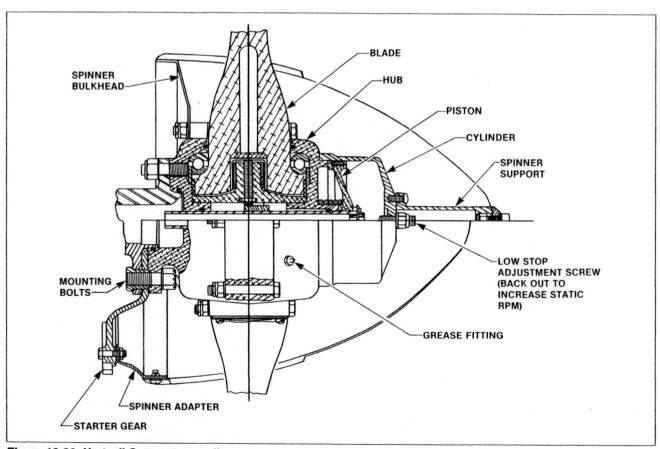

Figure 13-26. Hartzell Compact propeller.

governor contains a high-pressure transfer valve which is used to block the governor constant-speed mechanism out of the propeller control system when the propeller is feathered or unfeathered.

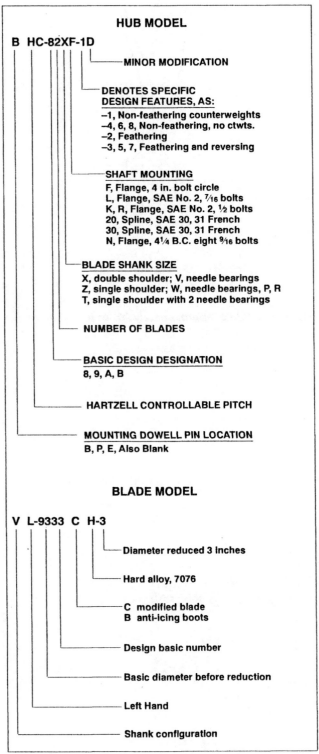

Figure 13-27. Hartzell propeller and blade designation system.

A pressure cut-out switch is located on the side of the governor and is used to automatically stop the feathering operation.

c. Feathering System Components

The cockpit control for the feathering system is a push button approximately 1¼″ in diameter, and is used to feather and unfeather the propeller. The feathering button incorporates a holding coil to electrically hold the button in after it is pushed.

An electrically operated feathering pump is used to supply oil under high pressure of about 600 PSI to the propeller when the feathering system is actuated. The pump takes its oil from the engine oil supply tank, at a level below the standpipe feeding the engine lubrication system.

d. Principles of Operation

The Hydromatic propeller uses governor oil pressure on one side of the propeller piston, opposed by engine oil pressure on the other side of the piston. Depending on the model of the propeller, governor oil pressure may be directed to the outboard side or inboard side of the piston.

For discussion purposes, consider that governor oil pressure is on the inboard side of the propeller piston and engine oil pressure is on the outboard side of the piston.

The Hydromatic propeller does not use any springs or counterweights for operation. The fixed force is the engine oil pressure, which is about 60 PSI. And the governor oil pressure (200 or 300 PSI, depending on the system) is controlled by the pilot valve during constant-speed operation.

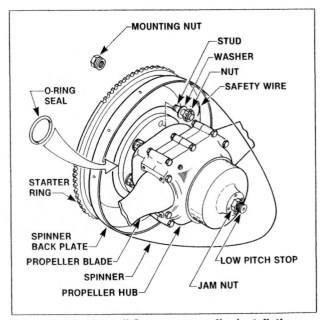

Figure 13-28. Hartzell Compact propeller installation.

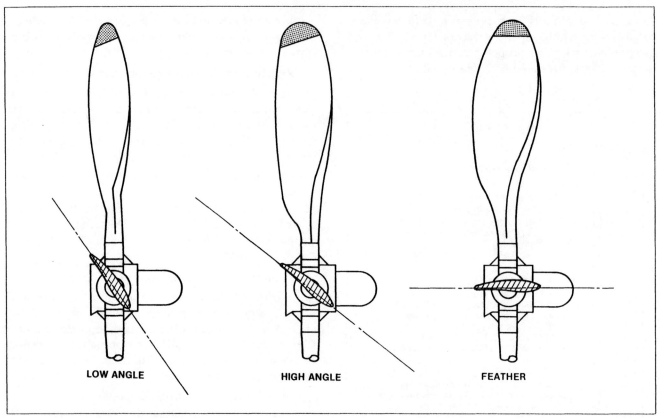

LOW ANGLE

HIGH ANGLE

FEATHER

Figure 13-29. When a propeller is feathered, its blades are turned to an angle of approximately 90° to the plane of propeller rotation.

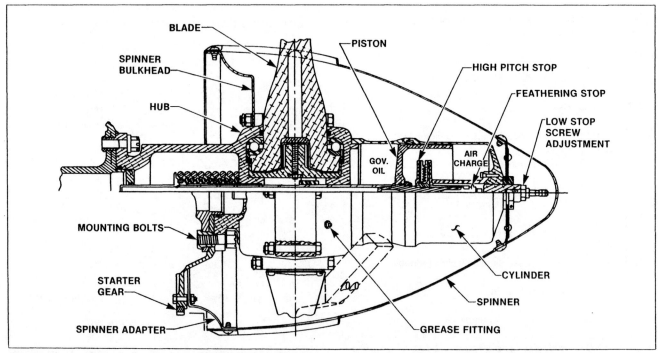

Figure 13-30. Hartzell Compact feathering propeller.

e. Over/Underspeed Operations

When the system is in an over-speed condition, the pilot valve in the governor is raised and governor oil pressure flows to the inboard (rear) side of the propeller piston via the crankshaft transfer bearing and the distributor valve. The increase in pressure on the inboard side of the piston forces the piston

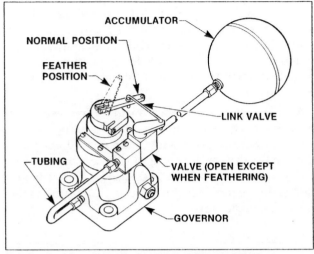

Figure 13-31. Propeller governor with an external accumulator adapter to aid in unfeathering the propeller in flight.

outboard (forward). As the piston moves outboard, it rotates, following the slot in the stationary cam, and this causes the rotating cam to rotate. As the rotating cam turns, the gears on the bottom of the cam, which mesh with the gears on the blade segment and rotate the blade to a higher blade angle. With this increase in blade angle, the system RPM slows down and the governor returns to the on-speed condition. The oil in the outboard side of the piston is forced back into the engine lubrication system.

When the system is under speed, the pilot valve is lowered, and the governor oil pressure in the inboard side of the piston is released. This causes engine oil pressure on the outboard side of the piston to force the piston inboard. As the piston moves inboard, the rotation created by the piston and the cams causes the blades to rotate to a lower blade angle, allowing system RPM to increase to the on-speed condition.

f. Feathering

To feather the propeller, the feather button in the cockpit is pushed. When this is done, electrical contacts close and energize the holding coil which holds the feather button in. Another set of feather button electrical contacts close at the same time and cause the feathering relay to close.

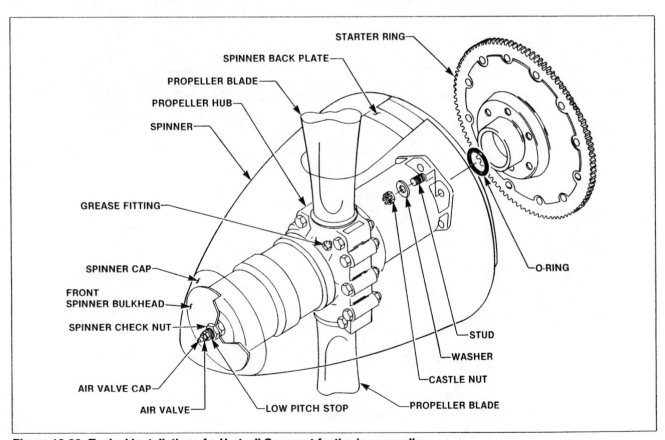

Figure 13-32. Typical installation of a Hartzell Compact feathering propeller.

The feathering relay completes the circuit from the battery to the auxiliary pump, and the high-pressure oil generated by the pump shifts the high-pressure transfer valve in the governor to block the governor constant-speed components out of the system. This high-pressure oil is then directed to the inboard side of the piston, and it moves the blades toward the feather angle.

When the rotating cam contacts the high-pitch stop, the piston stops moving and the blades have reached the feather angle. Since the piston cannot move any further, the pressure in the system starts to build rapidly. This increasing pressure is sensed by the pressure cutout switch on the governor, and it breaks the circuit to the feather button holding coil when the pressure reaches about 650 PSI. This releases the feather relay and shuts off the auxiliary pump. With the engine stopped and the propeller in feather, all oil pressures drop to zero. The blades are held in their full-feather position by aerodynamic forces.

To unfeather the propeller, the feather button is pushed and held in to prevent the button popping back out when the pressure cutout switch opens. The auxiliary pump starts building pressure above the setting of the pressure cutout switch. This causes the distributor valve to shift and reverse the flow of oil to the piston. Auxiliary pump pressure is then directed to the outboard side of the piston, and engine oil lines are open to the inboard side of the piston. The piston moves inboard and causes the blades to rotate to a lower blade angle through the action of the cams. With this lower blade angle, the propeller starts to windmill, allowing the engine to be restarted.

At this point, the feather button is released and the system will return to constant-speed operation. If the feather button is not released, the dome relief valve in the distributor valve will off-seat and release excess oil pressure (above 750 PSI) from the outboard side of the piston after the rotating cam contacts the low blade angle stop.

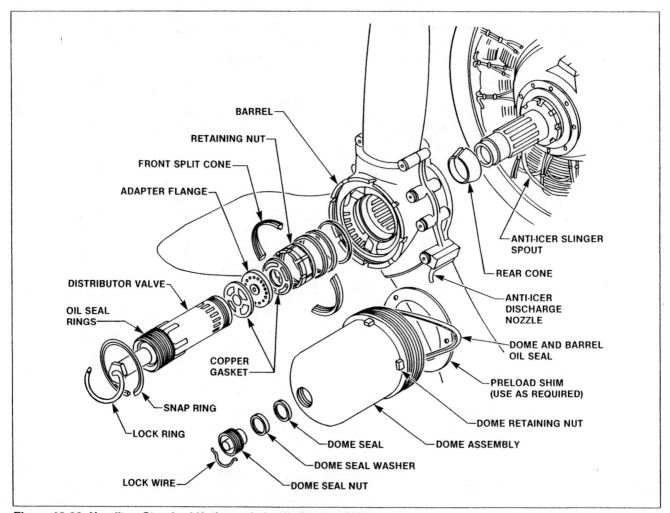

Figure 13-33. Hamilton-Standard Hydromatic feathering propeller.

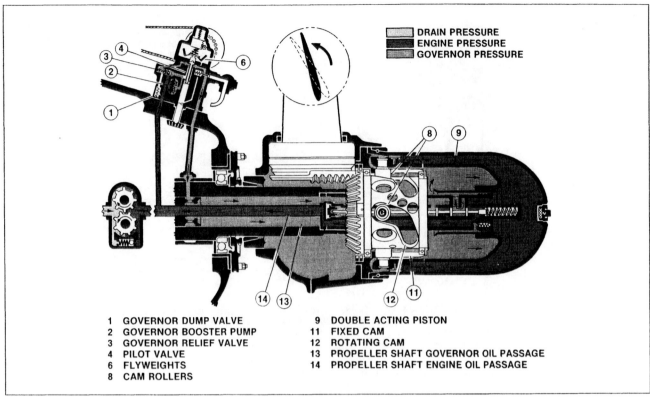

1	GOVERNOR DUMP VALVE	9	DOUBLE ACTING PISTON
2	GOVERNOR BOOSTER PUMP	11	FIXED CAM
3	GOVERNOR RELIEF VALVE	12	ROTATING CAM
4	PILOT VALVE	13	PROPELLER SHAFT GOVERNOR OIL PASSAGE
6	FLYWEIGHTS	14	PROPELLER SHAFT ENGINE OIL PASSAGE
8	CAM ROLLERS		

Figure 13-34. Hydromatic propeller installation in an over-speed condition.

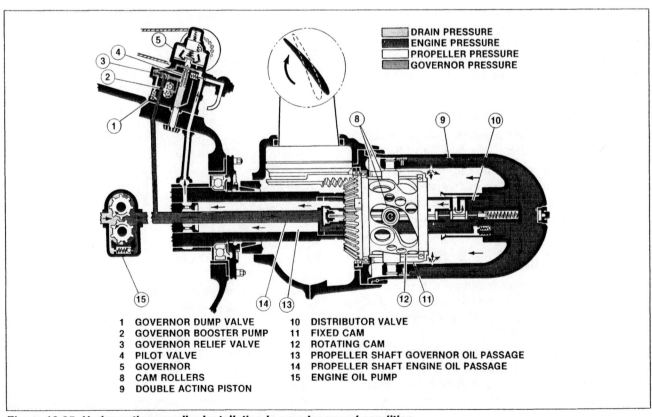

1	GOVERNOR DUMP VALVE	10	DISTRIBUTOR VALVE
2	GOVERNOR BOOSTER PUMP	11	FIXED CAM
3	GOVERNOR RELIEF VALVE	12	ROTATING CAM
4	PILOT VALVE	13	PROPELLER SHAFT GOVERNOR OIL PASSAGE
5	GOVERNOR	14	PROPELLER SHAFT ENGINE OIL PASSAGE
8	CAM ROLLERS	15	ENGINE OIL PUMP
9	DOUBLE ACTING PISTON		

Figure 13-35. Hydromatic propeller installation in a under speed condition.

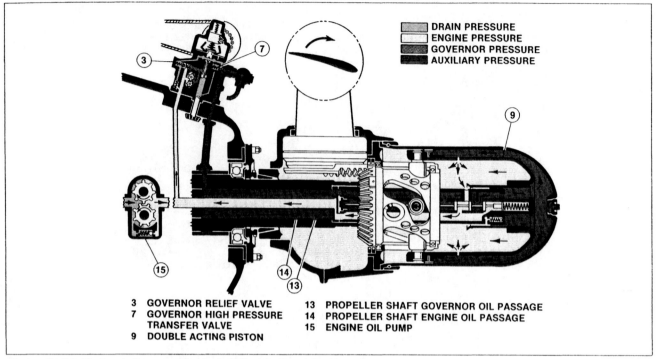

3	GOVERNOR RELIEF VALVE	13	PROPELLER SHAFT GOVERNOR OIL PASSAGE
7	GOVERNOR HIGH PRESSURE TRANSFER VALVE	14	PROPELLER SHAFT ENGINE OIL PASSAGE
9	DOUBLE ACTING PISTON	15	ENGINE OIL PUMP

Figure 13-36. Hydrostatic propeller installation being unfeathered.

D. Hydraulic Governors

As we have seen in the above description of how various propeller systems operate, the constant-speed function is controlled by a balance of two forces. One of these forces is always governor oil pressure. The flyweight-type hydraulic governor is really a very simple and reliable mechanism. We will examine here three of the basic types used on aircraft propeller systems.

1. Hamilton-Standard Governors

The Hamilton-Standard propeller governor is divided into three parts: the head, the body, and the base.

The head of the governor contains the flyweights and flyweight cup, the speeder spring, a speeder rack and pinion mechanism, and a control pulley. Cast on the side of the head is a flange for the pulley adjustment stop screw. Some head designs incorporate a balance spring above the speeder rack to set the governor to cruise RPM if the control cable breaks.

The body of the governor contains the propeller oil flow control mechanism, which is composed of the pilot valve, oil passages, and the pressure relief valve which is set for 180-200 PSI.

The base contains the governor boost pump, the mounting surface for installation on the engine, and oil passages which direct engine oil to the pump and return oil from the propeller to the engine sump.

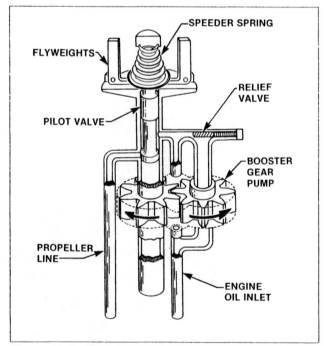

Figure 13-37. Basic configuration of a typical propeller governor.

The head, body, and base are held together with studs and nuts. The governor drive shaft extends below the base to mate with the engine drive gear. The drive shaft passes up through the base where it drives the oil pump, through the body where it has oil ports so oil can flow to and from the propeller, and into the head, where it is attached to the flyweight cup and rotates the flyweights.

The governor designation system indicates the design of the head, body, and base used on a particular governor. For a governor model 1A3-B2H, the basic design of the head is indicated by the "1" with minor modifications to the head design indicated by the "B" following the dash. The body design is "A" with minor modification "2". The base is a 3 altered by an "H" minor modification.

The propeller governor is an RPM sensing device which responds to a change in system RPM by directing oil to or releasing oil from the propeller to change the blade angle and return the system RPM to the original value. The governor may be set up for a specific RPM by the cockpit propeller control.

The basic governor contains a drive shaft which is connected to the engine drive train, and it rotates at a speed that is proportional to the engine RPM. An oil pump drive gear is mounted on the drive shaft, and it meshes with an oil pump idler gear. These gears take oil at engine oil system pressure and boost it to the propeller operating pressure. Excess pressure built up by the booster pump is returned to the inlet side of the pump by a pressure relief valve.

The boosted oil is routed through passages in the governor to a pilot valve which fits in the center of the hollow drive shaft. This pilot valve can be moved up and down in the drive shaft, and it directs oil through ports in the drive shaft to or from the propeller to vary the blade angle.

The position of the pilot valve is determined by the action of the flyweights attached to the end of the drive shaft. The flyweights are designed to tilt outward when the RPM increases and inward when RPM decreases. When the flyweights tilt outward, they raise the pilot valve, and when they tilt inward, the pilot valve is lowered. The movement of the pilot valve in response to changes in RPM directs oil flow to adjust the blade angle to maintain the selected RPM.

The action of the flyweights is opposed by a speeder spring located above the flyweights and adjusted by the pilot through a control cable, pulley, and speeder rack. When a higher RPM is desired, the cockpit control is moved forward to compress the speeder spring. This increased speeder spring compression tilts the flyweights inward and the pilot valve is lowered. This causes the blade angle to decrease, and the RPM will increase until the centrifugal force on the flyweights overcomes the force of the speeder spring and returns the pilot valve to the neutral position.

✳ The opposite action occurs if the cockpit control is moved aft. When the speeder spring compression

is reduced, the flyweights tilt outward, the pilot valve is raised, and the blade angle increases until the engine slows down and the centrifugal force on the flyweights decreases. The pilot valve returns to its neutral position.

Whenever the flyweights tilt outward and the pilot valve is raised, the governor is said to be in an over-speed condition, with the RPM higher than the governor speeder spring setting calls for. When the flyweights tilt inward, the governor is in an under-speed condition, with the RPM lower than the speeder spring setting calls for. When the RPM is the same as the governor setting is calling for, the governor is in its on-speed condition.

The same governing action of the flyweights and pilot valve occurs with changing flight conditions. If the aircraft is in a cruise condition and the pilot begins a climb, airspeed will decrease and cause an increase in the angle of attack of the propeller blades. This increase produces more drag, and the RPM decreases. The governor senses this decrease in RPM by the reduced centrifugal force on the flyweights, and they tilt inward, lowering the pilot valve and producing an under-speed condition. When the pilot valve is lowered, the blade angle is reduced and the RPM increases to its original value. The system returns to the on-speed condition.

If the aircraft is placed in a dive from cruising flight, an over-speed condition is created, and the governor will cause an increase in blade angle to return the system to the on-speed condition.

A change in throttle setting will have the same effect as placing the aircraft in a climb or dive. Increasing the throttle will cause an increase in the blade angle to prevent an RPM increase. Retarding the throttle will result in a decrease in blade angle.

2. McCauley Governors

McCauley governors use the same principles of operation as the Hamilton-Standard governors, except that oil is released from the propeller to decrease blade angle, directly opposite from the oil flow in the Hamilton-Standard system. The governor relief valve is set for an oil pressure of about 290 PSI. The governor control lever is spring-loaded to the high RPM setting. The overall construction of the governor is simpler than the Hamilton-Standard governor, being lighter and smaller. All governors incorporate a high RPM stop, while some also use an adjustable low RPM stop.

The McCauley governor uses a control arm instead of a pulley to connect the governor control shaft to the cockpit control cable. The push-pull cockpit control is adjustable in length through a limited range by an adjustable rod end, and the governor

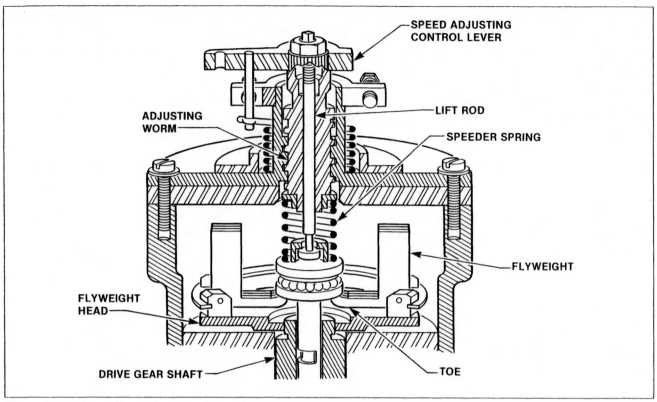

Figure 13-38. Propeller governor in the on-speed condition.

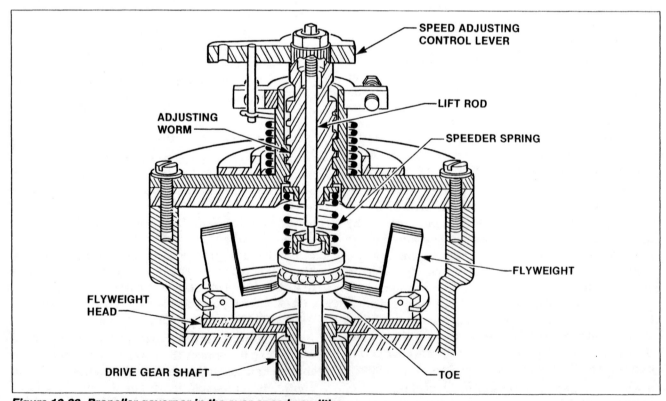

Figure 13-39. Propeller governor in the over-speed condition.

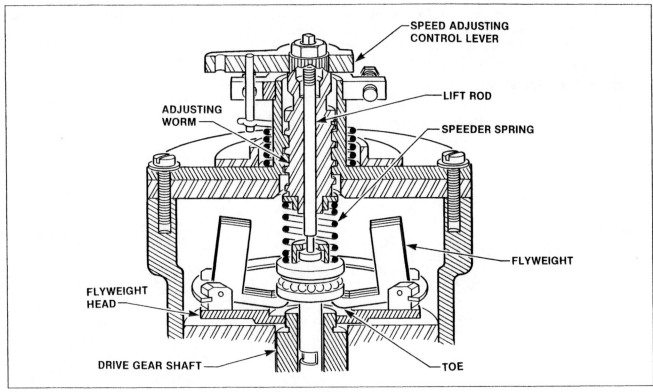

Figure 13-40. Propeller governor in the under speed condition.

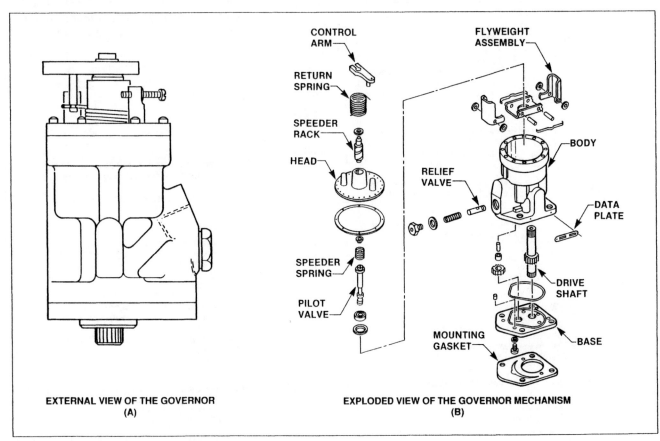

EXTERNAL VIEW OF THE GOVERNOR
(A)

EXPLODED VIEW OF THE GOVERNOR MECHANISM
(B)

Figure 13-41. McCauley constant-speed governor.

high RPM limit can be adjusted by the set screw on the head of the governor, with one turn of the screw changing the RPM by 17, 20, or 25 RPM, depending upon the engine gear ratio and the governor.

3. Hartzell Governors

Hartzell governors may be reworked Hamilton-Standard governors or Woodward governors. The Hartzell governor designation system is shown in figure 13-45.

E. Propeller Synchronization Systems

The propeller synchronization system is used to set all propellers at exactly the same RPM, thereby

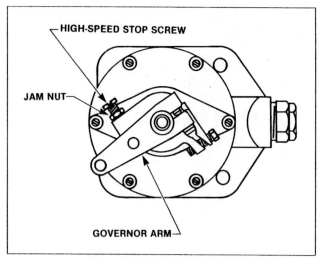

Figure 13-42. High RPM stop screw adjustment on a McCauley propeller governor.

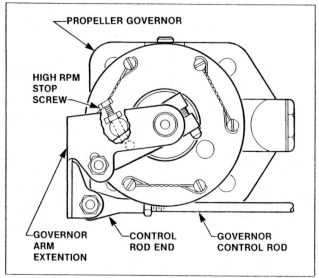

Figure 13-44. The amount of travel of a propeller governor control arm may be regulated by the amount the governor control rod is screwed into the control rod end.

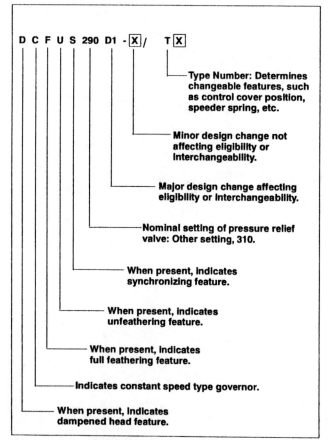

Figure 13-43. McCauley governor designation system.

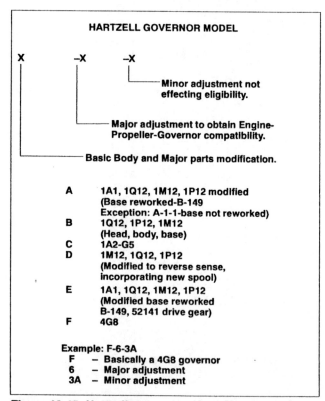

Figure 13-45. Hartzell governor designation system.

242

eliminating excess noise and vibration. It is used for all flight operations except takeoff and landing.

1. Master Motor Synchronization

An early type, which may still be found on some aircraft, consists of a synchronizer master unit, four alternators, a tachometer, engine RPM master control levers, switches and wiring. These components automatically control the speed of each engine and synchronize all engines at any desired RPM.

A synchronizer master unit incorporates a master motor which mechanically drives four contactor units; each contactor unit is electrically connected to an alternator. The alternator is a small 3-phase, alternating current generator driven by an accessory drive of the engine. The frequency of the voltage produced by the generators is directly proportional to the speed of the engine. In automatic operation, the desired engine RPM may be set by manually adjusting the RPM control lever until a master tachometer on the instrument panel indicates the desired RPM. Any difference in RPM between an engine and the master motor will cause the corresponding contactor unit to operate the pitch-change mechanism of the propeller until the engine is on-speed.

2. One Engine Master Control System

Synchronizer systems are also installed in light twin-engine aircraft. Typically, such systems consist of a special propeller governor on the left-hand engine, a slave governor on the right-hand engine and an actuator in the right-hand engine nacelle.

A frequency generator built into the propeller governor generates a signal that is proportional to the RPM of the engine. A comparison circuit in the control box compares the RPM signal from the slave engine to the RPM signal from the master engine and sends a correcting signal to the slave engine governor control mechanism.

The comparison unit has a limited range of operation, and the slave engine must be within about 100 RPM of the master engine for synchronization to occur.

3. Synchrophasing

Synchrophasing is a refinement of synchronization which allows the pilot to set the angular difference in the plane of rotation between the blades of the slave engines and the blades of the master. Synchrophasing is used to reduce the noise and vibration created by the engines and propellers, and the synchrophase angle can be varied by the pilot to adjust for different flight conditions and still achieve a minimum noise level.

A pulse generator is keyed to the same blade of each propeller, blade No. 1 for example, and a signal is generated to determine if both No. 1 blades are in the same relative position at any given instant. By comparison of the signals from the two engines, a signal is sent to the governor of the slave engine to cause it to establish the phase angle selected by the pilot.

A propeller manual phase control in the cockpit allows the pilot to select the phase angle which produces the minimum vibration and noise.

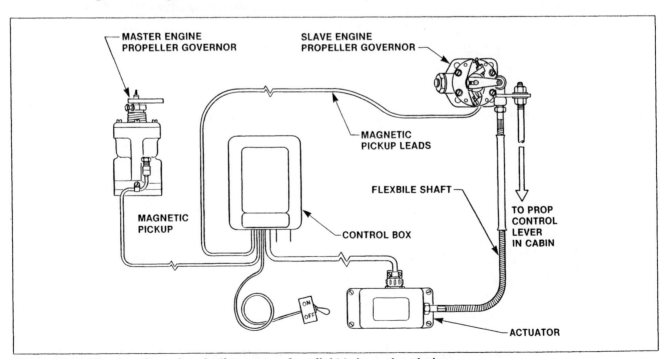

Figure 13-46. Woodward synchronization system for a light twin-engine airplane.

F. Propeller Ice Control Systems

As aircraft use has become a more vital part of our transportation system, the necessity to fly in nearly all weather conditions has brought about the development of systems permitting the aircraft to operate safely in these adverse environments.

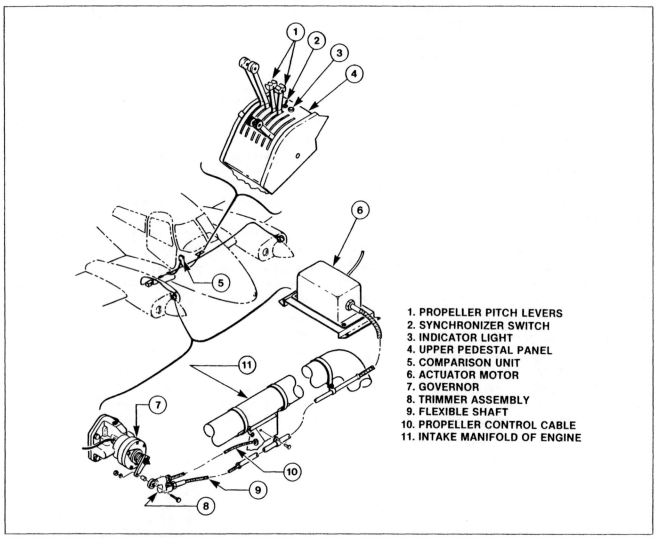

1. PROPELLER PITCH LEVERS
2. SYNCHRONIZER SWITCH
3. INDICATOR LIGHT
4. UPPER PEDESTAL PANEL
5. COMPARISON UNIT
6. ACTUATOR MOTOR
7. GOVERNOR
8. TRIMMER ASSEMBLY
9. FLEXIBLE SHAFT
10. PROPELLER CONTROL CABLE
11. INTAKE MANIFOLD OF ENGINE

Figure 13-47. Installation of a synchronization system in a light twin-engine airplane.

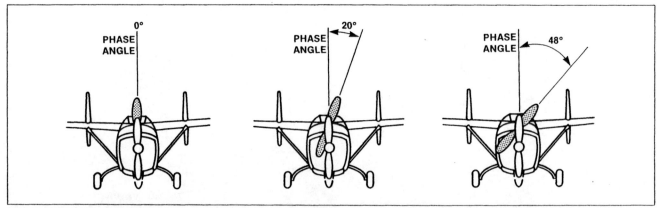

Figure 13-48. Synchrophasing allows the pilot to adjust the phase angle between the propellers on the various engines to reduce the noise and keep vibration to a minimum.

1. Effects of Propeller Icing

Ice formation on a propeller blade, in effect, produces a distorted blade airfoil section which causes loss in propeller efficiency. Generally, ice collects unsymmetrically on a propeller blade and produces propeller unbalance and destructive vibration.

2. Fluid Systems

A typical fluid system (figure 13-50) includes a tank to hold a supply of anti-icing fluid. This fluid is forced to each propeller by a pump. The control system permits variation in the pumping rate so that the quantity of fluid delivered to a propeller can be varied, depending on the severity of the icing. Fluid is transferred from a stationary nozzle on the engine nose case into a circular U-shaped channel (slinger-ring) mounted on the rear of the propeller assembly. The fluid under pressure of centrifugal force is transferred through nozzles to each blade shank.

Because airflow around a blade shank tends to disperse anti-icing fluids to areas on which ice does not collect in large quantities, feed shoes, or boots, are installed on the blade leading edge. These feed shoes are a narrow strip of rubber, extending from the blade shank to a blade station that is approximately 75% of the propeller radius. The feed shoes are molded with several parallel open channels in which fluid will flow from the blade shank toward the blade tip by centrifugal force. The fluid flows laterally from the channels over the leading edge of the blade.

Isopropyl alcohol is used in some anti-icing systems because of its availability and low cost. Phosphate compounds are comparable to isopropyl alcohol in anti-icing performance and have the advantage of reduced flammability. However, phosphate compounds are comparatively expensive and, consequently, are not widely used.

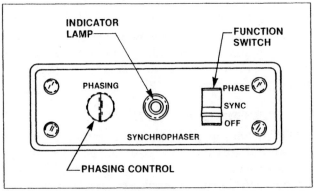

Figure 13-49. Synchrophasing control panel for a light twin-engine airplane.

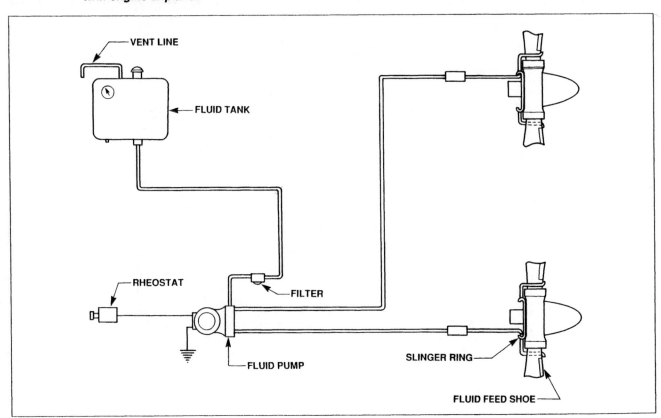

Figure 13-50. Typical propeller fluid anti-icing system.

3. Electric Deicing Systems

An electrical propeller icing control system (figure 13-51) consists basically of an electrical energy source, a resistance heating element, system controls, and necessary wiring. The heating elements are mounted internally or externally on the propeller spinner and blades. Electrical power from the aircraft system is transferred to the propeller hub through electrical leads, which terminate in slip rings and brushes. Flexible connectors are used to transfer power from the hub to the blade elements.

Icing control is accomplished by converting electrical energy to heat energy in the heating element. Balanced ice removal from all blades must be obtained as nearly as possible if excessive vibration is to be avoided. To obtain balanced ice removal, variation of heating current in the blade elements is controlled so that similar heating effects are obtained in opposite blades.

Electrical deicing systems are usually designed for intermittent application of power to the heating elements to remove ice after formation but before excessive accumulation. Proper control of heating intervals aids in preventing run-back, since heat is applied just long enough to melt the ice face in contact with the blade.

If heat supplied to an icing surface is more than that required to melt just the inner ice face, but insufficient to evaporate all the water formed, water will run back over the unheated surface and freeze. Run-back of this nature causes ice formation on uncontrolled icing areas of the blade or surface.

Cycling timers are used to energize the heating element circuits for periods of 15-30 sec., with a complete cycle time of 2 min. A cycling timer is an electric motor driven contactor which controls power contactors in separate sections of the circuit.

Controls for propeller electrical deicing systems include on-off switches, ammeters in the circuits, and protective devices, such as current limiters or circuit breakers. The ammeters or loadmeters permit monitoring of individual circuit currents and reflect operation of the timer.

To prevent element overheating, the propeller deicing system is generally used only when the propellers are rotating, and for short periods of time during ground run-up.

G. Turboprop Propellers

The turboprop propeller is operated by a gas turbine engine through a reduction gear assembly. It has proved to be an extremely efficient power source. Turboprop engines are used on aircraft ranging in size from large 4-engine transports to relatively small single-engine business and utility aircraft.

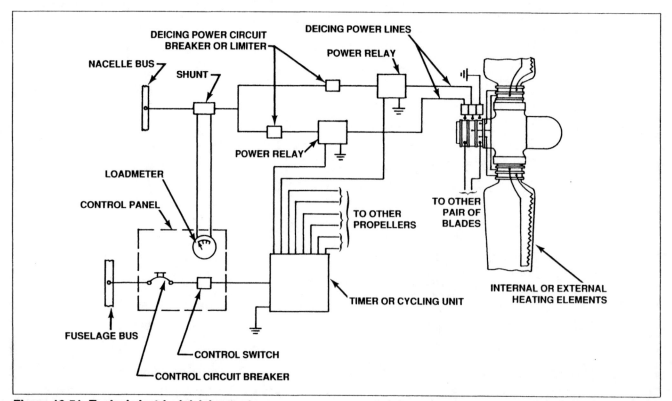

Figure 13-51. Typical electrical deicing system.

Because the engine and propeller must work together to produce the required thrust for a turboprop installation, there are a few unique relationships. The turboprop fuel control and the propeller governor are connected and operate in coordination with each other. The power lever directs a signal from the cockpit to the fuel control for a specific amount of power from the engine. The fuel control and the propeller governor together establish the correct combination of RPM, fuel flow, and propeller blade angle to provide the desired power.

The propeller control system is divided into two types of control: one for flight and one for ground operation. For flight, the propeller blade angle and fuel flow for any given power setting are governed automatically according to a predetermined schedule. This is known as the alpha range. Below the "flight idle" power lever position, the coordinated RPM blade angle schedule becomes incapable of handling the engine efficiently. Here the ground handling range (referred to as the beta range) is encountered. In the beta range of the throttle quadrant, the propeller blade angle is governed by the propeller governor, but is controlled by the power lever position. When the power lever is moved below the start position, the propeller pitch is reversed to provide reverse thrust for rapid deceleration of the aircraft after landing.

1. Reduction Gear Assembly

The reduction gear assembly may be integral with the engine power unit, or it may be separately located and driven by the power unit through an extension shaft. The reduction gear assembly may incorporate sensors for the NTS (negative torque signal), TSS (thrust sensitive signal), and a propeller brake.

The negative torque signal control system provides a signal which increases propeller blade angle to limit negative shaft torque.

If a power loss occurs during takeoff, the thrust sensitive signal increases propeller blade angle and causes the propeller to feather, automatically.

The propeller brake is designed to prevent the propeller from windmilling when it is feathered in flight, and to decrease the time for the propeller to come to a complete stop after engine shutdown.

2. Turbo-Propeller Assemblies

In this section of the text, we will discuss the Hartzell reversing propellers used with the Garrett AiResearch TPE-331, and the Pratt and Whitney of Canada PT6 engines.

a. Hartzell Reversing Propeller System used on TPE-331

The Hartzell propeller on the TPE-331 is used on aircraft such as the Mitsubishi MU-2, the Short Skyvan, and the Aero Commander 690.

The TPE-331 engine is a fixed turbine engine that produces more than 600 HP when the engine is turning at about 40,000 RPM. A reduction gear assembly on the front of the engine couples the engine drive shaft to the propeller drive shaft and reduces the engine speed to about 2,200 RPM at the propeller drive shaft.

The engine gear ratio and the method of mounting the reduction gearing to the engine varies with the installation. Some engines have the propeller drive shaft below the engine centerline, and other installations have the propeller above the engine centerline.

(1) Propeller

The propeller commonly used on the TPE-331 is a 3- or 4-bladed Hartzell steel hub reversing propeller. The propeller is spring-loaded and counterweighted to the feather position and uses engine oil pressurized by the governor to decrease the blade angle. The propeller is flange-mounted on the drive shaft, and it locks in a flat angle of about 2° when the engine is shut down on the ground. This prevents excessive strain on the engine starter when the engine is being started.

The propeller is constructed similar to the feathering steel hub designs. The principal additional component is the beta tube, which passes through the center of the propeller and serves as an oil passage and follow-up device during propeller operation.

The same designation system is used for the reversing Hartzell propellers as is used for Hartzell feathering and constant-speed propellers.

The cockpit controls for the TPE-331 turboprop installation include a power lever which controls the horsepower output of the engine, a speed lever which controls system RPM, a feather handle, and an unfeathering switch.

The power lever is similar to the reciprocating engine throttle in that it controls system horsepower. During ground operation, the power lever directly controls the propeller blade angle by positioning the propeller pitch control unit, and during flight operations, the power lever directly controls the engine fuel control unit.

The speed lever is similar to the propeller control lever in a reciprocating engine system in that it controls the system RPM. During ground operation, the speed lever adjusts the underspeed governor on the fuel control unit to vary the fuel flow and maintain a fixed RPM as the blade angle is changed by the power lever. During flight operations, the speed lever sets the RPM on the propeller governor which varies the blade angles when the engine power is changed with the power lever or when flight operations change to keep the RPM constant.

Many aircraft use a feather handle connected to the feathering valve on the engine. Other aircraft connect the feathering valve to the speed lever so that full aft movement of the lever will cause the propeller to feather. When the feathering valve is moved by the cockpit control, oil is released from the propeller and the propeller feathers.

An unfeathering switch is used to control the electric unfeathering pump to unfeather the propeller.

(2) System Operation

The two basic operating modes of the TPE-331 system are the Beta mode, meaning any ground operation including start, taxi, and reverse operation, and the alpha mode, which is any flight operation from takeoff to landing. Typically, Beta mode includes operation from 65% to 95% RPM, and alpha mode includes operation from 95% to 100% of system rated RPM.

When the engine is started, the power lever is set at the ground idle position and the speed lever is in the start position. When the engine starts, the propeller latches are retract by reversing the propeller with the power levers, and the propeller moves to a 0° blade angle as the propeller pitch control is positioned by the power lever over the beta tube. The Beta tube is attached to the propeller piston, and it moves forward with the piston as the propeller moves to the low blade angle. The propeller blade angle stops changing when the Beta tube moves forward to the neutral position in the propeller pitch control.

The speed lever is used to set the desired RPM through the underspeed governor during ground operation, and the power lever is used to vary the blade angle to cause the aircraft to move forward or rearward. If the power lever is moved forward, the propeller pitch control moves rearward, so that the oil ports on the end of the Beta tube are open to the gear reduction case and the oil in the propeller is forced out by the springs and counterweights. As the blade angle increases, the propeller piston moves inward until the Beta tube returns to its neutral position in the propeller pitch control unit. This causes a proportional response of the propeller to the power lever movement.

With the increase in blade angle, the engine will start to slow down, but the underspeed governor, which is set by the speed lever, will adjust the fuel flow to the engine to maintain the selected RPM.

If the power lever is moved rearward, the propeller pitch control moves forward over the Beta tube, and governor oil pressure flows out to the propeller piston and causes a decrease in blade angle. As the piston moves outward, the Beta tube moves with it and returns to the neutral position as the blade angle changes. With this lower blade angle, the engine RPM will try to change, but the underspeed governor will reduce the fuel flow to maintain the selected RPM.

In the Alpha mode of operation, flight operation, the speed lever is moved to a high RPM setting of between 95% to 100%, and the power lever is moved to the flight idle position. When this is done, the underspeed governor is fully opened and no longer affects system operation. RPM control is now accomplished through the propeller governor.

When the power lever is moved to flight idle, the propeller pitch control moves forward so that the beta tube is fully in the propeller pitch control and it no longer functions to adjust the blade angle. The power lever now controls the fuel flow through the engine fuel control unit.

With a fixed power lever setting in the alpha mode, the propeller governor is adjusted by the speed lever to set the system RPM in the same manner as for any constant-speed system.

With a fixed speed lever setting in the alpha mode, the power lever adjusts the fuel control unit to control the amount of fuel delivered to the engine. When the power lever is moved forward, fuel flow will increase and the propeller blade angle will be increased by the propeller governor to absorb the increased engine power and maintain the set RPM. When the power lever is moved aft, fuel flow will decrease and the propeller blade angle will decrease by the action of the propeller governor to maintain the selected RPM.

Whenever it is desired to feather the propeller, the feather handle is pulled or the speed lever is moved full aft, depending on the aircraft design. This action shifts the feathering valve, located on the rear of the gear reduction assembly, and releases the oil pressure from the propeller, returning the oil to the engine sump.

The springs and counterweights on the propeller force the oil out of the propeller, and the blades go into the feather angle.

To unfeather the propeller, the electric unfeathering pump is turned on with a toggle switch in the cockpit, and oil pressure is directed to the propeller to reduce the blade angle. This causes the propeller to start windmilling in flight and an air start can be accomplished. On the ground, the propeller can be unfeathered in the same manner before starting the engine.

b. Hartzell Reversing Propeller System on the Pratt & Whitney of Canada PT6 Engine

The Hartzell propeller on the PT6 engine is used on the Piper Cheyenne, DeHavilland Twin Otter, and most models of the Beechcraft King Air series.

The PT6 engine is a free-turbine turboprop engine that produces more than 600 HP at 38,000 RPM. A geared reduction mechanism couples the engine power turbine to the propeller drive shaft with the propeller rotating at 2,200 RPM at 100% RPM. The free-turbine design means that the power turbine is not mechanically connected to the engine compressor,

but rather is air coupled. The hot gases generated by the gas generator section of the engine flow through the power turbine wheel and cause the power turbine and the propeller to rotate.

Another turbine section is mechanically linked to the compressor section and is used to drive the compressor. It is possible, during engine start, for the compressor and its turbine to be rotating while the propeller and the power turbine do not move. During engine start, the power turbine will eventually reach the speed of the compressor, but the starter motor is not under a load from the propeller and the power turbine during engine start. For this reason, the propeller can be shut down in feather and does not need a low blade angle latch mechanism for engine starting.

(1) Propeller

The propeller commonly used with the PT6 is a 3- or 4-bladed Hartzell steel hub reversing propeller. The propeller is flange-mounted on the engine and is

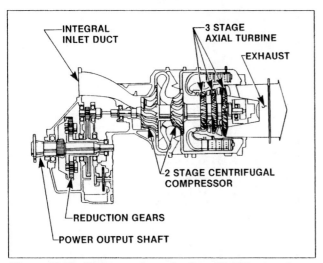

Figure 13-52. Cutaway view of a Garrett-AIResearch TPE-331 turboprop engine.

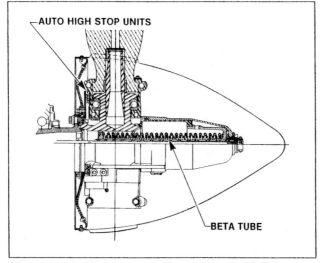

Figure 13-53. Hartzell propeller used on a TPE-331 engine.

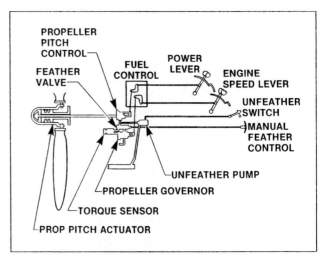

Figure 13-54. System components located on the gear reduction assembly of a TPE-331 engine.

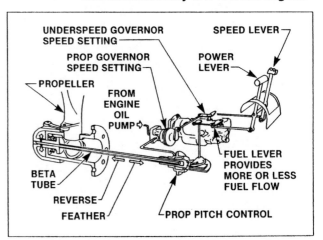

Figure 13-55. Control system for a TPE-331 engine.

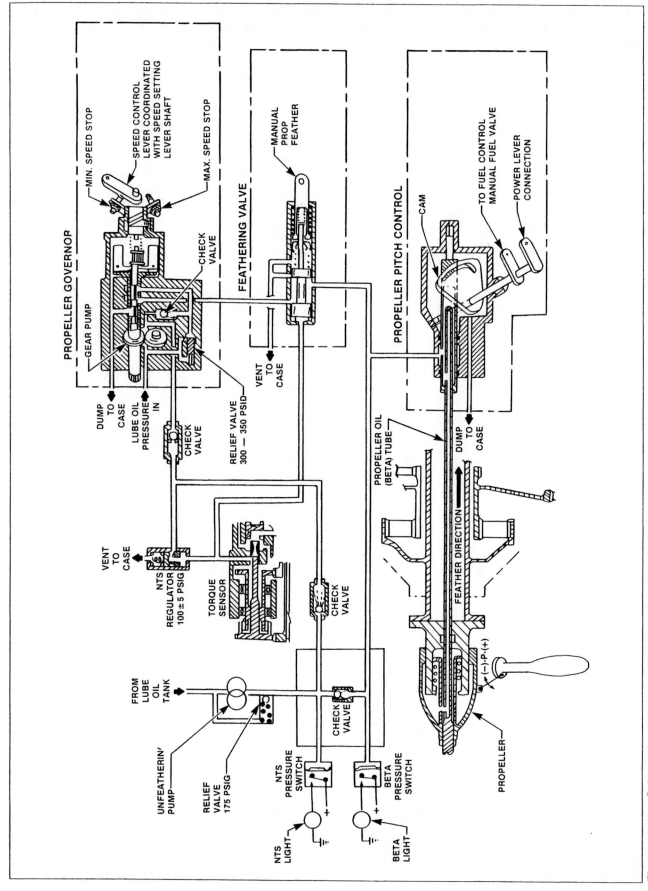

Figure 13-56. Schematic of the propeller control system for a TPE-331 engine.

250

spring-loaded and counterweighted to the feather position, with oil pressure being used to decrease the blade angle. A Beta slip ring assembly on the rear of the propeller serves as a follow-up mechanism in giving proportional propeller response to control inputs in the Beta mode.

(2) Governor

The propeller governor used with the PT6 is basically the same as other governors discussed for constant-speed operation. It uses a speeder spring and flyweights to control a pilot valve which directs oil flow to and from the propeller. A lift rod is incorporated in the governor to allow the propeller to feather.

For Beta mode operation, the governor contains a beta control valve operated by the power lever linkage, and it directs oil pressure generated by the governor

boost pump to the propeller, or else it relieves oil from the propeller to change the blade angle.

(3) System Components

A propeller over-speed governor is mounted on the gear reduction assembly and it releases oil from the propeller whenever the propeller RPM exceeds 100%. The release of oil pressure results in a higher blade angle and a reduction in RPM. The over-speed governor is adjusted by the overhaul facility, and it cannot be adjusted in flight. There are no cockpit controls to this governor except for a test mode in some aircraft.

A power turbine governor is installed on the gear reduction assembly as a safety backup in case the other propeller governing devices should fail. If the power turbine speed reaches about 105%, the power

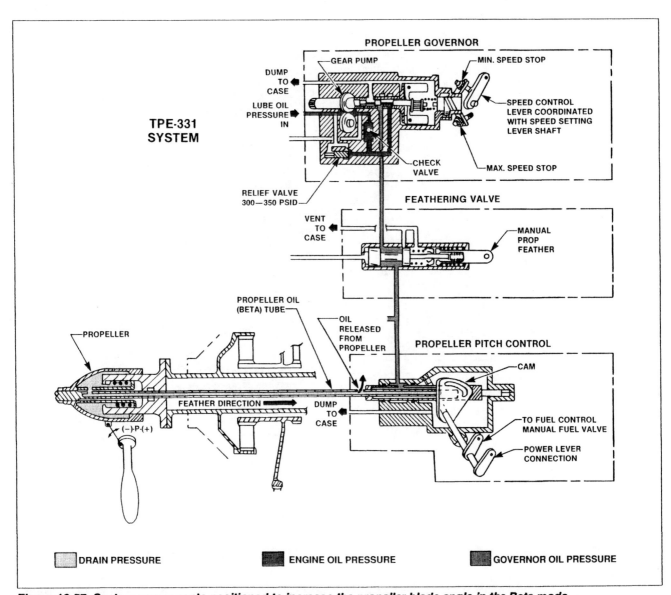

Figure 13-57. System components positioned to increase the propeller blade angle in the Beta mode.

turbine governor will reduce the fuel flow to the engine. The power turbine governor is not controllable from the cockpit.

The engine fuel control unit is mounted on the rear of the engine and is linked through a cam assembly to the Beta control valve on the propeller governor and also to the Beta slip ring on the propeller. This interconnection with the fuel control unit is used during Beta mode operation.

(4) Cockpit Controls

The cockpit controls for the PT6 turboprop installation consist of a power lever controlling engine power output in all modes and propeller blade angle in the Beta mode. There is also a propeller control lever which adjusts the system RPM when in the Alpha mode, and

a fuel cutoff lever which turns the fuel at the on or off fuel control.

The power lever is linked to the cam assembly on the side of the engine and, from there, rearward to the fuel control unit and forward to the propeller governor Beta control valve. The power lever adjusts both engine fuel flow and propeller blade angle when operating in the Beta mode which is reverse to flight idle. But in the Alpha mode, the lever controls only fuel flow to the engine.

The propeller control lever adjusts system RPM in the Alpha mode through conventional governor operation. Full aft movement of the lever raises the lift rod in the governor and causes the propeller to feather.

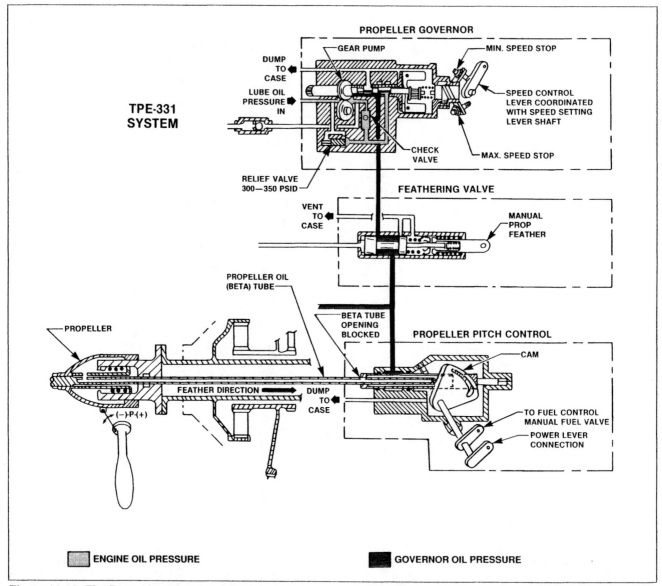

Figure 13-58. The Beta tube stops propeller blade angle change in the Beta mode by moving to the neutral position in the propeller pitch control unit.

The fuel cut-off lever turns the fuel to the engine on and off at the engine fuel control unit. Some designs have an intermediate position (lo-idle) to limit system power while operating on the ground.

(5) System Operation

Beta mode operation is generally in the range of 50-85% RPM. In this range, the power lever is used to control both fuel flow and propeller blade angle. When the power lever is moved forward, the cam assembly on the side of the engine causes the fuel flow to the engine to increase. At the same time, the linkage to the propeller governor moves the Beta control valve forward out of the governor body, and oil pressure in the propeller is released.

As the propeller cylinder moves rearward in response to the loss of oil, the slip ring on the rear of the cylinder moves rearward and, through the carbon block and linkage, returns the Beta control valve to a neutral position. This gives a proportional movement to the propeller.

When the power lever is moved rearward, fuel flow is reduced and the Beta control valve moves into the governor body, directing oil pressure to the propeller to decrease the blade angle. And as the propeller cylinder moves forward, the Beta control valve returns to its neutral position by the action of the slip ring, carbon block, and linkage. This again gives a proportional response.

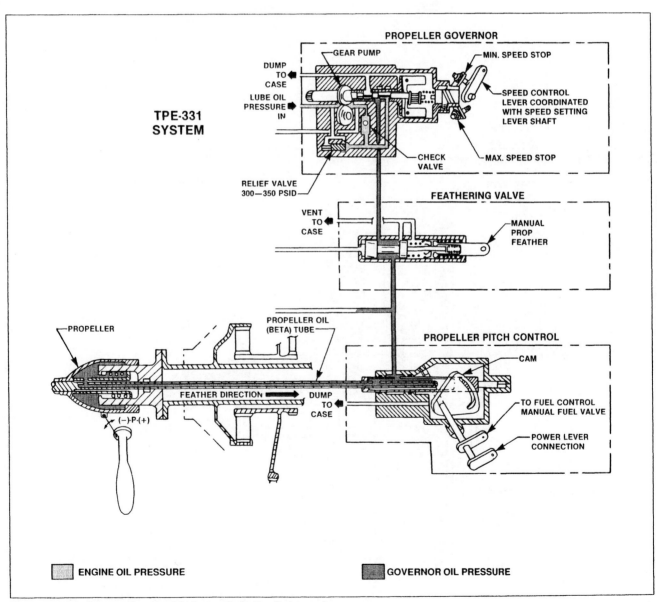

Figure 13-59. Decreasing the blade angle in the Beta mode.

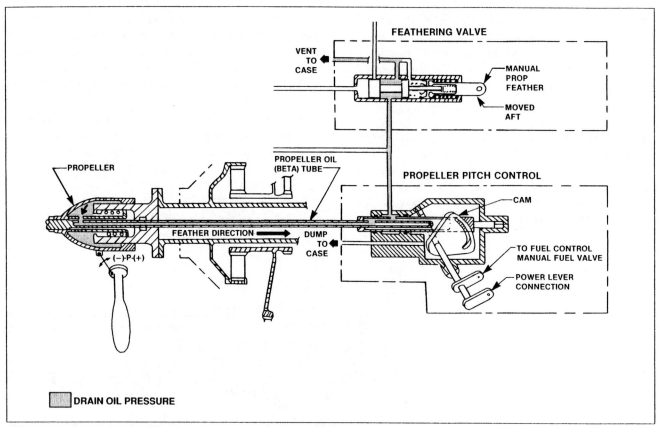

FEATHERING VALVE

VENT
TO
CASE

MANUAL
PROP
FEATHER

MOVED
AFT

PROPELLER

PROPELLER OIL
(BETA) TUBE

PROPELLER PITCH CONTROL

CAM

FEATHER DIRECTION → DUMP
TO
CASE

(−)P·(+)

TO FUEL CONTROL
MANUAL FUEL VALVE

POWER LEVER
CONNECTION

DRAIN OIL PRESSURE

Figure 13-60. Feathering the propeller by the cockpit controls.

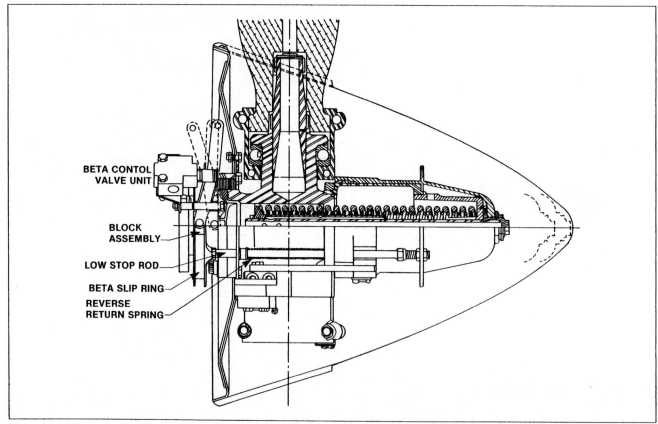

BETA CONTOL
VALVE UNIT

BLOCK
ASSEMBLY

LOW STOP ROD

BETA SLIP RING

REVERSE
RETURN SPRING

Figure 13-61. Hartzell propeller for use on a Pratt & Whitney of Canada PT6 engine.

If the power lever is moved aft of the zero thrust position, fuel flow will increase and the blade angle goes negative to allow a variable reverse thrust. This change in fuel flow is caused by the cam mechanism on the side of the engine.

During operation in the Beta mode, the propeller governor constant-speed mechanism is underspeed and the pilot valve is lowered. The governor oil pump supplies the oil pressure for propeller operation in the Beta mode.

In the Alpha mode, the system RPM is high enough for the propeller governor to operate, and the system is in a constant-speed mode of operation. When the power lever is moved forward, more fuel flows to the engine to increase the horsepower, and the propeller governor causes an increase in propeller blade angle to absorb the power increase and maintain the selected system RPM. If the power lever is moved aft, the blade angle will be decreased by the governor to maintain the selected RPM.

To feather the propeller, move the propeller control lever full aft. This raises the pilot valve in the governor by a lift rod, and releases all of the oil pressure in the propeller. The springs and counterweights in the propeller will take it to feather.

To unfeather the propeller, start the engine. As it begins to rotate, the power turbine will rotate, and the governor or Beta control valve will take the propeller to the selected blade angle or governor RPM setting. When the engine is restarted, the engine will be started before the propeller is rotating at the same proportional speed because of the free-turbine characteristic of the engine.

If the propeller RPM should exceed 100%, the propeller over-speed governor will raise its pilot valve and release oil from the propeller to increase blade angle and prevent over-speeding of the propeller. The over-speed governor is automatic and is not controllable in flight.

The power turbine governor prevents excessive over-speeding of the propeller by reducing fuel flow to the engine at approximately 105% RPM. This governor is not controllable in flight and is automatic in operation.

3. Blade Cuffs

A blade cuff is a metal, wood, or plastic structure designed for attachment to the shank end of the blade, with an outer surface that will transform the round shank into an airfoil section. The cuff is designed primarily to increase the flow of cooling air to the engine nacelle.

The cuffs are attached to the blades by mechanical clamping devices or by using bonding materials. Rubber-based adhesives and epoxy adhesives generally are used as bonding agents. Organic adhesives may cause corrosion, which results from moisture entrapment between the inner cuff surface and the outer shank surface.

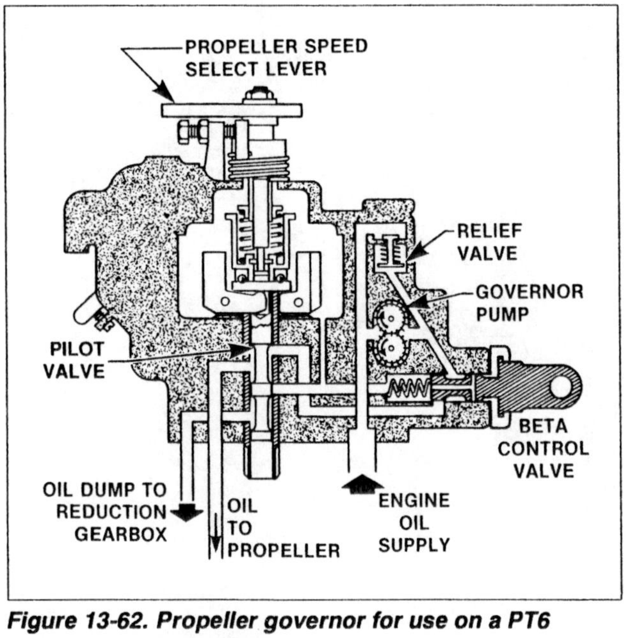

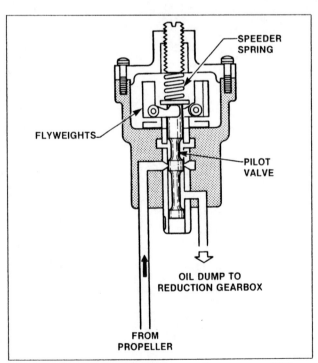

Figure 13-62. Propeller governor for use on a PT6 installation.

Figure 13-63. Over-speed governor for use on a PT6 installation.

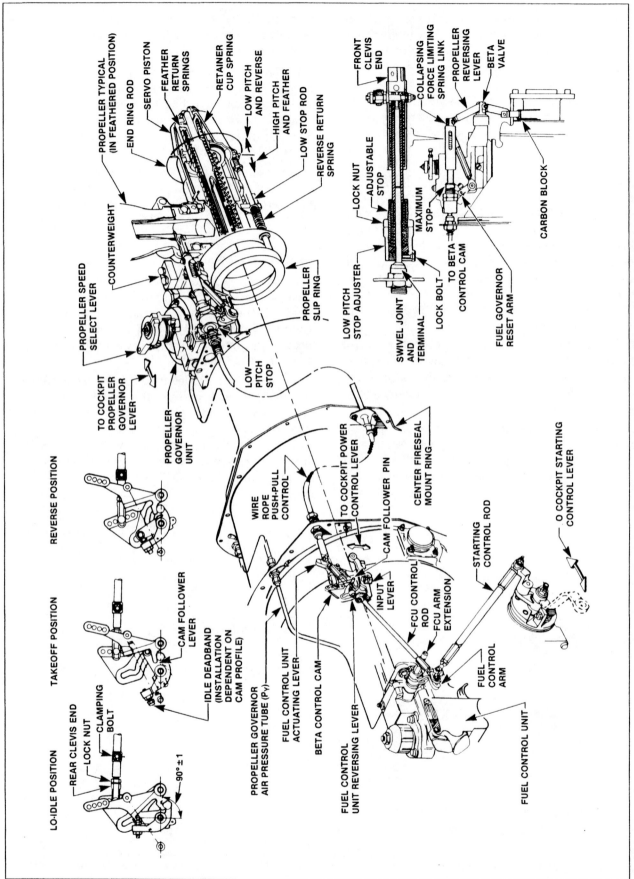

Figure 13-64. *Side view of a PT6 engine showing the position of the fuel control, the cam mechanism, and the propeller installation.*

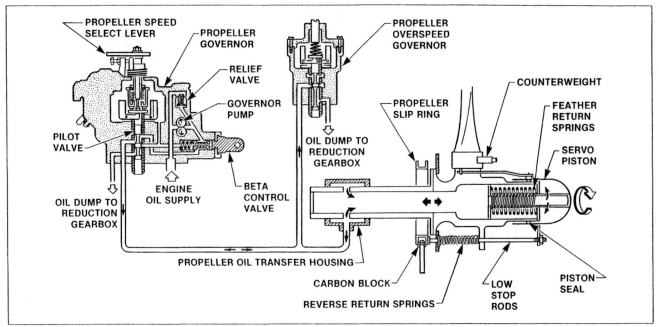

Figure 13-65. PT6 propeller system configuration.

PART IV

Aircraft Auxiliary Systems

Chapter XIV

Aircraft Cabin Atmospheric Control Systems

Humans live at the bottom of an ocean of air. This air, called the atmosphere, is a physical mixture of gases. Because it is a mixture, it is possible for its composition to vary, but actually it is quite consistent. Nitrogen makes up approximately 78% of the air we breathe, and while it is an inert gas, it is needed to dilute the oxygen which makes up 21% of the mixture. The other gases in the air, such as argon, neon, and krypton are relatively unimportant elements. Water vapor and carbon dioxide, on the other hand, are extremely important compounds.

The density of the air decreases as the pressure decreases. This change in air density is very important in the operation of high altitude aircraft. Aircraft should operate as high as possible, since the air resistance becomes less when the air density decreases.

Turbine engine powered aircraft are efficient at high altitude, but the human body is unable to exist in this cold and oxygen deficient air, so some provision must be made to provide an artificial environment to sustain life.

A. Aircraft Oxygen Systems

1. Characteristics of Oxygen

Oxygen is one of the most abundant elements on the earth. As an uncombined gas, it makes up more than one-fifth of the air we breathe. Nearly 90% of the weight of water is oxygen, and oxygen is found in most of the soil and rock that makes up the earth's crust.

As a gas, oxygen is colorless, odorless and tasteless, and it is extremely active chemically and will combine with almost all other elements and with many compounds. When any fuel burns, it unites with oxygen to produce heat, and in the human body, our tissues are continually being oxidized which causes the heat our bodies produce. This is the reason an ample supply of oxygen must be available at all times to support our life.

Oxygen is produced commercially by liquefying air, and when the nitrogen is allowed to boil off, relatively pure oxygen is left. Gaseous oxygen may also be produced by the electrolysis of water. When electrical current is passed through water (H_2O), it will break down into its two elements, hydrogen and oxygen.

Oxygen will not burn, but it does support combustion so well that special care must be taken when handling it that it is not used where there is any fire, hot material or any petroleum products. If pure oxygen is allowed to come in contact with oil, grease or any such product, it will combine violently and generate enough heat to ignite the material, and it will burn with a very hot flame.

Iron and steel may be cut by heating it red hot with an oxyacetylene flame and then directing a jet of pure oxygen onto the hot metal. The oxygen will combine with the hot metal and produce a flame hot enough to burn through it, cutting it as though with a knife.

Commercial oxygen is used in great quantities for welding and cutting and for medical use in hospitals and ambulances. Aviator's breathing oxygen is similar to that used for commercial purposes, except that it is additionally processed to remove almost all of the water that could freeze and stop the flow of oxygen when it is so vitally needed. Because of the additional purity required, you must never service an aircraft oxygen system with any oxygen that does not meet the specifications for aviators breathing oxygen. This is usually military specification MIL-O-21749 or MIL-O-27210. These specifications require the oxygen to have no more than 2 ml of water per liter of gas.

2. Forms of Oxygen

a. Gaseous Oxygen

Most of the aircraft in the general aviation fleet use gaseous oxygen usually stored in steel cylinders (figure 14-1) under a pressure of between 1,800 and 2,400 PSI. The main reason for using gaseous oxygen is its ease of handling and the fact that it is available at most of the airports used by these aircraft. It does have the disadvantage of all of the dangers associated with any high-pressure gas, and also there is a weight penalty because of the heavy storage cylinders.

b. Liquid Oxygen

Almost all military aircraft now carry their oxygen in its liquid state. Liquid oxygen is a pale blue, transparent liquid that will remain in its liquid state as long as it is stored at a temperature of below 181°F. This is done in aircraft installations by keeping it in a Dewar bottle which resembles a double-wall sphere having a vacuum between the walls. The vacuum prevents heat transferring into the inner container.

Liquid oxygen installations (figure 14-2) are extremely economical of space and weight and there is no high pressure involved in the system. They do have the disadvantage, however, of the dangers involved in handling the liquid at its extremely low temperature, and even when the oxygen system is not used, it will require periodic replenishing because of losses from the venting system.

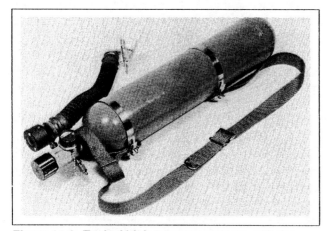

Figure 14-1. Typical high-pressure oxygen cylinder.

Figure 14-2. Liquid oxygen converter.

c. Chemical (Solid) Oxygen

A handy method of carrying oxygen for emergency use and for aircraft which require it only occasionally is the solid oxygen candle. This method of oxygen generation has been used for many years in submarines, and more recently in aircraft, and now a number of the large transport aircraft use it as a supplemental source of oxygen in the event of cabin depressurization.

Essentially, a solid oxygen generator (figure 14-3) consists of a shaped block of a chemical such as sodium chlorate encased in a protective steel case. It is ignited either electrically or by a mechanical igniter, and once it starts burning, it cannot be extinguished, but it must be used until it is exhausted. Solid oxygen candles have an almost unlimited shelf life and do not require any special conditions for their storage. They are safe to use and store because no high pressure is involved and the oxygen presents no fire hazard. They are relatively inexpensive and lightweight. On the negative side, they cannot be tested until they are actually used, and there is enough heat generated when they are used that they must be installed in such a way that

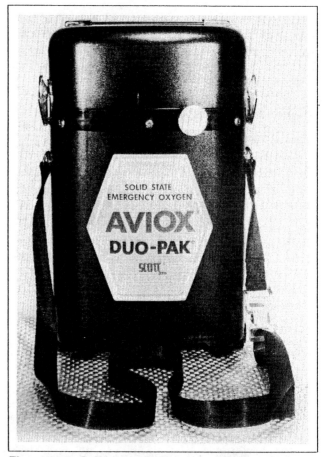

Figure 14-3. Solid (chemical) oxygen candle.

the heat can be dissipated without any damage to the aircraft structure.

d. Mechanically-separated Oxygen

A new procedure for producing oxygen is its extraction from the air by a mechanical separation process. Air is drawn through a patented material called a molecular sieve. As it passes through, the nitrogen and other gases are trapped in the sieve and only the oxygen passes through. Part of the oxygen is breathed, and the rest is used to purge the nitrogen from the sieve and prepare it for another cycle of filtering. This method of producing oxygen is currently being used in some medical facilities and is installed in some military aircraft. It appears to have the possibility of replacing all other types of oxygen because of the economy of weight and space, and the fact that the aircraft is no longer dependent upon ground facilities for its oxygen supply.

3. Oxygen Systems and Components

a. Gaseous Oxygen Systems

(1) Storage Cylinders

(a) Low-pressure Cylinders

Most military aircraft at one time used a low-pressure oxygen system in which the gaseous oxygen was stored under a pressure of approximately 450 PSI in large steel cylinders painted yellow. These cylinders were so large for the amount of oxygen they carried that they never became popular in civilian aircraft, and even the military has stopped using these systems.

(b) High-pressure Cylinders

Today, almost all gaseous oxygen is stored in green painted steel cylinders under a pressure of between 1,800 and 2,400 PSI. All cylinders approved for installation in an aircraft must be approved by the Department of Transportation (DOT) and may be of either the DOT 3AA 1800 or the DOT 3HT 1850 type.

Both types of cylinders must be hydrostatically tested to 5/3 of their working pressure, which means that the DOT 3AA cylinders are tested with water pressure of 3,000 PSI every 5 years and stamped with the date of the test. DOT 3HT cylinders must be tested with a water pressure of 3,083 PSI every 3 years, and these cylinders must be taken out of service after 15 years, or after they have been filled 4,380 times, whichever comes first.

All oxygen cylinders must be stamped near the filler neck with the approval number, the date of manufacture, and the dates of all of the hydrostatic tests. It is extremely important before servicing any oxygen system that you ensure that all cylinders are

proper for the installation and that they have all been inspected within the appropriate time limit.

Oxygen cylinders may be mounted permanently in the aircraft and connected to an installed oxygen plumbing system, or for light aircraft where oxygen is needed only occasionally, they may be carried as a part of a portable oxygen system. The cylinders for either type of system must meet the same requirements, and should be painted green and identified with the words AVIATOR'S BREATHING OXYGEN written in white letters on the cylinder.

(2) Regulators

It is the oxygen regulator that determines the type of system we have. There are two basic types of regulators in use, and in each type we have variations. For low-demand systems, such as are used in the smaller piston-engine powered general aviation aircraft, we normally use a continuous flow regulator that allows oxygen to flow from the storage cylinder regardless of whether the user is inhaling or exhaling. Continuous flow systems are not economical of the oxygen, but their simplicity and low cost make them desirable when the demands are low. The emergency oxygen systems that drop the mask to the passengers of large jet transport aircraft in the event of cabin depressurization are also of the continuous flow type.

Oxygen is almost always supplied to the crew of an aircraft by an efficient system that uses one of the demand-type regulators. Demand regulators allow a flow of oxygen only when the user is inhaling and shuts it off during exhale. There are several types of these regulators, as we will see.

(a) Continuous Flow Regulators

1) Manual Continuous Flow Regulator

A typical manually adjusted continuous flow oxygen regulator is shown in figure 14-4. The gauge on the right shows the pressure of the oxygen in the system and indicates indirectly the amount of oxygen available. The gauge on the left is a flow indicator and is adjusted by the knob in the lower center of the regulator. As the airplane ascends into the less dense air, the occupants need more oxygen, and with this type of regulator the user is able to adjust the flow to correspond with the altitude being flown, and the regulator will meter the correct amount of oxygen.

2) Automatic Continuous Flow Regulator

An automatic regulator, such as the one in figure 14-5, has a barometric control valve that automatically adjusts the oxygen flow to correspond with the altitude being flown. The flight crew need only open the valve on the front of the regulator, and the correct amount of oxygen will be metered into the system for the altitude being flown.

(b) Demand Regulators

The simple demand-type oxygen regulator, such as the one seen on the cylinder in figure 14-6, meters oxygen to the user only during inhale. This type of regulator is far more economical of the oxygen than the continuous flow type, but there are regulators that are even more efficient.

Figure 14-4. Manual continuous flow oxygen regulator.

Figure 14-5. Automatic continuous flow oxygen regulator.

(c) Diluter Demand Regulators

The oxygen regulator used by the flight crews for most commercial jet aircraft are of the diluter demand type. In figure 14-7, we have a very basic schematic of this type of regulator. When the supply lever is turned on, oxygen can flow from the supply into the regulator. There is a pressure reducer at the inlet of the regulator that decreases the pressure to a value that is usable by the regulator. The demand valve shuts off all flow of oxygen to the mask until the wearer inhales and decreases the pressure inside the regulator. This decreased pressure pulls the demand diaphragm over and opens the demand valve so oxygen can flow through the regulator to the mask.

A diluter demand regulator dilutes the oxygen supplied to the mask with air from the cabin. This air enters the regulator through the inlet air valve and passes around the air metering valve. At low altitude, the air inlet passage is open and the passage to the oxygen demand valve is restricted so the user gets mostly air from the cabin. As the aircraft goes up in altitude, the barometric control bellows expands and opens the oxygen passage while closing off the air passage. At an altitude of around 34,000', the air passage is completely closed off, and every time the user inhales, pure oxygen is metered to the mask.

If there is ever smoke in the cabin, or if for any reason the user wants pure oxygen, the oxygen selector on the face of the regulator can be moved

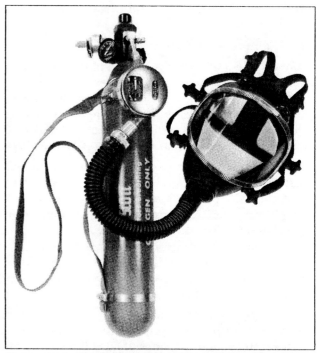

Figure 14-6. Portable oxygen system fitted with a demand regulator feeding oxygen to a full-face type mask.

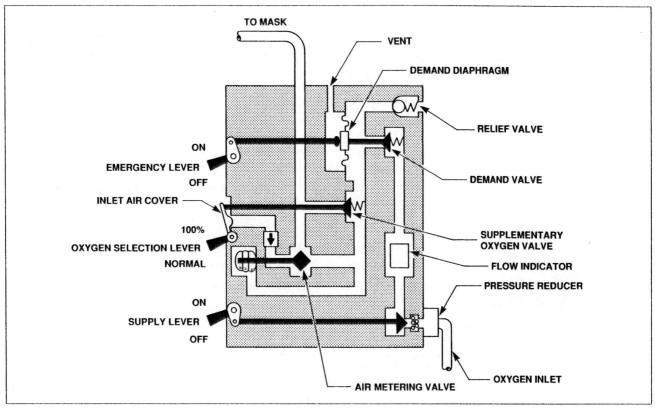

Figure 14-7. Operating principle of a diluter demand oxygen regulator.

from the NORMAL position to the 100% position. This closes the outside air passage and opens a supplemental oxygen valve inside the regulator so pure oxygen can flow to the mask.

An additional safety feature is incorporated that bypasses the regulator. When the emergency lever is placed in the EMERGENCY position, the demand valve is held open and oxygen flows continuously from the supply system to the mask as long as the supply lever is in the ON position.

(d) Pressure Demand Regulators

Military aircraft fly at altitudes of more than 40,000' and at this altitude they must have provision to supply 100% oxygen under a positive pressure to the mask. When we breathe normally, we expand our lungs and the atmospheric pressure forces air into them. But at altitudes above 40,000' we cannot get enough oxygen into our lungs even with the regulator on 100%.

Pressure demand regulators (an example is shown in figure 14-8) operate in much the same way as diluter demand regulators except at the extremely high altitudes, where the oxygen is forced into the mask under a positive pressure. Breathing at this high altitude requires a different technique from that required in breathing normally. The oxygen flows

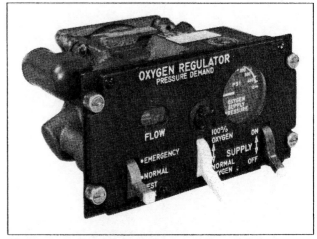

Figure 14-8. Pressure demand oxygen regulator.

into the lungs without effort on the part of the user, but muscular effort is needed to force the used air out of the lungs. This is exactly the opposite of normal breathing.

(3) Masks

(a) Continuous Flow Masks

Almost all of the masks used with a continuous flow oxygen system are of the rebreather type and vary from the simple bag-type disposable mask used with some of the portable systems to the rubber bag-type mask used for some of the flight crew systems.

Oxygen enters a rebreather mask (figure 14-9) at the bottom of the bag, and the mask fits the face of the user very loosely so air can escape around it. If the rebreather bag is full of oxygen when the user inhales, the lungs fill with oxygen. Oxygen continues to flow into the bag and fill it from the bottom at the same time the user exhales used air into the bag at the top. When the bag fills, the air that was in the lungs longest will spill out of the bag into the outside air, and when the user inhales, the first air to enter the lungs is that which was first exhaled and still has some oxygen in it. This air is mixed with pure oxygen, and so oxygen rich air is always breathed with this type of mask. More elaborate rebreather-type masks have a close-fitting cup over the nose and mouth with a built-in check valve which allows the air to escape, but prevents the user breathing air from the cabin.

The oxygen masks that automatically drop from the overhead compartment of a jet transport aircraft in the event of cabin depressurization are of the rebreather type. The plastic cup that fits over the mouth and nose has a check valve in it, and the plastic bag attached to the cup is the rebreather bag.

(b) Demand-type Masks

All demand-type masks must fit tightly to the face so no outside air can enter to disturb the metering of the regulator (figure 14-10). Demand masks all connect to the regulator with a large diameter corrugated hose, whereas the continuous flow masks all use a small diameter tube to carry the oxygen to the mask.

A full-face mask is available for use in case the cockpit should ever be filled with smoke. These masks cover the eyes as well as the mouth and nose, and the positive pressure inside the mask prevents any smoke entering.

(4) Plumbing and Valves

Most of the rigid plumbing lines that carry high-pressure oxygen are made of stainless steel, with the end fittings silver soldered to the tubing. Lines that

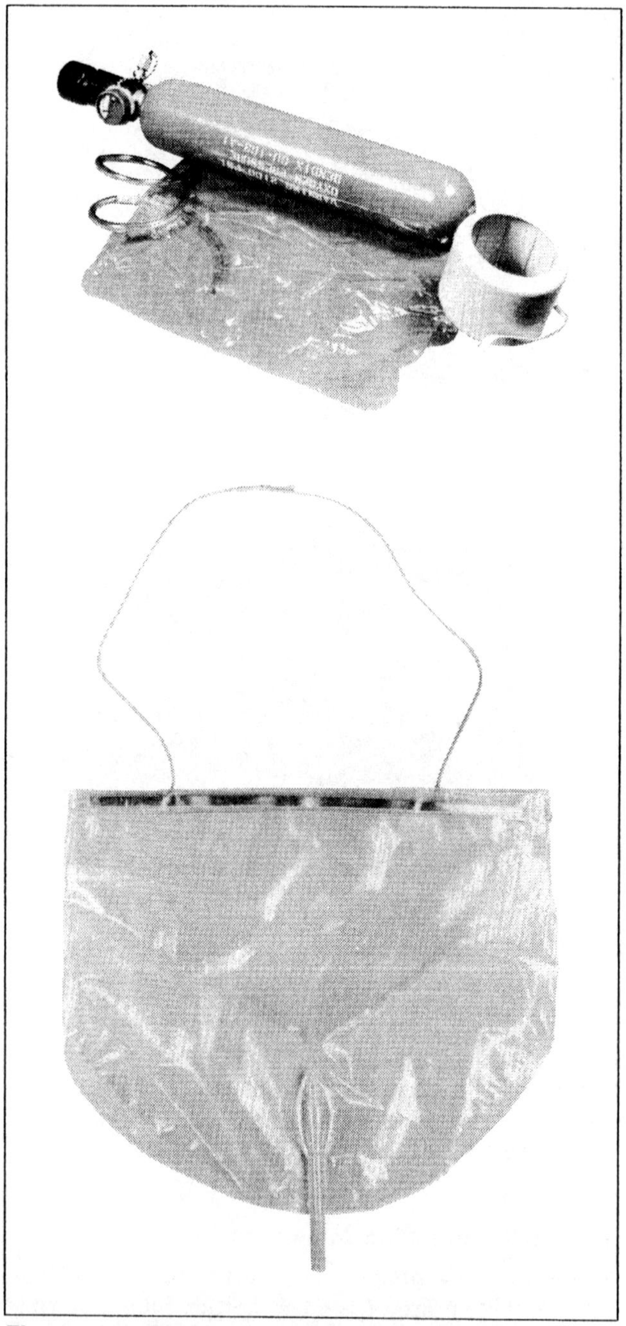

Figure 14-9. Rebreather-type mask used with continuous flow oxygen regulators.

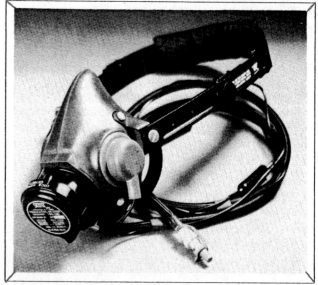

Figure 14-10. Oxygen mask used with demand-type oxygen regulator.

carry low-pressure oxygen are made of aluminum alloy and are terminated with the same type fittings used for any other fluid-carrying line in the aircraft. The fittings may be of either the flared or flareless type. It is essential in any form of aircraft maintenance that only approved components be used. This is especially true of oxygen system components. Only valves carrying the correct part number should be used to replace any valve in an oxygen system.

Many of the valves used in oxygen systems are of the slow-opening type to prevent a rapid in-rush of oxygen that could cause excessive heat and become a fire hazard. Other valves have restrictors in them to limit the flow rate through a fully open valve.

(5) Typical Installed Oxygen Systems

(a) Continuous Flow System

In figure 14-11, a typical continuous flow oxygen system is illustrated which is installed in a single-engine general aviation type of aircraft. The external filler valve is installed in a location that is convenient to service and is usually covered with an inspection door. It has an orifice that limits the filling rate and is protected with a cap to prevent contamination when the charging line is not connected. The storage cylinder is of an approved type and is installed in the aircraft in such a location that is most appropriate for weight and balance considerations. The shutoff valve on the cylinder is of the slow-opening type and requires several turns of the knob to open or close it to prevent too rapid a change in the flow rate which could place too much strain on the system or could generate too much heat. Some installations use a pressure reducing valve on the cylinder, and when the reducer is placed here, the pressure gauge must be mounted on the cylinder side of the reducer to determine the amount of oxygen in the cylinder.

The pressure gauge is used as an indication of the amount of oxygen in the cylinder. This is not, of course, a direct indication of quantity, but within the limitations seen when discussing system servicing, it can be used to indicate the amount of oxygen on board.

The pressure regulator reduces the pressure in the cylinder to a pressure that is usable by the masks. This regulator may be, as has been seen, either a manual or an automatic type. There must be provision, one way or another, to vary the amount of pressure supplied to the masks as the altitude changes.

The mask couplings are fitted with restricting orifices to meter the amount of oxygen needed at each mask. In figure 14-11, the pilot's coupling has

an orifice considerably larger than that provided for the passengers. The reason is that the pilot and other flight crew members require more oxygen since they are more active, and their alertness is of more vital importance than that of the passengers.

Some installations incorporate a therapeutic mask adapter. This is used for any passenger that has a health problem that would require additional oxygen. The flow rate through a therapeutic adapter is approximately three times than that through a normal passenger mask adapter.

Each tube to the mask has a flow indicator built into it. This is simply a colored indicator that is visible when no oxygen is flowing. When oxygen flows, it pushes the indicator out of sight.

(b) Diluter Demand System for Crew, with Continuous Flow System for Passengers

Pressurized aircraft do not normally have oxygen available for passengers all of the time, but FAR Part 91 requires that under certain flight conditions, the pilot operating the controls wear and use an oxygen mask. Because of this requirement, most executive aircraft that operate at high altitude are equipped with diluter demand or pressure demand oxygen regulators for the flight crew and a continuous flow system for the occupants of the cabin. A schematic of this type of system is shown in figure 14-12.

(c) Pressure Demand Systems

These systems are used primarily for high altitude military aircraft and were described earlier in this discussion.

b. Liquid Oxygen Systems

Civilian aircraft do not generally use liquid oxygen (LOX) systems because of the difficulty in handling this form of oxygen, and because it is not readily available to the fixed-base operators who service general aviation aircraft. The military, on the other hand, uses liquid oxygen almost exclusively because of the space and weight savings it makes possible. One liter of liquid oxygen will produce approximately 860 liters of gaseous oxygen at the pressure required for breathing.

The regulators and masks are the same as those used for gaseous oxygen systems, the difference in the systems being in the supply. Shown in figure 14-13 is a sketch of a typical LOX converter and supply system. Liquid oxygen is held in the spherical converter and in normal operation the buildup and vent valve is back-seated so some of the LOX can flow into the buildup coil where it absorbs enough heat to evaporate and pressurize the system to the amount allowed by the container pressure regulator,

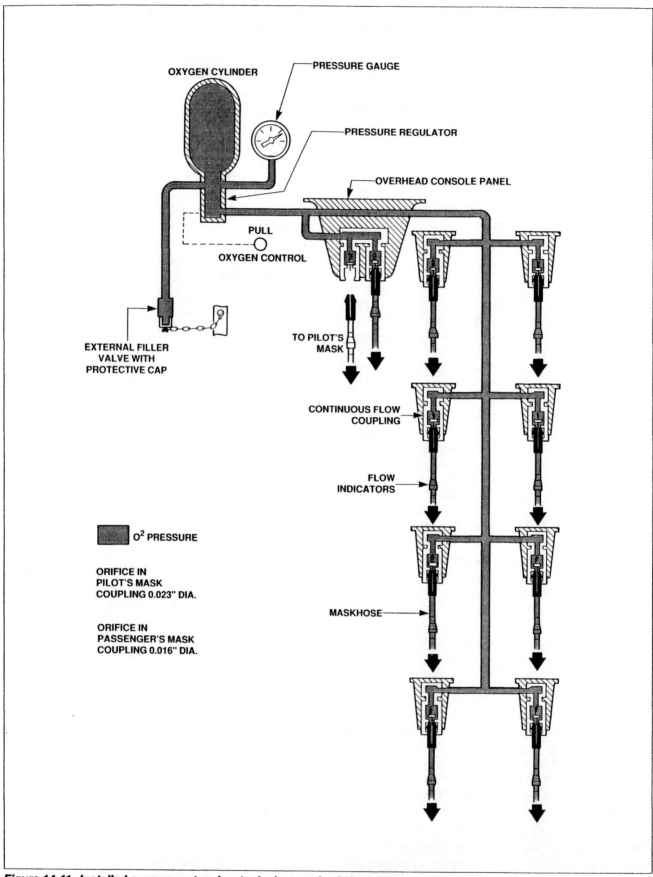

OXYGEN CYLINDER

PRESSURE GAUGE

PRESSURE REGULATOR

OVERHEAD CONSOLE PANEL

PULL

OXYGEN CONTROL

EXTERNAL FILLER
VALVE WITH
PROTECTIVE CAP

TO PILOT'S
MASK

CONTINUOUS FLOW
COUPLING

FLOW
INDICATORS

MASKHOSE

O^2 PRESSURE

ORIFICE IN
PILOT'S MASK
COUPLING 0.023" DIA.

ORIFICE IN
PASSENGER'S MASK
COUPLING 0.016" DIA.

Figure 14-11. Installed oxygen system in a typical general aviation airplane.

normally about 70 PSI. This gaseous oxygen maintains a relatively constant pressure in the converter and supplies the oxygen to the regulator.

When the supply valve on the regulator is turned on, LOX flows from the converter into the supply evaporator coil where it absorbs heat and turns into gaseous oxygen.

If, for any reason, excessive pressure should build up in the system, it will vent overboard through one of the relief valves.

c. Chemical Oxygen Systems

Sodium chlorate mixed with appropriate binders and a fuel is formed into a block, called a candle (figure 14-14). When this candle is burned, it releases oxygen. The shape and composition of the candle determines the oxygen flow rate. An igniter, actuated either electrically or by a spring, starts the candle burning, and as the sodium chlorate decomposes, it produces oxygen by a chemical action that looks something like this:

$$2\ NaClO_3 + HEAT \rightarrow 2\ NaCl + 2O_2$$

The core of the candle is insulated to retain the heat needed for the chemical action and to prevent the housing from getting too hot, and filters are located at the outlet to prevent any contaminants entering the system.

The long shelf life of unused chemical oxygen generators makes them an ideal source of oxygen for occasional flights where oxygen is needed, and for the emergency oxygen supply for pressurized

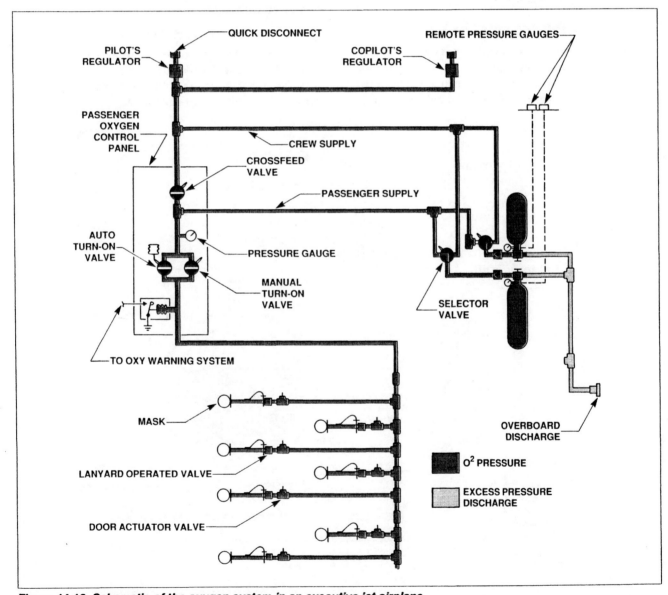

Figure 14-12. Schematic of the oxygen system in an executive jet airplane.

aircraft where oxygen is required only as a standby in case cabin pressurization is lost.

, The emergency oxygen systems for pressurized aircraft have the oxygen generators mounted in either the overhead rack, in seat backs, or in bulkhead panels. The masks are located with these generators and are enclosed, hidden from view by a door that may be opened electrically by one of the flight crew members or automatically by an aneroid valve in the event of cabin depressurization. When the door opens, the mask drops out where it is easily accessible to the user. Attached to the mask is a lanyard that, when pulled, releases the lock pin from the flow initiation mechanism, so the striker (figure 14-15) can hit the igniter and start the candle burning. Once a chemical oxygen candle is ignited, it must burn until it is exhausted.

B. Aircraft Pressurization Systems

The air that forms our atmosphere allows people to live and breathe easily because of sufficient air pressure at low altitudes to force the needed amount of air into our lungs. But flight is most efficient at high altitudes where the air is thin and the aerodynamic drag is low, and where there are a minimum of weather problems.

1. Pressure of the Atmosphere

The atmosphere envelops the earth and extends upward for more than 20 mi., but because air has mass and is compressible, the gravity of the earth pulls on it and causes the air at the lower levels to be more dense than the air above it. This accounts for the fact that more than one-half of the mass of the air surrounding the earth is below about 18,000'.

Standard conditions have been established for all of the important parameters of the earth's atmosphere. The pressure exerted by the blanket of air is considered to be 29.92", or 760 mm of mercury, which is the same as 14.69 PSI at sea level, and it decreases with altitude.

2. Temperature and Altitude

The standard temperature of the air at sea level is 15°C (59°F). The temperature also decreases with altitude. Above 36,000 ft., the temperature of the air stabilizes, remaining at 55°C (69.7°F).

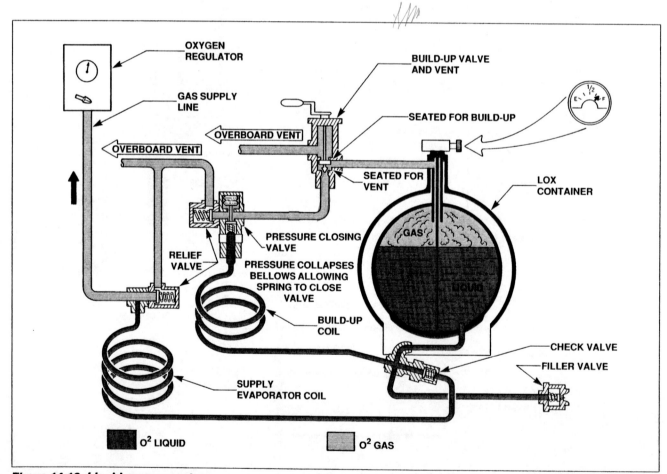

Figure 14-13. Liquid oxygen system.

3. Pressurization

Turbine engines operate effectively at these high altitudes, but piston engines (as well as human occupants of an aircraft) require additional oxygen to be supplied. Superchargers compress the air before it enters the cylinders of a reciprocating engine, and we can supply the occupants with supplemental oxygen.

The pressurization of modern aircraft is achieved by directing air into the cabin from either the compressor of the jet engine, from a turbosupercharger, or from an auxiliary compressor. The amount of air pumped into the cabin is in excess of that needed, and the cabin pressure is controlled by varying the amount of air allowed to leave the cabin through the controller-operated outflow valve.

Most of the cabin pressurization systems have two modes of operation: the isobaric mode in which the cabin is maintained at a constant altitude (thus the name iso is the same, and baric means pressure), and the constant pressure differential mode. In the isobaric mode, the pressure regulator controls the outflow valve as the aircraft goes up in altitude to maintain the same pressure in the cabin. When the

pressure differential between that inside the cabin and that outside reaches the maximum structural pressure limitation, the pressure controller shifts to the constant differential mode and maintains a constant pressure differential. As the flight altitude increases, so does the cabin altitude, always maintaining the same differential pressure between the inside and the outside.

4. Sources of Pressurizing Air

a. Reciprocating Engine Aircraft

When pressurization was first used, it was for large aircraft such as the Lockheed Constellations and the Douglas DC-6s. These large cabins required great volumes of compressed air, and this was provided by a positive displacement Roots-type compressor or by a variable displacement centrifugal compressor driven by one of the engines.

Pressurization air for the smaller single- and twin-engine piston-engine-powered aircraft is provided by bleed air from the engine turbochargers and from the exhaust of the dry-type air pumps that are used to operate some of the flight instruments. A typical turbocharger pressurization supply system is shown in figure 14-16.

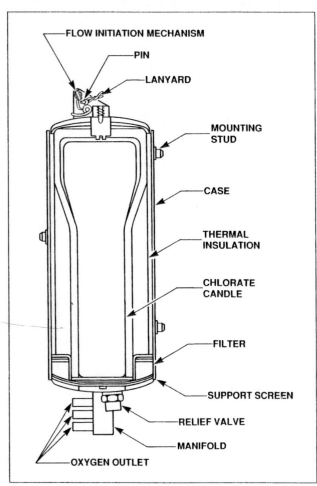

Figure 14-14. Chemical oxygen candle.

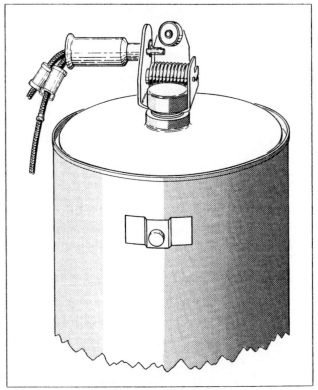

Figure 14-15. Strike for a chemical oxygen candle. Pulling the lanyard removes the safety pin and allows the spring to drive the striker down onto the flow initiation mechanism.

b. Turbine Engine Aircraft

The compressor in a turbine engine is a good source of air to pressurize the cabin, and since this air is quite hot it is used to provide heat as well as pressurization.

Engine power is required to compress this air, and this power must be taken from that available to power the aircraft.

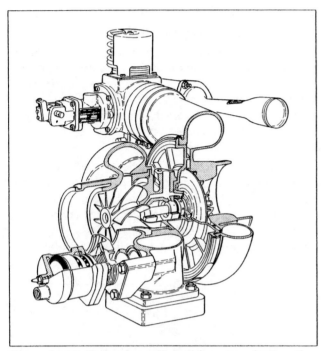

Figure 14-16. Turbochargers supply pressurization air through the venturi which serves as a flow limiter.

Compressor bleed air may be used directly or it may be used to drive a turbocompressor (figure 14-17). Outside air is taken in and compressed, and then, before it enters the cabin, it is mixed with the engine compressor bleed air that has been used to drive the turbocompressor.

A jet pump flow multiplier will provide cabin pressurization air without the complexity of the turbocompressor. Compressor bleed air flows through the nozzle of a jet pump (figure 14-18) at a high velocity and produces a low pressure that draws air in from the outside of the aircraft. The bleed air and the outside air mix and flow into the cabin to provide the air needed for pressurization.

5. Control of Cabin Pressure

It would be impractical to build the pressure vessel of an aircraft that is airtight, as pressurization is accomplished by flowing more air into the cabin than is needed and allowing the excess air to leak out. There are two types of leakage in an aircraft pressure vessel; controlled and uncontrolled. The uncontrolled leakage is that in which air escapes around door and window seals, control cables and other openings in the sealed portion of the structure, and the controlled leakage through the outflow valve and the safety valve. This controlled leakage is far more than the uncontrolled, and it determines the amount of pressure in the cabin. Pressurization control systems can be of the pneumatic or electronic type with the electronic type incorporating electrically controlled outflow valves.

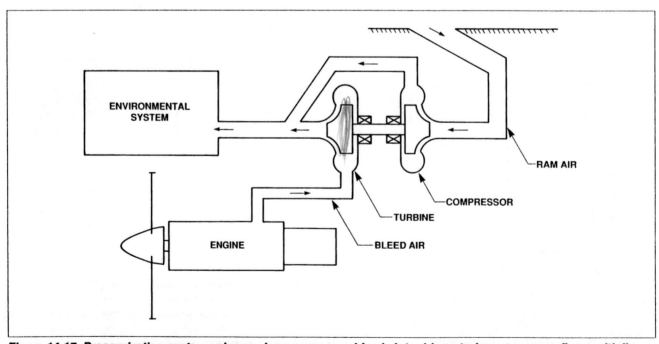

Figure 14-17. Pressurization system using engine compressor bleed air to drive a turbocompressor flow multiplier.

a. Pressurization Cockpit Controls

Most pressurization systems have three basic cockpit indicators, cabin altitude, cabin rate of climb, and the pressure differential indicator (figure 14-19). The cabin altitude gauge measures the actual cabin altitude. The cabin altitude is almost always much below that of the aircraft, except when the aircraft is on the ground. An example would be an aircraft cruising at 40,000' would normally gave a cabin altitude of about 8,000'. The cabin rate-of-climb indicator tells the pilot or flight engineer the rate the cabin is either climbing or descending. Normal climb rate is 500' per minute and normal descending rate is 300' per minute. The cabin rate-of-climb can be automatic or manual according to the type of aircraft. The differential pressure gauge reads the current difference in pressure between the aircraft's cabin interior and the outside air. The modes of operation of the pressurization system are generally automatic and manual control. In the manual control mode, the pilots can control the outflow valves directly through switches and indicators that are used to position the outflow valves if the automatic mode fails. If the cabin altitude exceeds 10,000', on most aircraft, an alarm (intermittent horn) will sound alerting the flight crew to take action.

b. Cabin Air Pressure Regulator and Outflow Valve Operation

The outflow valve and the safety valve are normally located in the pressure bulkhead at the rear of the aircraft cabin. The outflow valve is controlled by the altitude controller and can be closed, open or modulated, which means that it is working at a position somewhere between the two extremes to maintain the pressure called for by the controller. The safety valve is normally open or closed and is used primarily as a backup in case of a malfunction of the outflow valve.

The altitude controller contains an altitude selector and a rate controller. In figure 14-20, there is a schematic of the pressurization controls, and in figure 14-21, the operation of the outflow valve is illustrated. The safety valve is essentially the same as the outflow valve except for its controls.

The outflow valve is closed until it receives a signal from the controller, and as soon as the safety valve closes, the cabin begins to be pressurized at the rate allowed by the rate controller. This increase in pressure is sensed by the controller. When the cabin reaches the selected altitude, the diaphragm in the controller moves back and vacuum is sent into the outflow valve to open it and allow some of the pressurizing air to escape from the cabin. This modulation of the outflow valve will maintain the cabin

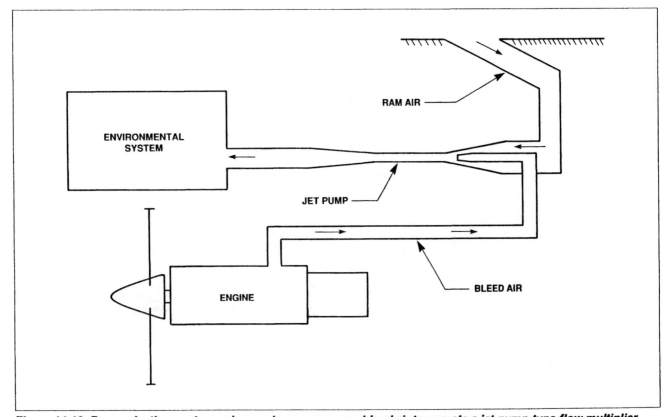

Figure 14-18. Pressurization system using engine compressor bleed air to operate a jet-pump-type flow multiplier.

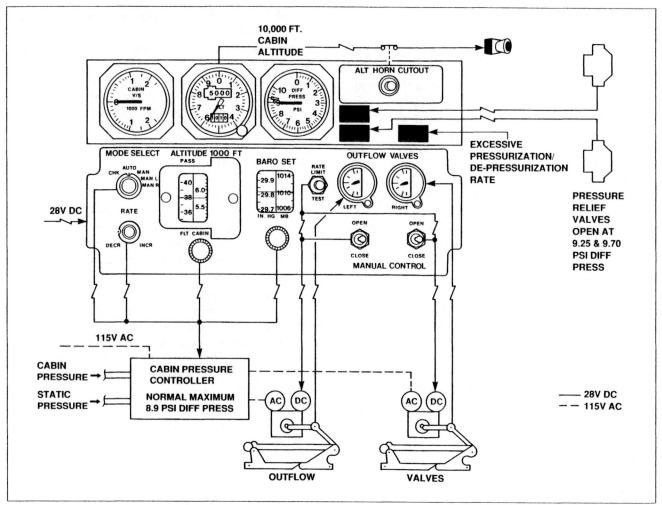

Figure 14-19. Pressurized cockpit indicators.

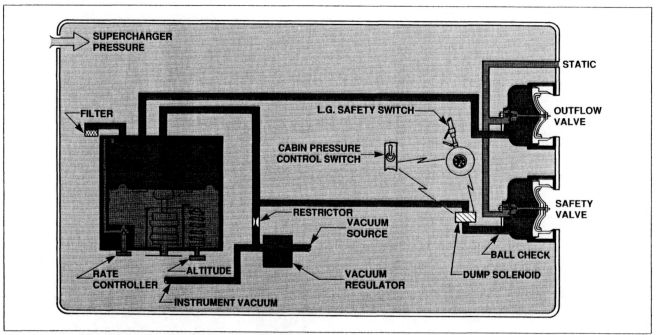

Figure 14-20. Pneumatic pressurization control system.

pressure at the altitude selected. As the flight altitude increases, the outside pressure decreases, and when it becomes low enough that the cabin differential pressure reaches close to the structural limit, the upper diaphragm in the outflow valve moves up until the adjusting screw depresses the valve and releases some of the reference pressure to the outside air. This decrease in pressure allows the outflow valve to open so it can maintain the cabin pressure at a constant amount above the outside air pressure.

c. Cabin Air Pressure Safety Valve Operation

When the aircraft is on the ground and prepared for flight, the cabin is closed and the safety valve is held off its seat by vacuum from the vacuum pump acting on the diaphragm. The dump solenoid in the vacuum line is held open because the circuit through the landing gear safety switch is completed when the weight of the aircraft is on the landing gear.

As soon as the aircraft takes off, the safety switch circuit opens and the dump solenoid shuts off the vacuum line to the safety valve, and the valve closes. If for any reason the pressure in the cabin should exceed a set limit, the safety valve will open fully. This will prevent the cabin from being overly pressurized which could cause the structure of the aircraft to fail.

d. Air Distribution

The air distribution system on most aircraft takes cold air from the packs (air-conditioning packages) and hot engine bleed air and mixes the two in the air mix manifold. The air is then mixed together depending on the temperature called for by the flight crew. The air is then distributed to side wall or overhead vents in the cabin. The cabin air is drawn back into the air mixing manifold by recirculating fans, mixed with new incoming air, then redistributed to the aircraft cabin. A Boeing 747 distribution system is shown in figure 14-22. A gasper fan provides air for the overhead air outlets for the passengers. Each passenger can turn the gasper fan air on or off by turning the air outlet.

C. Aircraft Heaters

1. Types of Heaters

a. Exhaust Shroud Heaters

The most common type of heater for small single-engine aircraft is the exhaust shroud heater. A sheet metal shroud is installed around the muffler in the engine exhaust system, and cold air is taken into this shroud and held against the muffler so it can absorb some of the heat that is being wasted. This air is then routed into the cabin through a heater valve in the firewall. When the heater is not on, this air is directed overboard. This type of heater is quite economical for these small aircraft, as it requires no energy other than that which is otherwise wasted.

One of the problems with this type of heater is the possibility of carbon monoxide poisoning if there should be a crack in the exhaust system. For this

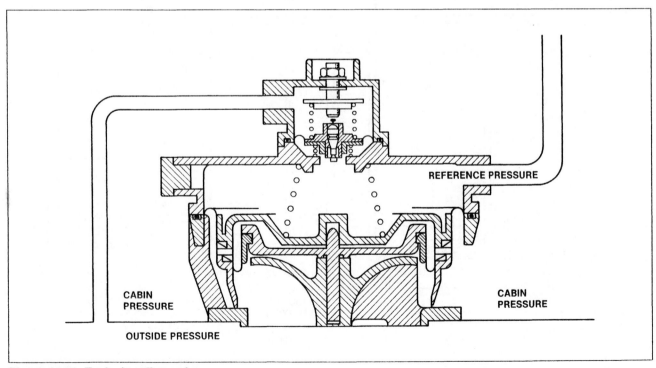

Figure 14-21. Typical outflow valve.

reason, it is very important that the shrouds be removed and the exhaust pipes and mufflers carefully inspected on the schedule recommended by the aircraft manufacturer.

The amount of heat that is transferred to the air from the muffler is determined by the amount of the muffler's surface area. Some manufacturers have increased this area by using welded-on studs (figure 14-23). This type of muffler is more efficient but it must be checked with special care as it is possible for minute cracks to start where the studs are welded on.

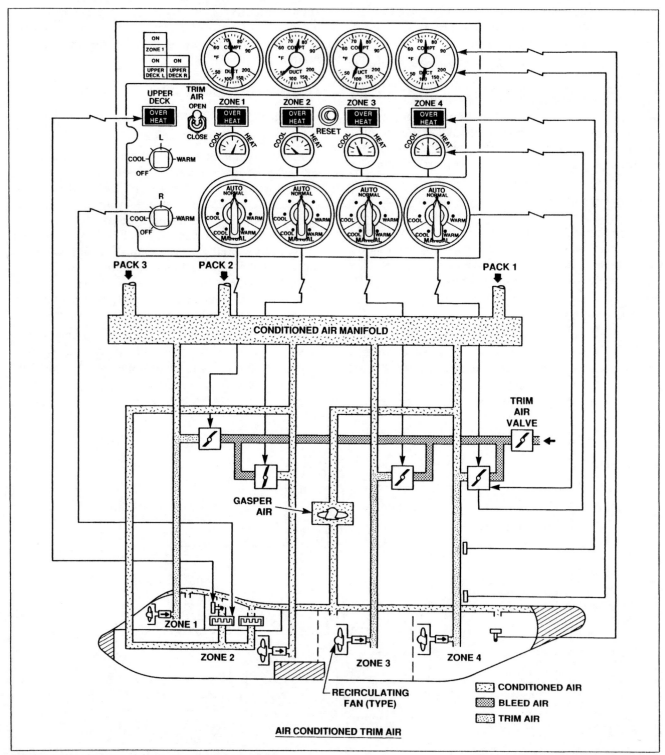

Figure 14-22. Boeing 747 air distribution system.

b. Electric Heating Systems

Electric heating on most aircraft is generally a supplemental heating source. The heaters use heating elements that create heat through electrical resistance. Some aircraft use this type of heat when the aircraft is on the ground and the engines are not running. A fan blows air over the heating coils in the heating elements which heats and circulates the air back into the cabin. Safety devices are installed in these systems to prevent them from overheating if the ventilating fan should become inoperative.

c. Combustion Heaters

Exhaust shroud heaters are used for small single-engine aircraft, and compressor bleed air heating is primarily used on large turbine-powered aircraft. The light- and medium-twin engine aircraft are often heated with combustion heaters (figure 14-24).

These popular heaters consist of two stainless steel cylinders, one inside the other. Combustion air from outside the aircraft is forced into the inner cylinder, and aviation gasoline drawn from the fuel tank is sprayed over a spark plug that is continually sparking. This results in a very hot flame that heats the combustion chamber, and then the gases are exhausted overboard. Ventilating air flows through the outer cylinder around the combustion chamber and picks up the heat and distributes it through the cabin. This type of heater has a number of safety features that prevent it creating a fire hazard in the event of a malfunction. A complete schematic of a combustion heater system is illustrated in figure 14-25.

(1) Combustion Air System

The air that is used in the combustion process is picked up from a scoop on the outside of the aircraft and is forced into the combustion chamber by the combustion air blower.

Figure 14-23. Engine muffler with studs welded on its surface to increase the amount of heat transfer.

(2) Fuel System

Fuel is taken from the aircraft fuel system and pressurized with a constant pressure pump, and after it passes through a fuel filter, it is controlled by a solenoid valve that may be turned off by the overheat switch, the limit switch, or by the pressure switch. There is a second solenoid valve in the fuel line that is controlled by the cabin thermostat. It shuts off the fuel just before it enters the combustion chamber.

(3) Ventilation Air System

Ram air is taken into the heater from outside the aircraft, and it flows over the outside of the combustion chamber, where it picks up heat and carries it inside the aircraft. There is a ventilating fan in the heater that operates when the aircraft is on the ground, but when the aircraft becomes airborne, a switch on the landing gear shuts off the ventilating fan. The ventilating air pressure is slightly higher than the pressure of the combustion air, so in the event of a crack in the combustion chamber, ventilating air will flow into the combustion chamber rather than allowing the combustion air that contains carbon monoxide to mix with the ventilating air.

(4) Controls

The only action required by the pilot to start the combustion heater is to turn the cabin heater switch ON and adjust the cabin thermostat to the temperature wanted by the heater to maintain. When the cabin heater switch is turned on, the fuel pump starts, as well as both the ventilating air and the combustion air blowers. As soon as the combustion air blower moves the required amount of air, it trips a pressure switch which starts the ignition coil supplying sparks to the igniter plug. The fuel supply solenoid valve is opened and fuel can get to the heater. When the thermostat calls for heat, the second fuel solenoid valve opens and fuel sprays into the combustion chamber and burns. As soon as the temperature reaches the value for which the thermostat is set, the contacts inside the thermostat open and de-energize the fuel solenoid valve, shutting off the fuel to the heater, and the fire goes out. The ventilating air cools the combustion chamber, and the cool air causes the thermostat to call for more heat. The cycle then repeats itself.

(5) Safety Features

(a) Duct Limit Switch

This switch is in the circuit to the main fuel solenoid, and if for any reason there is not enough ventilating area to carry the heat out of the duct, or if the duct temperature reaches the preset value, the limit switch will cause the fuel to be shut off to the heater.

(b) Overheat Switch

This is the final switch in the system, and if the temperature put out by the heater reaches the limit allowed by this switch, which is considerably higher than that at which the duct limit switch is set, but below a temperature that could cause a fire hazard, the switch will close the fuel supply solenoid valve and will also shut off the combustion air flow and the ignition. A warning light will turn on, notifying the pilot that the heater has been shut down because of an overheat condition. This switch, unlike the others, cannot be reset in flight, but must be reset on the ground at the heater itself.

D. Aircraft Air Conditioning Systems

We have become accustomed to thinking of air conditioning as the cooling of air, but actually it means much more than just this. A complete air-conditioning system for an aircraft should control both the temperature and humidity of the air, heating or cooling it as is necessary. It should provide adequate movement of the air for ventilation, and there should be provision for the removal of cabin odors.

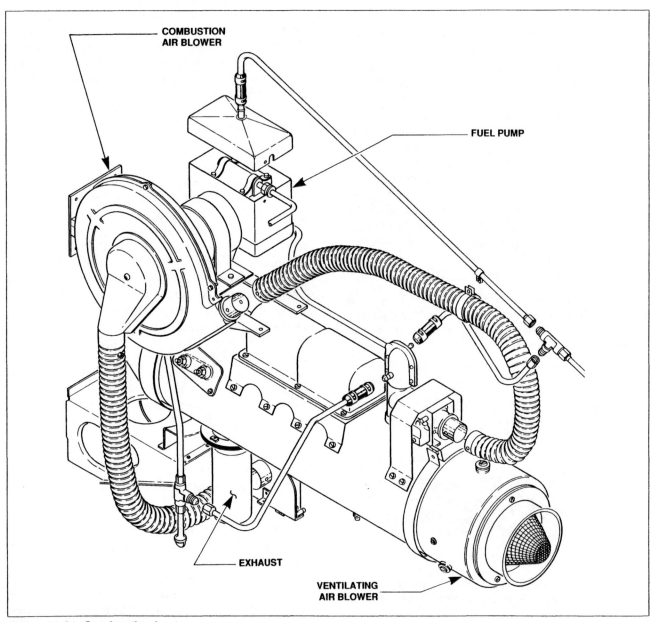

Figure 14-24. Combustion heater.

1. Air-cycle Air Conditioning

a. System Operation

Shown in figure 14-26 is a complete air-conditioning system for a twin-engine jet-powered transport airplane. Notice that hot compressor bleed air is taken from the 13th stage of the two engine compressors. Some of this air flows directly into the mixing chamber, while the rest of it flows through the primary heat exchanger where some of its heat is removed. It then goes into the air-cycle machine and is cooled. Any water that condenses out of the

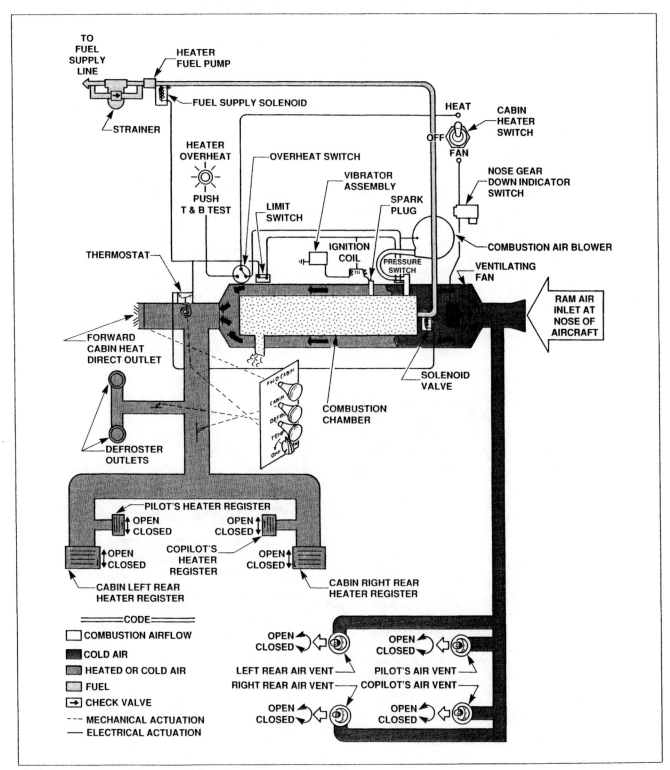

Figure 14-25. Schematic of a combustion heater system.

cool air is removed by the water separators before it goes into the mixing chamber.

In the mixing chamber, the hot and cold air are mixed in the proportion needed to provide air of the correct temperature for the cabin.

Notice that only the cold air system supplies air to the gasper fan on this airplane. The gasper system consists of the overhead ventilating air outlets above the passenger seats. Cooling air is blown over the passengers which is refreshing, but only when the passenger opens the air outlet for that seat.

The hot air ducts are normally in such locations that they will blow warm air over our feet and the lower parts of our bodies.

b. Component Operation

(1) Primary Heat Exchanger

The primary heat exchanger is a radiator which cold ram air passes through to cool the hot bleed air from the engines. Any heat exchanger's function is to exchange heat, as the cold ram air comes in contact with the radiators fin-like tubes, which bleed air is passing through, the bleed air is cooled. On the ground there is not enough air passing through the cooling doors which control the flow of ram air into the heat exchangers, so fans called pack fans provide adequate air flow to cool the heat exchangers on the ground.

(2) Primary Heat Exchanger Bypass Valve

Some of the hot bleed air from the engines can be bypassed around the air-conditioning package if warm air is needed in the cabin. There would be no purpose in cooling all the air if warm air is called for by the temperature controls.

(3) Shutoff Valve

The air-conditioning shutoff valve, sometimes called the pack valve, is used to control the flow of air into the system. It can shut off the air flow or it will modulate the flow of air to provide that which is needed to operate the air-conditioning package.

(4) Refrigeration Bypass Valve

This valve is used to prevent ice from clogging the air-cycle machine's outlet. It keeps the temperature of the air exiting the ACM (air cycle machine) from becoming too cold. Generally this air is kept at about 35°F by bypassing warm bleed air around the ACM and mixing it with the output air of the ACM.

(5) Secondary Heat Exchanger

This heat exchanger is another stage in cooling the hot engine bleed air after is has passed through the primary heat exchanger and the ACM's compressor. Its functional operation is similar to the primary heat exchanger.

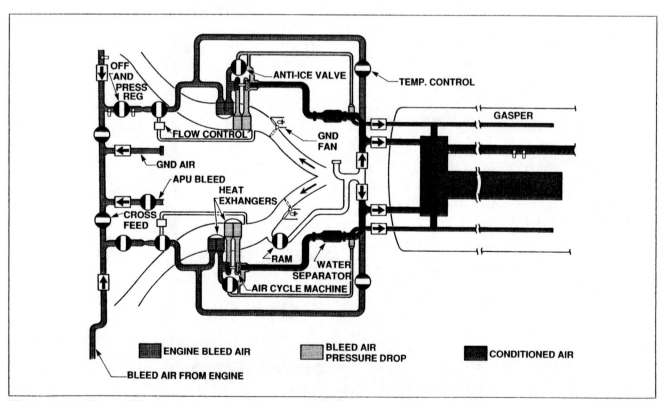

Figure 14-26. Air-conditioning system of a jet transport airplane using an air-cycle system.

(6) Refrigeration Turbine Unit

From the study of physics, it is found that the relationship between pressure and temperature, both manifestations of energy, are interchangeable forms of energy. The turbine engine extracts energy from the burning fuel to turn the compressor, and this energy raises both the pressure and the temperature of the air. Compressed air with this energy in it is taken from the engine and passed through a primary heat exchanger, where some of the heat is transferred into ram air passing around the tubes in this radiator-like cooler. The high-pressure air, somewhat cooled, is then ducted into the air cycle machine where most of the remainder of its energy is extracted by the air cycle machine which consists of a centrifugal air compressor and a cooling turbine that drives the compressor. When the compressor bleed air passes through the primary heat exchanger, it loses some of its heat but almost none of its pressure. This air then enters the compressor of the air cycle machine, and its pressure is further increased. With the increase in pressure, there is some increase in its temperature, but this is removed by the secondary heat exchanger. Now the somewhat cooled high-pressure air flows into the cooling turbine where a large percent of its remaining energy is used up to drive the compressor. There

are two forms of cooling used in this system. Some is done by transferring heat into the ram air, but most of the heat is removed by converting it into work to drive the compressor. This type of cooling system is called a bootstrap system is illustrated in figure 14-27.

(7) Water Separators

The rapid cooling of the air in the turbine causes moisture to condense in the form of a fog, and when this foggy air passes through the water separator, the tiny droplets of water coalesce in a fiberglass sock and form large drops of water. The louvers over which the sock fits are shaped to impart a swirling motion to the air, and the drops of water are slung to the sides of the container where they drain down and are carried overboard through the drain valve.

This water is kept from freezing by mixing the air in the separator with warm air. A temperature sensor in the outlet of the water separator controls a temperature control valve in a bypass line around the air cycle machine. If the temperature of the air at the outlet of the water separator ever drops below 38°F, the control valve will open so warm air can mix with that in the water separator, keeping the water from freezing.

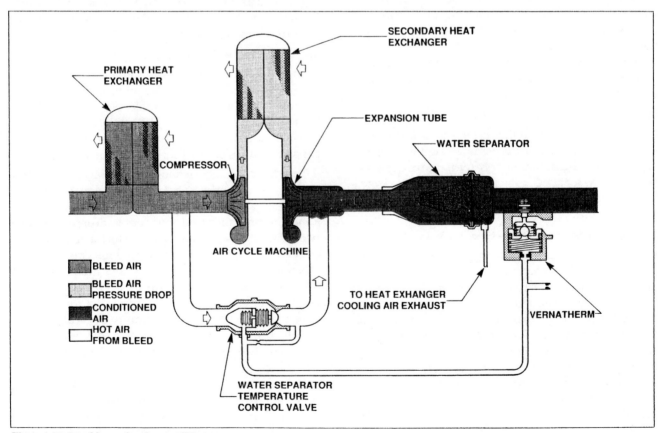

Figure 14-27. Air-cycle air conditioner.

(8) Ram Air Valve

This valve is used on some aircraft during nonpressurized flight to allow cool outside air to enter the air-conditioning system to ventilate the cabin for fresh air. It is generally fully open or closed and is seldom used. Sometimes the ram air valve is used to describe the cooling doors which open to allow air to flow through the heat exchangers in the air-conditioning packages.

c. Electronic Cabin Temperature Control System

(1) Cabin Temperature Pickup Unit

Normally, temperature sensors are located in each passenger zone in the aircraft's cabin. Some sensors are for temperature indications in the cabin while others are for the purpose of controlling the zone temperature. Air from the passenger cabin is drawn across the sensors to constantly monitor cabin temperature. The indicating sensors sends signals, proportional to temperature, to a signal conditioner which converts them to voltage signals. These signals are used by the zone temperature controller to adjust the temperature as needed.

(2) Cabin Air Temperature Selector

Selectors provide automatic temperature control of each cabin zone. The selected zone temperature signal is sent to the zone controller and compared with the sensed temperature signal from the respective zone temperature sensor. The difference between the selected temperature and the sensed temperature is the demand signal for each cabin zone sent to the air mixing valves.

(3) Cabin Air Temperature Control Regulator

The cabin zone controller uses the sensed error between the temperature demand signal from the selector and the actual supply temperature to position the associated air mix valve. Each zone's temperature demand is satisfied by the pack controllers interacting with the zone controllers.

(4) Typical System Operation

When a temperature is selected for a cabin zone by repositioning its temperature selector, a signal is provided to its zone temperature controller, where it is compared with the actual temperature in that zone. Any difference between the two results in the controller generating a demand signal in order to bring the zone to the selected temperature. A discriminator function in the zone controller selects the lowest temperature demand signal and sends this signal to the pack controllers as a pack demand signal. This signal will reposition the packs output to meet the current temperature requirements of the zone.

2. Vapor-cycle Air Conditioning

a. Theory of Refrigeration

The vapor-cycle air-conditioning system operates on the same refrigeration cycle as the mechanical refrigerator we use to cool our food and water. A refrigerant changes its state from a liquid into a vapor, and in doing so, it absorbs heat from the cabin. This heat is taken outside of the aircraft and is given off to the outside air as the refrigerant returns to its liquid state.

(1) Transfer of Heat

Heat, we must remember, is a form of energy, and we have neither the prerogative to create nor destroy energy. We can, however, transform it, or move it from one place or material to another. This energy continues to exist regardless of its form or location.

Heat will flow from an object having a certain level of energy into an object having a lower level. And any material that allows this transfer easily is said to be a conductor of heat, while any material that blocks or impedes the transfer is called an insulator.

The refrigerant used in an aircraft air-conditioning system is a liquid under certain conditions, but when it is surrounded by air having a higher level of heat energy, heat will pass from the air into the liquid, and as it is absorbed by the liquid, will change its state and become a gas. The air that gave up its heat to the refrigerant is cooled.

(2) Basic Vapor Cycle of Refrigeration

Heat is a form of energy that manifests itself in the molecular movement within a material. If there were no heat, there would be no molecular motion. When heat is added to a material, its molecular movement increases, and the material even increases in physical size. This is called thermal expansion.

Temperature is a measure of the effect of heat on a body or material, and is a convenient way of expressing, in numbers, this physical phenomenon. You will remember that four temperature scales are used. Two, Rankine and Kelvin, start with their zero position at the point at which molecular motion stops. Fahrenheit and Celsius scales are both based on the difference in temperature between the changes of state of pure water, its freezing and boiling points. While heat and temperature naturally relate, it will soon be seen that heat can be added or removed to a refrigerant without its temperature changing.

Hot and cold are relative terms, with cold referring to an absence of hotness. When we think of "hot," we must divorce our thinking from "heat" because, as will soon be seen, a refrigerant can have heat added to it in order to boil it, and still be very cold. "Hot" generally refers to a condition completely opposite from cold.

If a pan of water is placed on a heating element and heat is added to the water, a thermometer in the water will show that the temperature rises as the heat is added. This heat is called sensible heat. But, if heat is continued to be put into the water, it will begin to boil, or change its state from a liquid to a vapor, and when this change takes place, the temperature will no longer rise.

The heat put into a material as it changes its state without changing its temperature is called latent heat, and this heat will be returned when the material reverts to its original state.

As its name implies, this cooling process acts in a continuous cycle. Heat is picked up from the aircraft cabin by the refrigerant and is carried outside the aircraft where it is given up to the air, and then the refrigerant returns inside to pick up another load of heat.

This system (figure 14-28) is divided into two sides, one that accepts the heat and the other that disposes of it. The side that accepts the heat is called the low side, because here the refrigerant has a low temperature and is under a low pressure. The heat is given up on the high side, where the refrigerant is under high pressure and has a high temperature. Notice in figure 14-28, the system is divided at the compressor where the refrigerant vapor is compressed, increasing both its pressure and temperature, and at the expansion valve where the pressure and temperature of the liquid refrigerant are both dropped.

We can trace the refrigeration cycle by starting at the receiver-dryer which acts as a reservoir to store any of the liquid refrigerant that is not actually passing through the system at any given time. If any refrigerant is lost from the system, it is replaced from that in the receiver-dryer. A tiny droplet of water in the refrigerant is all that is needed to freeze in the orifice of the expansion valve to completely stop the system operation, so a desiccant agent is used in the

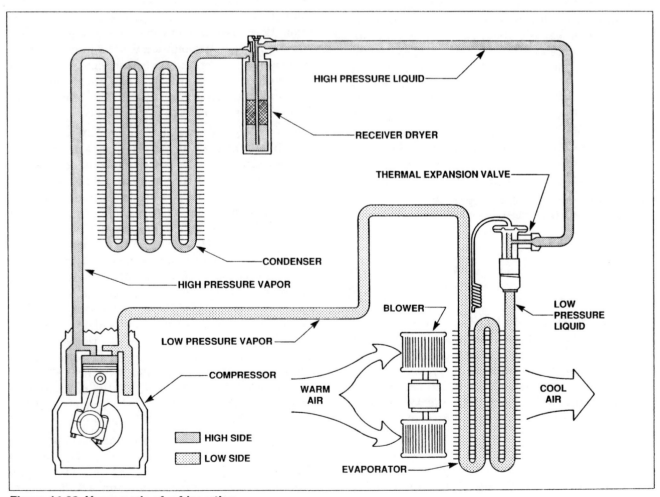

Figure 14-28. Vapor cycle of refrigeration.

receiver-dryer to trap and hold any moisture that should possibly be in the system.

Liquid refrigerant leaves the receiver-dryer and flows under pressure to the expansion valve where it sprays out through its tiny metering orifice into the coils of the evaporator. The refrigerant is still a liquid, but it is in the form of tiny droplets, each having the maximum amount of surface area so it can absorb the maximum amount of heat.

The evaporator is the unit in an air-conditioning system that produces the cold air. It is in this unit that heat from the aircraft cabin is absorbed by the refrigerant, and a blower forces warm air through the thin metal fins that fit over the evaporator coils. Heat from the air is absorbed into the refrigerant, and when it emerges from the evaporator, it is cool. When heat is absorbed by the refrigerant, it changes from a liquid into a gas without increasing its temperature. The heat remains in the refrigerant in the form of latent heat.

The refrigerant vapor which has the heat from the cabin is taken into the compressor, where additional energy is added to it to increase both its pressure and temperature. It leaves the compressor as a hot, high-pressure vapor. The heat trapped in the refrigerant vapors in the condenser escapes into the walls of the coil and then into the fins that are pressed onto these coils. Relatively cool air from outside the aircraft flows through these fins and picks up the heat that is given up by the refrigerant. When it loses its heat energy, the refrigerant vapor condenses back into a liquid and then flows into the receiver-dryer where it is held until it passes through the system for another cycle.

b. Components of a Vapor-cycle Air Conditioning System

(1) Refrigerant

Almost any volatile liquid can be used as a refrigerant, but for maximum effectiveness, one is needed that has a very low vapor pressure and therefore a low boiling point.

The vapor pressure of a liquid is the pressure that will exist above the liquid in an enclosed container at any given temperature. For example, liquid refrigerant in an open container at a temperature of 70°F will boil vigorously as the liquid turns into a gas. If the container is closed, the liquid will continue to change into a vapor and the pressure of the vapor will increase.

When the pressure reaches 70.1 PSI, no more vapor can be released from the liquid. The vapor pressure of this particular material is then said to be 70.1 PSI at 70°F.

Many different materials have been used as a refrigerant in commercial systems, but for aircraft air-conditioning systems, dichlorodifluoromethane is almost universally used. This is a halogen compound very similar to carbon tetrachloride, except that some of the chlorine atoms have been exchanged for fluorine atoms. It is a stable compound at both high and low temperatures, it does not react with any of the materials in an air-conditioning system, and it will not attack the rubber used for hoses and seals. It is colorless and practically odorless, is non-injurious to humans or plants, and it does not contaminate water or foodstuff. It is non-flammable, so much so in fact, that it is often used as a fire extinguishing agent.

Rather than calling this refrigerant by its long chemical name, it is just referred to as Refrigerant-12, or, even more simply as R-12. It may also be known by one of its many trade names such as Freon-12®, Genetron-12®, Isotron-12®, Ucon-12®, or by some other proprietary name. The important thing to remember is the number. Any of these trade names associated with another number is a different product. Freon-22®, for example, is similar to Freon-12, except that its vapor pressure is different. It is the refrigerant commonly used in commercial refrigerators and freezers. When servicing an aircraft air-conditioning system, it is extremely important that only the refrigerant specified in the aircraft manufacturer's service manual be used.

One of the characteristics of R-12 that makes it desirable for aircraft air-conditioning systems is its temperature-vapor pressure relationship. In the temperature range between 20 and 80°F, the range with which we are most concerned, there is an approximate relationship of 1 PSI of vapor pressure for each degree of Fahrenheit temperature. Notice in the chart of figure 14-29 that for 20°F the vapor pressure is 21 PSI, for 30°F the pressure is 28.4 PSI, and for 50°F, it is 46.6 PSI. While this relationship is not exact, it is close enough to make servicing relatively easy. If the low-side pressure is 28 PSI, the temperature of the refrigerant in the evaporator coils is about 30°F. This is, remember, the temperature of the refrigerant and not of the air passing through the evaporator. That will be somewhat higher, about 34 or 35°F. This temperature will give the most effective cooling, since we want the evaporator coils to be extremely cold, but we do not want ice to form on them.

Refrigerant-12 boils at normal sea level pressure at 21.6°F, and if you get a drop of liquid R-12 on your skin it will drop to this temperature and give you frostbite. *CAUTION: Even a tiny drop of liquid R-12 in your eye is hazardous. If you should get any in your* eye, flood it with cool water and treat it with mineral oil or petroleum jelly until you can get to a physician or a hospital. It is extremely important to wear eye protection any time you are servicing an air conditioning system.

Refrigerant-12 is not toxic nor is it dangerous if it is breathed. It can, however, deprive you of the oxygen you need if it is released in a confined space. Be sure there is adequate ventilation when a system is being discharged.

When R-12 passes over an open flame, its characteristics change drastically. Rather than a harmless gas, it becomes deadly phosgene gas. The effects of phosgene are cumulative, and cause severe damage to your respiratory system if phosgene gas is breathed. R-12 also changes its nature when it comes in contact with water, forming hydrochloric acid.

(2) Refrigeration Oil

Since the air-conditioning system is completely sealed, the oil used to lubricate the compressor seals and expansion valve must be sealed in the system. The oil used is a special refrigeration oil, which is a highly refined mineral oil, free from such impurities as water, sulfur or wax. The identification number of the oil refers to its viscosity, and the lower the number, the lighter the oil. It is very important that the oil specified in the aircraft manufacturer's service manual be used when servicing the system.

Refrigeration oil should be kept tightly closed when it is not in use, and it should never be poured from one container into another. Oil that has been removed for compressor servicing should be discarded and new oil put into the system.

(3) Receiver-dryer

The receiver-dryer (figure 14-30) is the reservoir for the system and is located in the high side between the condenser and the expansion valve. Liquid refrigerant enters from the condenser and is filtered, and then it passes through a desiccant such as silica-gel which absorbs any moisture that might be

TEMP °F	PRESSURE PSI	TEMP °F	PRESSURE PSI	TEMP °F	PRESSURE PSI	TEMP °F	PRESSURE PSI	TEMP °F	PRESSURE PSI
0	9.1	35	32.5	60	57.7	85	91.7	110	136.0
2	10.1	36	33.4	61	58.9	86	93.2	111	138.0
4	11.2	37	34.3	62	60.0	87	94.8	112	140.1
6	12.3	38	35.1	63	61.3	88	96.4	113	142.1
8	13.4	39	36.0	64	62.5	89	98.0	114	144.2
10	14.6	40	36.9	65	63.7	90	99.6	115	146.3
12	15.8	41	37.9	66	64.9	91	101.3	116	148.4
14	17.1	42	38.8	67	66.2	92	103.0	117	151.2
16	18.3	43	39.7	68	67.5	93	104.6	118	152.7
18	19.7	44	40.7	69	68.8	94	106.3	119	154.9
20	21.0	45	41.7	70	70.1	95	108.1	120	157.1
21	21.7	46	42.6	71	71.4	96	109.8	121	159.3
22	22.4	47	43.6	72	72.8	97	111.5	122	161.5
23	23.1	48	44.6	73	74.2	98	113.3	123	163.8
24	23.8	49	45.6	74	75.5	99	115.1	124	166.1
25	24.6	50	46.6	75	76.9	100	116.9	125	168.4
26	25.3	51	47.8	76	78.3	101	118.8	126	170.7
27	26.1	52	48.7	77	79.2	102	120.6	127	173.1
28	26.8	53	49.8	78	81.8	103	122.4	128	175.4
29	27.6	54	50.9	79	82.5	104	124.3	129	177.8
30	28.4	55	52.0	80	84.0	105	126.2	130	182.2
31	29.2	56	53.1	81	85.5	106	128.1	131	182.6
32	30.0	57	55.4	82	87.0	107	130.0	132	185.1
33	30.9	58	56.6	83	88.5	108	132.1	133	187.6
34	31.7	59	57.1	84	90.1	109	135.1	134	190.1

Figure 14-29. Temperature vs. Vapor Pressure chart for Refrigerant-12.

in the system. A sight glass is normally installed in the outlet tube to indicate the amount of charge in the system. Bubbles can be seen in the glass when the charge is low. A pickup tube extends from the top of the receiver-dryer to near the bottom where the liquid refrigerant is picked up. A filter is installed either on the end of the pickup tube or between the

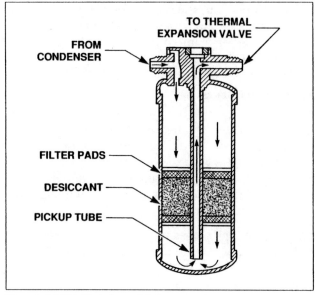

Figure 14-30. Receiver-dryer.

tube and the desiccant to prevent any particles getting into the expansion valve. It is of extreme importance to remove all of the moisture from the system, as a single drop can freeze in the expansion valve and stop the entire system operation. Water will also react with refrigerant to form hydrochloric acid which is highly corrosive to the metal in the system.

(4) Thermal Expansion Valve

The thermal expansion valve (TXV) is the control device which meters just the correct amount of refrigerant into the evaporator to evaporate completely by the time it reaches the end of the coils. The opening, or orifice, in the valve is controlled by the heat load in the aircraft cabin. There are two types of thermal expansion valves: the internally equalized valve and the externally equalized valve.

(a) Internally-equalized Thermal Expansion Valve

The internally-equalized thermal expansion valve (figure 14-31) is controlled by the amount of superheat in the evaporator. A capillary tube, filled with a gas and sealed, connects into the diaphragm chamber of the valve. The end of the capillary is coiled into a bulb and is held tightly against the discharge tube of the evaporator. Coiling this tube allows a greater area to be held in intimate contact with the tube and

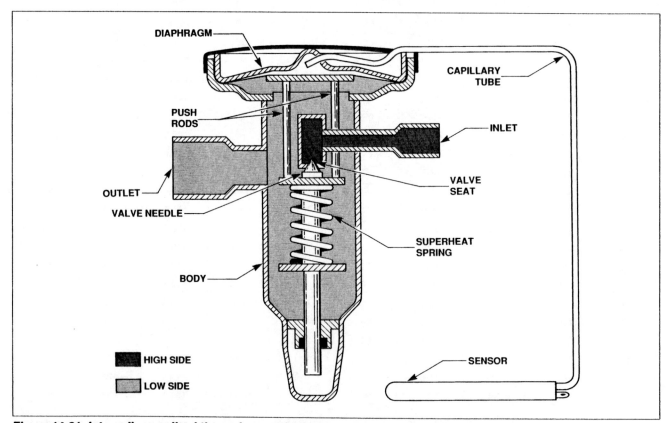

Figure 14-31. Internally-equalized thermal expansion valve.

a more accurate measurement of the temperature can be made. If the liquid refrigerant completely evaporates before it reaches the end of the evaporator, it will continue to absorb heat and become superheated. It is still very cold to touch, but it is considerably warmer than it would be if it had not absorbed this additional heat. The expansion valve is adjusted to a given amount of superheat, and when the pressure of the refrigerant vapor reaches this valve, the diaphragm pushes down against the superheat spring and opens the valve and allows more refrigerant to enter the evaporator. A balance between the vapor pressure on the diaphragm and the superheat spring controls the amount of refrigerant allowed to flow. These valves are calibrated at the factory and cannot normally be adjusted in the field. If there is a lot of heat in the cabin, the liquid refrigerant will evaporate quickly, and more superheat will be added to the vapor, so the valve will open and allow more refrigerant to flow into the evaporator. When the heat load is low, the liquid will use most of the evaporator length to evaporate. Little superheat will be added, and a smaller amount of refrigerant will be metered into the coils.

(b) Externally-equalized Expansion Valve

There is a noticeable pressure drop across large evaporators because of the opposition to the flow of refrigerant they produce. This pressure drop may be compensated for by increasing the flow of refrigerant into the evaporator. This increased flow will maintain a constant pressure across the evaporator, so the temperature sensing function of the valve will be able to meter the refrigerant as a function of the super-heat, or actually the heat load in the cabin. An externally-equalized thermal expansion valve is shown in figure 14-32.

(5) Evaporator

The actual cooling unit in an air-conditioning system is the evaporator. An evaporator consists of one or more circuits of copper tubing arranged in parallel between the expansion valve and the compressor. These tubes are silver-soldered into a compact unit, with thin aluminum fins pressed onto their surface. The evaporator is usually mounted in a housing with a blower so air from the cabin can be taken in by the blower and forced over the evaporator coils. Heat in this air is absorbed by the refrigerant, and the air that is blown out into the cabin is thus cooled. A drip pan is mounted below the evaporator to catch water that drips off of the coils when the system cycles. The capillary of the thermostat is stuck into the evaporator core between the fins to sense the temperature of the coil, and it is this temperature that controls the cycling of the system.

The evaporator (figure 14-33) is similar to the condenser in construction, and somewhat similar in appearance, but since it is in the low side of the system, the evaporator is not subject to such high pressures as the condenser. Operating pressures seldom go as high as 200 PSI, and the units normally have a design burst pressure of 1,000 PSI. The refrigerant should use the entire length of the evaporator when changing from a liquid into a vapor, yet there should be no liquid left at the evaporator discharge.

(6) Compressor

If we think of the expansion valve as the brains of an air-conditioning system, the compressor would logically compare with the heart, in that it circulates the refrigerant through the system. A reciprocating compressor is shown in figure 14-34.

Refrigerant leaves the evaporator as a low-pressure, low-temperature vapor and enters the compressor. Since the temperature of this vapor may be somewhere around 40°F, it can't be changed it into a liquid by lowering its temperature, but its pressure can be raised, and thus its temperature raised high enough to cause it to give up enough heat to the outside air as it passes through the condenser that it will turn back into a liquid.

Compressors used in aircraft air-conditioning systems are usually of the reciprocating type, having reed valves and a lubricating system that uses crankcase pressure to force oil into its vital parts. On small aircraft, these compressors are usually belt driven from pulleys on the engine, very similar to the arrangement used in an automobile. The compressors in systems used on larger aircraft are driven by electric or hydraulic motors, or by compressor bleed air powered turbines. Engine-driven compressors are single speed pumps whose output is controlled by a magnetically actuated clutch in the compressor drive pulley as shown in figure 14-35. When no cooling is needed, the clutch is de-energized and the compressor does not pump. But when the air conditioner is turned on, and the thermostat calls for cooling, the magnetic clutch is energized, causing the drive pulley to turn the compressor and pump refrigerant through the system.

Electric motor-driven compressors are controlled by a thermostat which turns the compressor motor on when cooling is required in the cabin, and off when the temperature drops sufficiently. Hydraulic motors are also actuated by control from the thermostat, and when cooling is needed, a solenoid valve opens, directing hydraulic fluid under pressure to the motor. When the motor is not being driven, the output of the engine-driven hydraulic pump is

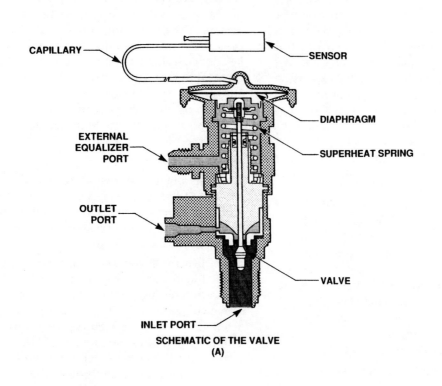

CAPILLARY

SENSOR

DIAPHRAGM

EXTERNAL
EQUALIZER
PORT

SUPERHEAT SPRING

OUTLET
PORT

VALVE

INLET PORT

SCHEMATIC OF THE VALVE
(A)

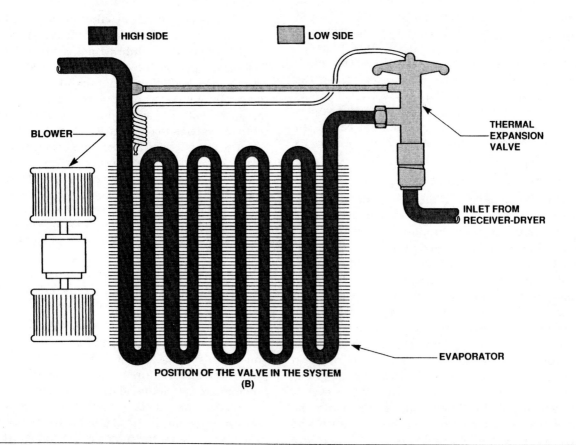

HIGH SIDE

LOW SIDE

BLOWER

THERMAL
EXPANSION
VALVE

INLET FROM
RECEIVER-DRYER

EVAPORATOR

POSITION OF THE VALVE IN THE SYSTEM
(B)

Figure 14-32. Externally-equalized thermal expansion valve.

returned to the reservoir. In all of these systems, the cabin blower operates continually, forcing the cabin air over the evaporator so heat can be transferred from it into the refrigerant.

Figure 14-33. The evaporator is the unit that actually produces the cool air.

(7) Condenser

The condenser is the radiator-like component which receives the hot, high-pressure vapors from the compressor and allows cool air to flow over its coils and remove the heat from the refrigeration vapors so they will change back into a liquid.

The condenser is made of copper tubing with aluminum fins pressed onto it, formed into a set of coils, and mounted in an aluminum housing. In some aircraft the condenser is mounted in an air duct where cooling air can be drawn in from the outside and blown over the coils. In some of the smaller airplanes it is mounted under the fuselage where it can be extended down into the airstream where the system is operating, and retracted into the fuselage when the system is off.

An interlock switch on the throttle retracts the condenser and de-energizes the compressor clutch when the throttle is opened for full power, to prevent the compressor loading the engine and the condenser causing drag when the airplane needs its maximum performance for takeoff.

The condenser and the evaporator are similar in both construction and appearance, differing primarily in strength. Since the condenser is in the high side of the system, it must be capable of withstanding the high pressure found there. Condensers normally operate at a pressure of about 300 PSI and have a burst pressure in excess of 1,500 PSI.

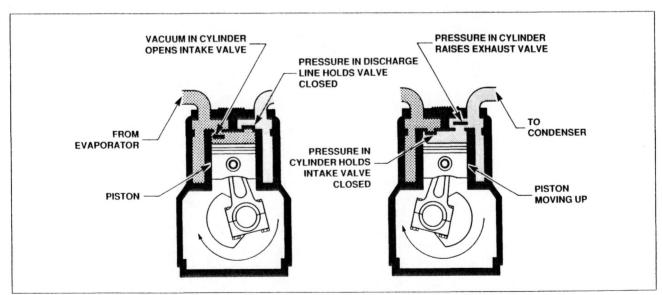

Figure 14-34. Piston-type compressor used in an aircraft air-conditioning system.

Figure 14-35. The magnetic clutch in this pulley operates at the command of the thermostat to drive the compressor only when cooling is required.

Chapter XV

Ice and Rain Control Systems

A. Ice Control Systems

1. Icing Effects

Ice in almost any form constitutes a hazard to flight and it must be removed before flight can be safely conducted. Some forms of ice that can present aircraft operational problems are frost, wing leading edge ice, horizontal stabilizer ice, carburetor ice, propeller ice, engine intake and windshield ice.

Frost forms on the surface of an aircraft that has been sitting outside when the temperature of the air drops at night and moisture precipitates out. If the air is warm, the water will form dew, but if the temperature is below freezing, the water will freeze as it precipitates out and it will form as frost in tiny crystals on the surface. Frost does not add appreciable weight, but it must be removed before flight because it creates a very effective aerodynamic spoiler that increases the thickness of the boundary layer and adds so much drag that flight may be impossible.

As an aircraft flies into clouds with the outside air temperature near freezing, it will quite likely collect an accumulation of ice on the wings and tail, as well as on the windshield and propeller, and on any radio antenna that is exposed. This ice adds a great deal of weight the aircraft must carry and it also changes the aerodynamic shape of the surfaces and destroys much of the lift. In the case of turbine engine intakes, the ice will disturb the flow of air into the engine or break off and be ingested into the engine's compressor, damaging it. Propellers will become inefficient and out of balance.

2. Anti-icing Systems

There are two types of ice control systems used on aircraft: anti-icing and deicing systems. Anti-icing systems prevents the formation of ice, while the deicing systems allow ice to accumulate, then it is removed. This discussion will concern itself with onboard or inflight deicing and anti-icing. Pneumatic anti-icing areas for a large transport aircraft are shown in figure 15-1. Ground deicing and anti-icing will be covered later in this chapter. Each deicing or anti-icing system may use several different methods to remove the ice. Anti-icing may be done by heating the surface or the component with hot air, engine oil, or using electric heating elements.

a. Thermal Anti-icing

Heated air can be directed through a specially designed heater duct in the leading edge of the wing (figure 15-2) and the tail surfaces to heat this portion of the airfoil and prevent the formation of ice. This air can be heated in reciprocating engine aircraft by using combustion heaters or heater shrouds around the engine exhaust system.

Most aircraft that use the thermal anti-icing systems today are turbine powered, and it is a very simple matter to use some of the engine's heated compressor bleed air to heat the leading edges and prevent the formation of ice.

The Boeing 727 takes bleed air from the two outboard engines and directs it through the wing anti-icing control valves to a common manifold and then out into the wing leading edge ducts. As can be seen in figure 15-3, the two inboard leading edge flaps and 8 leading edge slats are protected with this hot air. These portions of the wing are protected from overheating by overheat sensor switches. If they sense an overheat condition, they turn on an overheat warning light and close the anti-icing valves, shutting off the flow of hot air into the ducts. When the duct temperature drops to an allowable range, the overheat light will go out, and hot air will again flow into the duct.

Turbine engines are susceptible to ice damage if chunks of ice form on some of the exposed portions of the engine which can break off and be sucked into the engine's compressor. The engine intakes of most turbine engines are heated by compressor bleed air being circulated around the intake area of the engines preventing ice from forming (figure 15-4). Most large turbine engines have hot compressor bleed air directed through the inlet guide vanes, the engine bullet nose, and through the oil cooler scoop for the constant speed drive, as well as for the inlet duct for the center engine.

The Boeing 727 (figure 15-5) has the center engine's air intake at the rear top of the fuselage and, because of this, some of the anti-icing hot air is ducted to the upper VHF radio antenna to prevent

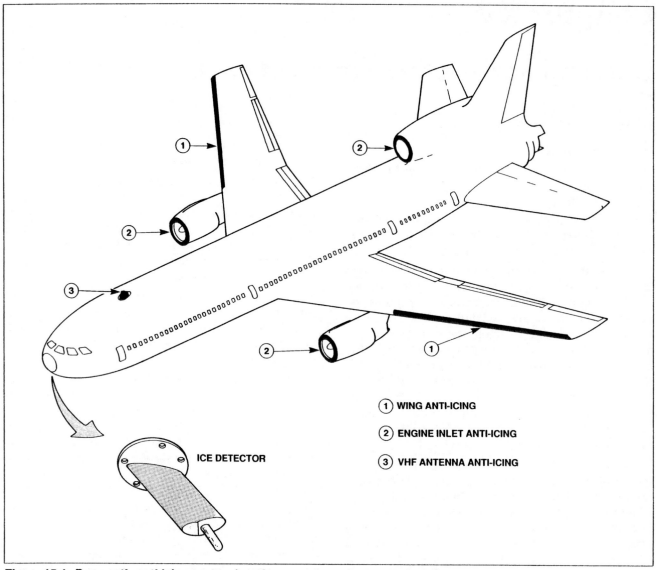

Figure 15-1. Pneumatic anti-icing system locations on a large transport aircraft.

① WING ANTI-ICING

② ENGINE INLET ANTI-ICING

③ VHF ANTENNA ANTI-ICING

ICE DETECTOR

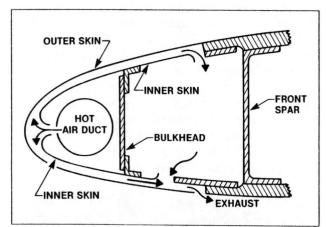

Figure 15-2. Thermal deicing is accomplished by flowing hot compressor bleed air from the engine through a duct in the leading edge of the wing.

ice forming on it and breaking off to be ingested into the center engine.

b. Electric Anti-icing

The pitot heads (tubes) installed on almost all aircraft that may possibly encounter icing are electrically heated. These heaters are so powerful that they should not be operated on the ground because, without an adequate flow of air over them, there is a possibility that they will burn out. Their operation is monitored in flight by indicator lights or watching the ammeter. These heaters require enough current that the ammeter will deflect noticeably when the heater is on. A heated pitot tube (figure 15-6) prevents ice from plugging the entry hole by warming it with an electric heater built inside the pitot tube housing. Static ports and stall warning vanes on many aircraft are also electrically heated.

The static port on some of the smaller aircraft are not heated, but if there is no provision for melting the ice off of this vital pressure pickup point, the aircraft should be equipped with an alternate source valve. This valve allows the pilot to reference the flight instruments to a static source inside the aircraft (nonpressurized) if the outside static port should become covered with ice.

Large transport aircraft that have flush toilets and lavatories have electric powered heating elements to prevent the drains and water lines from freezing.

Windshields and cockpit windows are electrically heated to prevent ice obstructing the vision of the pilot and the copilot. There are two methods of heating these components. One method uses a conductive coating on the inside of the outer layer of glass in the laminated windshield (figure 15-7) and the other method uses tiny resistance wires embedded inside the laminated windshield. It is heated by electric current flowing through a conductive film on the inside of the outer layer of glass.

The windshield of a high-speed jet aircraft is a highly complex and costly component. For all of the transport category aircraft, these windshields must not only withstand the pressures caused by pressurization and normal abuse and flight loads, but they must also withstand, without penetration, the impact produced by a 4-lb. bird striking the windshield at a velocity equal to the airplane's design cruising speed. For a windshield to be this strong, it is built as a highly complex sandwich, with some of the business jet windshields about an inch and a half thick, made of three plies of tempered glass with layers of vinyl between them. The inner surface of the outer ply of glass is coated with a conductive material through which electric current flows to produce enough heat to melt off any ice that forms on the windshield. There are temperature sensors and an elaborate electronic control system to

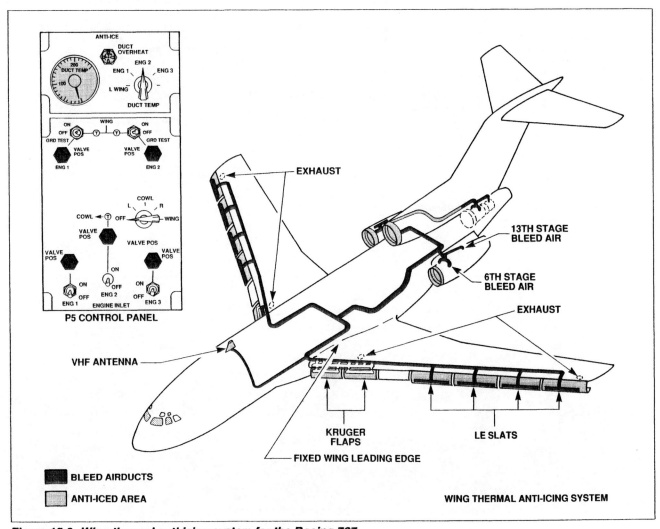

Figure 15-3. Wing thermal anti-icing system for the Boeing 727.

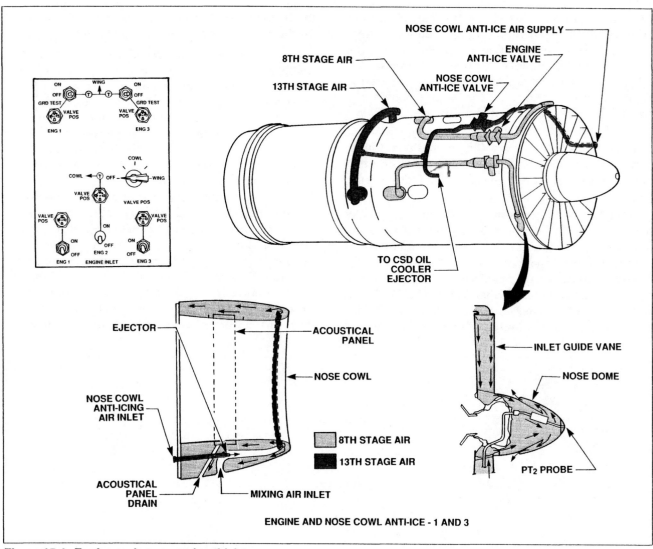

Figure 15-4. Engine and nose cowl anti-icing.

Figure 15-5. The Boeing 727 can fly through icing conditions because of the extensive used of thermal anti-icing.

prevent these windshields from becoming over-heated. The windshields are heated not only to prevent ice, but to strengthen them against bird strikes. When the windshield is heated, the vinyl layers are less brittle and will withstand an impact with much less chance of penetration than they will when they are cold.

The engine intakes of some turboprop aircraft are anti-iced by using electric heating elements which prevent ice build-up.

c. Chemical Anti-icing

Certain surfaces and components of an aircraft may be coated with either isopropyl alcohol, or a mixture of ethylene glycol and alcohol. Either of these chemicals lowers the freezing point of the water at the surface of the aircraft, and at the same time, makes the surface slick to prevent ice from getting a good grip on the surface.

Chemical anti-icing is normally done to the carburetors, the propellers, and to the windshield from a tank of anti-icing fluid carried in the aircraft. Ground chemical anti-icing is done by spraying all of the surfaces with ethylene glycol before the aircraft takes off, and will be discussed later in this chapter. Rubber deicer boots are often sprayed with a silicon spray that gives the rubber an extremely smooth surface so the ice cannot adhere to it.

Propeller anti-icing (figure 15-8) uses isopropyl alcohol which is sprayed onto the leading edges of the propeller blades, preventing icing. The alcohol is stored in a tank from which it is pumped to the propeller when needed. The pump is driven by an electric motor which is controlled by a rheostat. By controlling the pumps speed through the rheostat,

the pilot can control the amount of alcohol flowing to the propeller. Each propeller has a slinger ring that uses centrifugal force to distribute the alcohol to the blade nozzles. The length of time this system can be used is limited by the amount of alcohol the tank can carry.

3. Deicing Systems

Deicing systems remove the ice after it has formed, by the use of pneumatic deicer boots on the leading edges of wings and tails. Propeller deicing uses heating elements that are cycled to melt the accumulated ice and allow it to be removed by centrifugal force.

We have just noticed that an anti-icing system prevents the formation of ice on the protected component, but it has been found that for keeping the wings and tail surfaces of some of the slower airplanes free of ice, it is more effective to allow the ice to form on the surface and then crack it so the airflow over the surface will carry the ice away. This is more effective than melting the ice on the leading edge, because when this is done, the water flows back to an unheated portion of the surface and re-freezes, forming a ridge that becomes an effective aerodynamic spoiler.

a. Rubber Deicer Boot System

Airline flying was hindered in the early days of aviation because of aircraft ice accumulation. Pilots did not dare fly into clouds where ice could exist. But with improved instruments and radio, and with the introduction of newer models of aircraft, flight into icing conditions did occur. And to remove the ice, the BF Goodrich Company developed a rubber deicer boot that was installed on the leading edges of the wings and the empennage. An example of just such an aircraft is shown in figure 15-9.

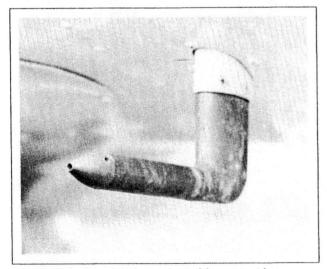

Figure 15-6. Pitot heads such as this prevent ice plugging the entry hole by warming them with an electric heater.

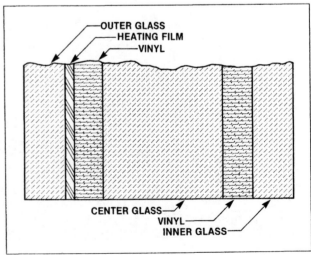

Figure 15-7. The windshield of a modern jet aircraft is made up of laminations of glass and vinyl.

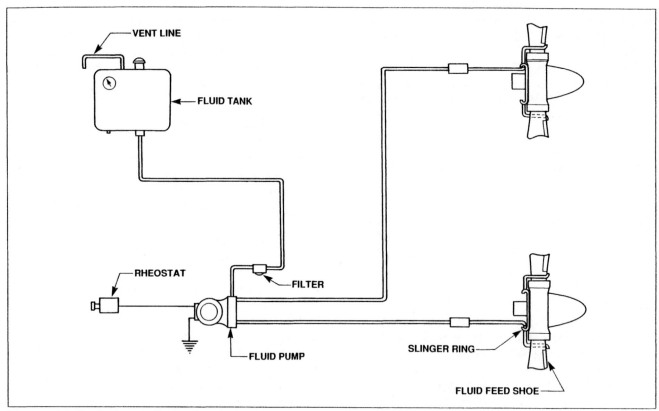

Figure 15-8. Typical propeller fluid anti-icing system.

Figure 15-9. This airplane can fly into icing conditions because the wing and tail surfaces are deiced with pneumatic deicer boots and the propeller is protected by electric deicers.

(1) Principle of Operation

A rubber boot containing several longitudinal tubes is fastened to the leading edge of the surface, and air from the discharge of the engine driven vacuum pump is passed through an oil separator to remove the oil that has been used to lubricate and seal the pump. Newer types of vacuum pumps do not need to use oil separators. This air is now passed through a timer-operated distributor valve into the tubes in a sequential manner. As can be seen in figure 15-10, the boot is installed on the leading edge of a wing with all of the tubes deflated. When they are deflated, suction from the suction side of the pump or from an ejector around the pump discharge line holds the tubes evacuated, so air flowing over the boot will not cause the tube to distort the shape of the leading edge of the wing. As shown in figure 15-11, the center tube is inflated and any ice that has formed over it will

crack. The center tube now deflates (figure 15-12) and the outer tubes inflate and push up the cracked ice so air flowing over the wing will get under it and blow it off of the surface. All of the tubes now deflate and are held tight against the boot by suction until the ice reforms, and then the cycle repeats itself.

The cycle of operation causes the tubes to inflate in a symmetrical manner so the disruption of lift during the inflation will be uniform and will not cause any flight control problems. The manufacturer of the aircraft has determined by flight tests the proper cycle time for the operation.

The larger aircraft that use this type of deicing system have an electric motor-driven timer to operate solenoid valves that, when the system is turned on, will continually cycle the system through all of the tubes, and then provide the proper duration of rest time to allow the ice to form over the boots; then the cycle is repeated. Any time the tubes are not inflated, suction is applied to them as mentioned earlier.

A smaller aircraft deicing system (figure 15-13) does not use the elaborate timer, but is turned on by the pilot when they detect an accumulation of ice on the leading edges that should be removed. When the deicing switch is turned on, the boots will cycle through one, two, or three operating cycles, depending upon the design of the system, and then the tubes will be connected to the vacuum side of the air pump to hold them tight against the leading edge.

(2) Source of Operating Air

The following provide operating air for deicing:

1. On many smaller turbine aircraft the source of pneumatic air is from the turbine engine

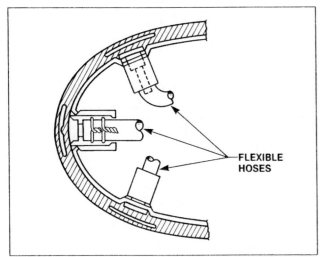

Figure 15-10. Pneumatic deicer boot with all tubes deflated.

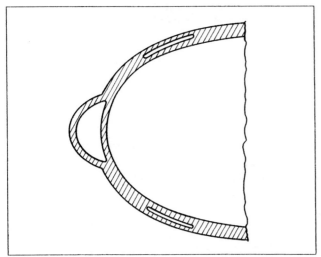

Figure 15-11. Pneumatic deicer boot with the center tube inflated and the outer tubes deflated.

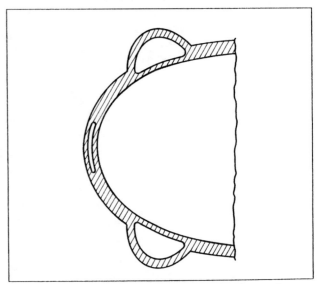

Figure 15-12. Pneumatic deicer boot with the center tube deflated and the two outer tubes inflated.

compressor bleed air. This air is under pressure and with the use of a regulator the pressure is made suitable for inflating the deicer boots. It can also be used to create a vacuum by using a venturi. This vacuum (negative pressure) is used to hold the boots down smoothly to the leading edge during the deflation cycle.

2. The air for inflating the boots can also come from the exhaust of the engine-driven air pump (instrument system vacuum pump). Some of these pumps are of the "wet" type which use engine oil taken into the pump through holes in the mount-

ing flange to lubricate and seal the steel vanes. This oil must all be removed by an oil separator and sent back into the engine crankcase before the air can be used to inflate the deicer boots.

3. Newer dry-type pumps are used for many installations, and these pumps do not require an oil separator as they use carbon vanes which make the pump self-lubricating.

4. Some deicing systems that are used only occasionally inflate the boots from a cylinder of compressed air that is carried just for this purpose.

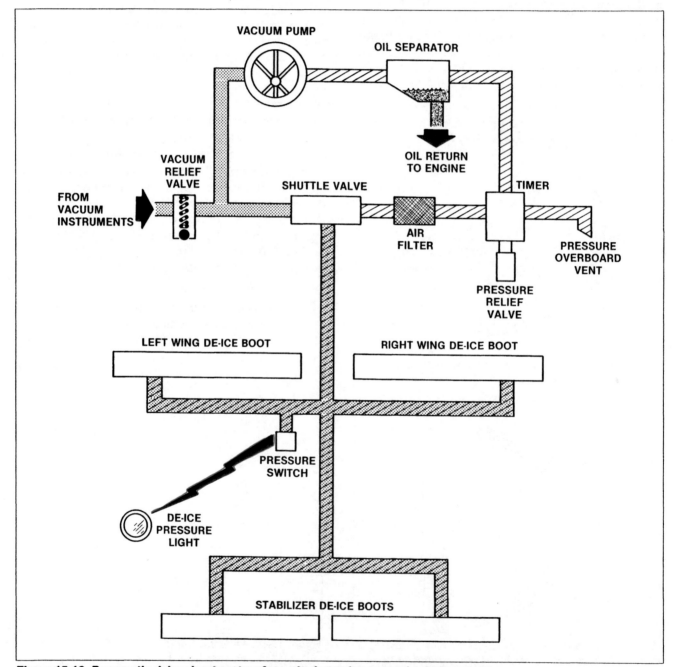

Figure 15-13. Pneumatic deicer boot system for a single-engine general aviation airplane.

(3) Deicing System Components (Typical)

Some of the main components in a pneumatic deicer system is the air pump (vacuum pump), vacuum regulator, pressure control valve, timer module, and deicer boots. The vacuum pump is normally used to create a vacuum for operating the flight instruments. The output side of the pump provides air pressure which is used to inflate the deicer boots. The oil separator, previously described, is used only with the older style vacuum pumps and its purpose is to separate the oil from the air to prevent oil from being blown overboard and deterioration of the deicer boots. The amount of vacuum applied to the deice boots and the instruments is controlled by the vacuum regulator. Likewise, the amount of pressure allowed in the system is controlled by the pressure control valve. The timer module is normally activated by a switch in the cockpit which sequences the deicer boots through one complete deice cycle. On some systems, the center deice boot cells or tubes are activated by the timer, then deflated, and the outer tubes are inflated. Normally, after one complete cycle, the system returns to off which applies vacuum to the cells or tubes until another cycle is called for by the pilot. Other components include filters, valves and miscellaneous tubing and lines.

(4) Construction and Installation of Deicer Boots

There are several configurations of deicer boots, but all accomplish their work in the same way. They allow the ice to form and then break it off as the tubes inflate. Figure 15-14 shows some of the more commonly used configurations. Some boots use span-wise tubes that inflate alternately, and some inflate simultaneously. Other configurations of boots have chord-wise tubes that may inflate either alternately or simultaneously. The configuration of the tubes is determined by flight test and, naturally, only the specific boot that is approved for the aircraft should be used.

When rubber deicer boots were first developed, adhesives had not been developed to the state they are today, and these boots were installed on the leading edge of the surfaces with machine screws driven into Rivnuts installed in the skin. This type of installation can be identified by a narrow metal fairing strip that covers the screw heads at the edges of the boots. Almost all of the newer boot installations fasten the boot to the surface with adhesives so that there is no need for Rivnuts and screws.

b. Electrothermal Propeller Deicing

Many of the modern propellers installed on both reciprocating and turboprop engines are deiced with an electrothermal deicer system. Rubber boots with heater wires embedded in the rubber are bonded to the leading edges of the propeller blades, and electrical current is passed through these wires to heat the rubber and melt any ice that has formed, so centrifugal force and wind can carry the ice away.

The boots in some installations are made in two sections on each blade. Current flows for about a half minute through the outboard section of all blades and then for the same time through the heaters on the inboard section of all of the blades. The time the current flows has been proven by flight tests to be sufficient to allow ice to form over the inactive section and long enough to loosen the ice from the section that is receiving the current.

The complete propeller deicer system (figure 15-15) consists of the following components:

1. Electrically heated deicers bonded to the propeller blades.
2. Slip-ring and brush block assemblies that carry the current to the rotating propeller.
3. Timer to control the heating time and sequence of the deicing cycle.
4. An ammeter to indicate the operation of the system.
5. All of the wiring, switches and circuit breakers necessary to conduct electrical power from the aircraft electrical system into the deicer system.

The slip-ring assembly is mounted on the propeller either through a specially adapted starter gear or attached to the spinner bulkhead or the crankshaft flange. The brush block is mounted on the engine so the three brushes will ride squarely on the slip rings. The timer controls the sequence of current to each of the deicers. The sequence of heating is important, to provide the best loosening of the ice so it can be carried away by the centrifugal force. It is also important that the same portion of each blade be heated at the same time to prevent an out-of-balance condition.

The ammeter monitors the operation of the system and assures the pilot that each heater element is taking the required amount of current. In this way, the pilot knows that there is even deicing of the propellers.

4. Ground Deicing of Aircraft

a. Frost Removal

Frost can be removed from the wing and tail surfaces by brushing it off with a long handled T-broom. Better yet, it can be prevented from forming on the surfaces by covering them with a nylon or canvas cover when the airplane is secured for the night.

Spraying the surfaces with a deicing solution of ethylene glycol and isopropyl alcohol just before flight will effectively remove all traces of the frost.

b. Ice and Snow Removal

Ice and snow removal is normally a 2-step process, a deicing and an anti-icing step. The deicing step is

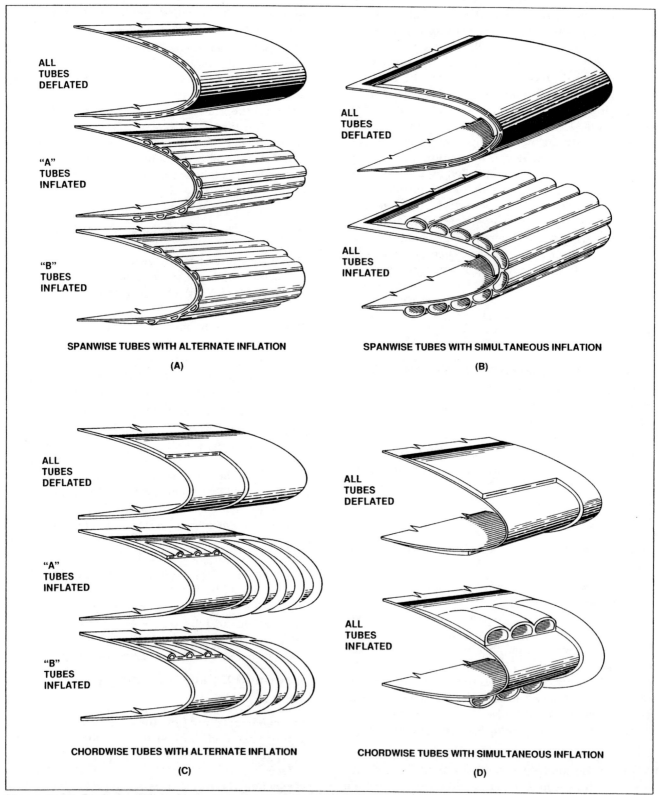

Figure 15-14. Typical configurations of pneumatic deicer boots.

used to remove any snow and ice on the aircraft's surfaces. This first step (figure 15-16) is done by applying a heated mixture of ethylene glycol and isopropyl alcohol to the aircraft's surfaces to melt any ice or snow that is present. The deicing fluid must keep any moisture from refreezing on the airplanes surfaces until the anti-icing fluid can be applied. The anti-icing fluid, as the name implies, is to prevent ice or snow from accumulating on the aircraft during taxi and while holding for takeoff on the ground. Each step should be completed separately with a different type or thickness of fluid used for each step.

B. Rain Control Systems

Almost all of the small general aviation aircraft use transparent acrylic plastic windshields, and this soft material is so easy to scratch that windshield wipers are seldom installed. One way to minimize the effect rain has on visibility in flight is to keep the windshield waxed so water will not be able to spread out over the surface, but will bead up so the propeller slip stream or wind can blow it away.

Larger and faster aircraft that routinely operate in rain have rather elaborate rain control systems. There are three methods used to control the effects

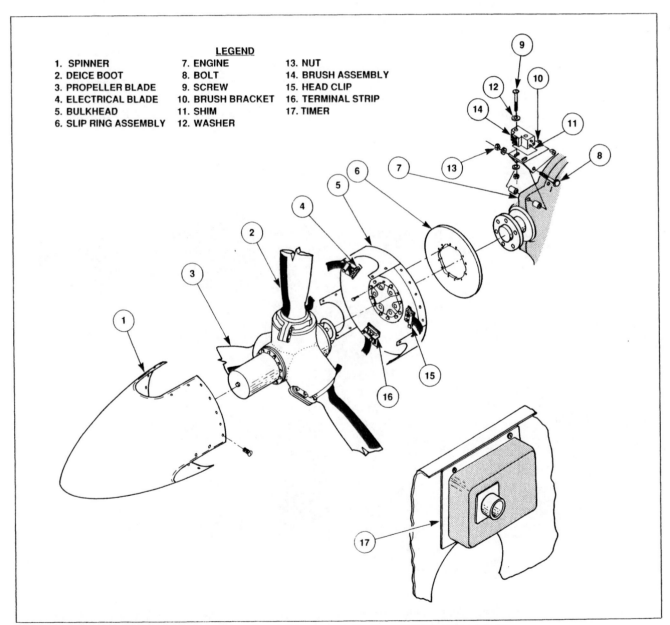

LEGEND
1. SPINNER
2. DEICE BOOT
3. PROPELLER BLADE
4. ELECTRICAL BLADE
5. BULKHEAD
6. SLIP RING ASSEMBLY
7. ENGINE
8. BOLT
9. SCREW
10. BRUSH BRACKET
11. SHIM
12. WASHER
13. NUT
14. BRUSH ASSEMBLY
15. HEAD CLIP
16. TERMINAL STRIP
17. TIMER

Figure 15-15. An electrical deicing system is used to remove ice from the propeller blades.

of rain and they may be used together. These three methods will be discussed separately. They are mechanical windshield wipers, chemical rain repellant, and a pneumatic rain removal systems.

1. Windshield Wipers Systems

Windshield wipers for aircraft are similar to those used on automobiles except they must be able to withstand the air loads caused by the high speeds of operation. A rain control panel of a large transport aircraft is shown in figure 15-17. Electrical windshield wipers are usually operated by a 2-speed DC motor that drives a converter. This converter changes the rotary output of the motor into the reciprocating motion needed for the wiper blades. When the windshield wiper switch is turned OFF, the control circuit is open, but the motor continues to run until the blades are driven to the PARK position. The motor then stops, but the control circuit is armed so the motor will start when the windshield wiper switch is turned to either the FAST or SLOW position. Some installations have a separate position on the speed selector switch that allows the pilot to drive the

wiper blades to the PARK position before putting the switch in the OFF position.

Some aircraft use hydraulic windshield wipers (figure 15-18) that use pressure from the main hydraulic power system to drive the wiper blades. Hydraulic fluid under pressure flows into the control unit, which periodically reverses the direction of the flow of fluid to the actuators. Inside the actuators are pistons which move a rack and pinion gear system. As the pistons move in one direction, the wiper will move one way, but when the flow is reversed, the piston and the wiper blades will move in the opposite direction. When the control valve is turned OFF, the blades are driven to and held in the PARK position. Speed control is accomplished by varying the flow rate through a variable orifice in the fluid line.

Windshield wipers must never be operated on a dry windshield, and the blades must be kept clean and free of any type of contaminants that could scratch the windshield. If the windshield wiper should ever have to be operated for maintenance or

Figure 15-16. Spraying an airplane with a mixture of isopropyl alcohol and ethylene glycol will remove frost and ice from the surface and prevent its refreezing.

adjustment, the windshield must be flooded with ample quantities of fresh, clean water and kept wet while the wiper blades are moving across the glass. Many transport airplanes keep the windows in the cabin area free of fog and frost by directing warm air between the panes of the windows.

2. Chemical Rain Repellant

Many of the jet transport aircraft have a chemical rain repellent system that uses a liquid chemical sprayed on the windshield to prevent the water reaching the surface of the glass. Since it cannot wet the surface and spread out, the water will form beads and the wind can easily carry it away and leave the glass free of water so the pilot's visibility will not be distorted.

The repellent is a syrupy liquid that is carried in pressurized cans connected into the rain repellent system. When the aircraft is flying in rain so heavy that the windshield wipers cannot keep the windshield clear, the pilot can depress the Rain Repellent button and a single timed application of the liquid will then be sprayed out onto the

windshield. The windshield wipers will then spread the liquid out evenly over the wiped surface.

The liquid should never be sprayed onto the windshield unless the rain is sufficiently heavy, because too much repellent can smear on the windshield and be difficult to see through. The repellent is difficult to remove if it is sprayed onto a dry windshield.

The operating system shown in figure 15-19 consists of two pressurized containers of repellent and two DC solenoid valves that, once actuated, are held open by a time-delay relay. When the Rain Repellent push-button switch is depressed, the fluid flows for the required period of time, which is less than a second, and then the valve closes until the push button is again depressed. The number of times the button is depressed is determined by the intensity of the rain.

3. Pneumatic Rain Removal Systems

High-pressure compressed air may be ducted from the engine bleed air system into a plenum chamber and then up against the outside of the windshield in the form of a high-velocity sheet of air. This air blast effectively prevents the rain hitting the windshield surface and adhering to it.

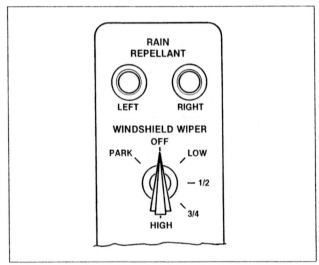

Figure 15-17. Rain control panel on a jet transport airplane.

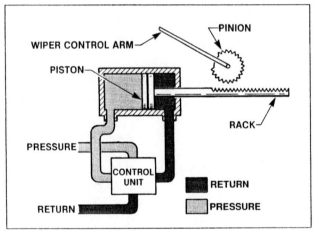

Figure 15-18. Hydraulically operated windshield wiper.

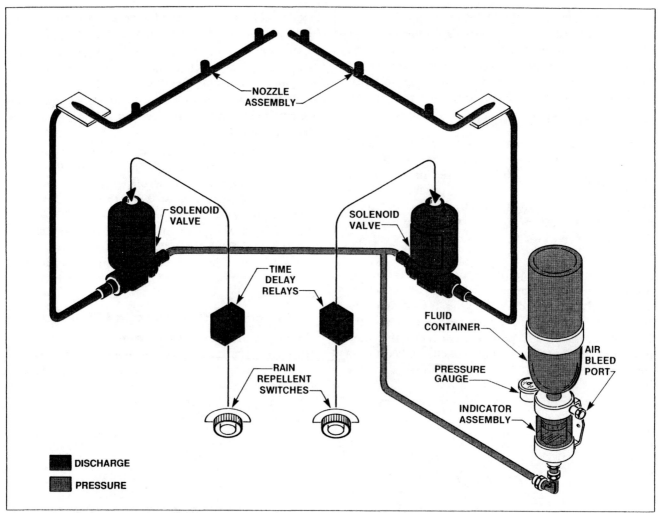

Figure 15-19. Chemical rain repellent system used on a jet transport airplane.

Chapter XVI

Fire Protection Systems

Because fire is one of the most dangerous threats to an aircraft, manufacturers and operators will install any of a variety of overheat, fire and smoke detection devices, and extinguishing equipment. Federal Aviation Regulations may require certain systems to be installed in some categories of aircraft, or for certain types of operation.

A. Principles of Fire Protection Systems

Chemically, fire is a reaction between oxygen and a material known as the fuel. This reaction, or oxidation, reduces the fuel to its chemical elements and in the process produces a good deal of heat. Paper, for example, is an organic material composed primarily of carbon and hydrogen. When it is heated to its kindling temperature in the presence of air (which contains oxygen), the carbon and hydrogen will unite with the oxygen and form carbon dioxide CO_2 and water H_2O. Other elements in the paper, and the products of incomplete combustion, will show up as ash and black carbon.

Three conditions have to be met for fire to occur. There must be fuel, there must be oxygen, and there must be enough heat to raise the temperature of the fuel to its ignition or kindling point.

1. Classes of Fires

In order to understand the way an aircraft fire protection system operates, we should be familiar with the classification of fires as they are listed by the National Fire Protection Association.

Class-A fires are ones in which solid combustible materials such as wood, paper, or cloth burn. Aircraft cabin fires are usually examples of class A fires.

Class-B fires have as their fuel, combustible liquids such as gasoline, oil, turbine fuel, and many of the paint thinners and solvents used in aviation maintenance.

Class-C fires are ones which involve energized electrical equipment. Special care must be exercised because of the dangers from the electricity as well as those from the fire itself.

Class-D fires involve some burning metal such as magnesium. The use of the wrong type of fire extinguisher can intensify a class-D fire rather than extinguish it.

2. Requirements for Overheat and Fire Protection Systems

Overheat and fire protection systems on modern aircraft do not rely on observation by crewmembers as a primary method of fire detection. An ideal fire protection system will include as many as possible of the following features:

1. A system which will not cause false warnings, under any flight or ground operating conditions.
2. Rapid indication of a fire and accurate location of the fire.
3. Accurate indication that the fire is out.
4. Indication that the fire has re-ignited.
5. Continuous indication for the duration of a fire.
6. Means for electrically testing the detector system from the aircraft cockpit.
7. Detectors which resist exposure to oil, water, vibration, extreme temperatures, and maintenance handling.
8. Detectors which are light in weight and easily adaptable to any mounting position.

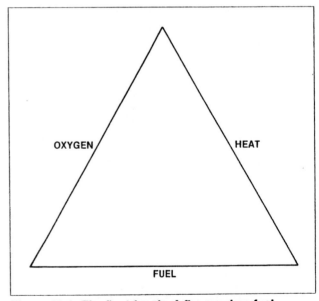

Figure 16-1. The fire triangle. A fire requires fuel, oxygen, and enough heat to raise the temperature or the fuel and oxygen to their combining point.

9. Detector circuitry which operates directly from the aircraft power system without inverters.

10. Minimum electrical current requirements when not indicating a fire.

11. Each detection system should actuate a cockpit light indicating the location of the fire, and an audible alarm system.

12. A separate detection system for each engine.

There are a number of overheat and fire detection systems that satisfy these requirements, and a single aircraft may utilize more than one type.

B. Fire Detection/Overheat Systems

Airplanes are so large today that elaborate systems must be installed to warn the flight crew of any fire, or of an overheat condition that could lead to a fire.

A fire detection system should signal the presence of a fire. Units of the system are installed in locations where there are greater possibilities of a fire. A fire will be indicated by both a cockpit light, showing the location of the fire, and a warning bell.

Overheat warning systems are used on some aircraft to indicate areas of high temperature that may lead to a fire. The number of overheat warning systems will vary with the type of aircraft. They may be used in engine turbine areas, nacelles, wheel well areas, and for the pneumatic manifold. When an overheat condition occurs in the detector area, the systems cause a light on the fire control panel to flash.

1. Thermal Switch Fire Detection System

The thermal switch fire detection system is a spot-type system that uses a number of thermally activated switches to warn of fire. The switches are wired in parallel with each other, and the entire group of switches are connected in series with the indicator light. The spot detector sensors operate using a bimetallic thermoswitch that closes when heated to a high temperature.

In figure 16-2, we see the basic circuit for this type of system. If the temperature of any thermal switch reaches the temperature for which it is set, the thermoswitch will close. This completes the circuit to ground, and the indicator light turns on, warning the flight crew of a fire condition. This circuit has a safety feature that allows all of the detectors to continue to operate even if the loop is broken. And the test circuit allows the flight crew to test for continuity of the loop and for the integrity of the entire system.

The Fenwall fire-detection system uses spot detectors (figure 16-3) wired parallel between two separate circuits. This circuit arrangement is illustrated in figure 16-4. This system can withstand one fault, either an electrical open circuit or a short to ground without sounding a false alarm. A double fault must exist before a false fire warning can occur. In case of a fire or overheat condition, the spot-detector switch closes and completes a circuit to sound an alarm.

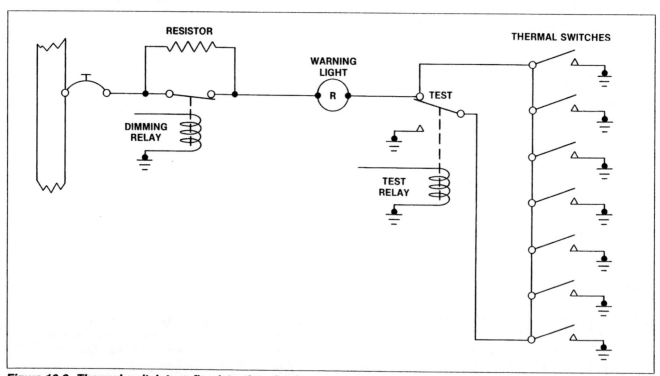

Figure 16-2. Thermal-switch type fire detection circuit.

2. Thermocouple-type Fire Detection System

This system operates on the rate of temperature rise principle, rather than operating when a specific temperature is reached. This system will not give a warning when an engine overheats slowly, or a short circuit develops. The thermocouple fire detection system may also be known as the Edison fire detection system, after its manufacturer. In figure 16-5, we see the basic circuit of this type of system. The system consists of a relay box, warning lights, and thermocouples. The wiring system of these units may be divided into the following circuits: The detector circuit, the alarm circuit, and the test circuit.

The relay box contains two relays, the sensitive relay and the slave relay, and the thermal test unit.

Such a box may contain from 1 to 8 identical circuits, depending on the number of potential fire zones. The relays control the warning lights. In turn, the thermocouples control the operation of the relays. The circuit consists of several thermocouples in series with each other and the sensitive relay.

The thermocouple is constructed of two dissimilar metals such as chromel and constantan. The point where these metals are joined and will be exposed to the heat of a fire is called a hot junction. A metal cage surrounds each thermocouple to give mechanical protection without hindering the free movement of air to the hot junction.

In a typical thermocouple system installation, the active thermocouples are placed in locations where fire is most likely to occur, and one thermocouple,

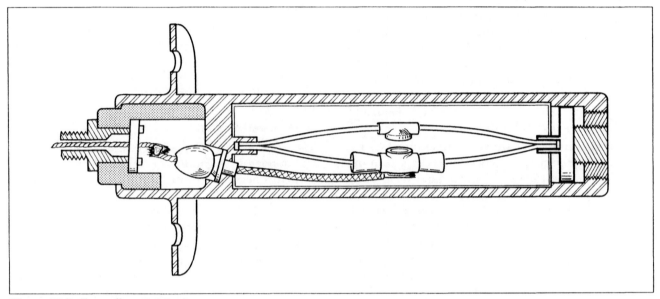

Figure 16-3. Fenwall spot detector.

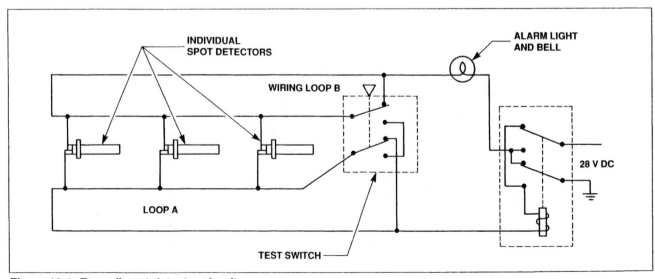

Figure 16-4. Fenwall spot detector circuit.

called the reference thermocouple, is placed in a location that is relatively well protected from the initial flame. The temperature of the reference thermocouple will eventually reach that of the other thermocouples, and there will be no fire warning if everything heats up uniformly as it does in normal operation. But, if a fire should occur, the active thermocouples will get hot much sooner than the reference thermocouple, and the difference in temperature will produce a current in the thermocouple loop. This current flows through the coil of the sensitive relay. Any time the current is greater than 4 milliamperes (0.004 ampere), the sensitive relay will close. The slave relay is energized by current through the contacts of the sensitive relay, and the warning light is turned on by the current through the contacts of the slave relay.

A test circuit includes a special test thermocouple in the loop with the other thermocouples. This test thermocouple and an electric heater are mounted inside the relay housing, and when the test switch on the instrument panel is closed, current flows through the heater and heats up the test thermocouple. This causes current to flow in the thermocouple loop, and the fire warning light will turn on.

The total number of thermocouples used in individual detector circuits depends on the size of the fire zone and the total circuit resistance. The total resistance usually does not exceed 5 ohms. As shown in the circuit diagram (figure 16-5), the circuit includes a resistor connected across the terminals of the slave relay. This resistor is used to absorb the coil's self induced voltage. This is to prevent arcing across the points of the sensitive relay, since the contacts of the sensitive relay are so fragile they would burn or weld if arcing were permitted.

When the sensitive relay opens, the circuit to the slave relay is interrupted and the magnetic field around its coil collapses. When this happens, the coil generates a voltage by self-induction. The resistor across the coil terminals provides a path for any current flow as a result of this voltage. Thus, arcing at the sensitive relay contacts is eliminated.

3. Continuous-loop Fire Detection System

A continuous-loop detector or sensing system permits more complete coverage of a fire hazard area than any type of spot-type temperature detectors. The continuous-loop system works on the same basic principle as the spot-type fire detectors, except that instead of using individual thermal switches the continuous-loop system has sensors in the form of a long Inconel tube.

These are overheat systems, using heat sensitive units that complete an electrical circuit at a certain temperature. There is no rate-of-heat-rise sensitivity in a continuous-loop system. Two widely used type of continuous-loop systems are the Fenwall and the Kidde systems.

a. Fenwall System

The Fenwall system (figure 16-6) uses a single wire surrounded by a continuous string of ceramic beads in an Inconel tube. The beads in this system are wetted with a eutectic salt which possesses the characteristics of suddenly lowering its electrical resistance as the sensing element reaches its alarm temperature.

At normal temperatures, the eutectic salt core material prevents electrical current from flowing. In case of fire or overheat condition, the core resistance drops and current flows between the signal wire and ground, energizing the alarm system.

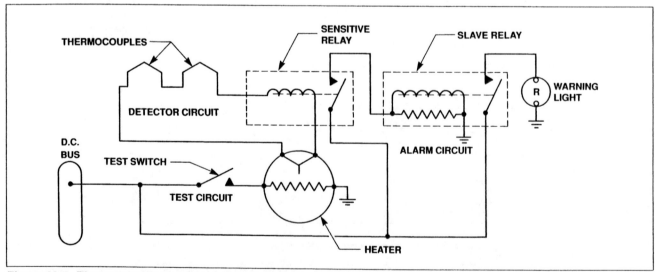

Figure 16-5. Thermocouple-type fire detection system.

The Fenwall system uses a magnetic amplifier control unit. This system is non-averaging but will sound an alarm when any portion of its sensing element reaches the alarm temperature.

b. Kidde System

In the Kidde continuous-loop system (figure 16-7), two wires are imbedded in a special ceramic core within an Inconel tube. One of the wires is welded to the case at each end and acts as an internal ground. The second wire is a hot lead (above ground potential) that provides a current signal when the ceramic core material changes its resistance with a change in temperature.

The Kidde sensing elements are connected to a relay control unit. This unit constantly measures the total resistance of the full sensing loop. The system senses the average temperature, as well as any hot spot.

Both systems continuously monitor temperatures in the affected compartments, and both will automatically reset following a fire or overheat alarm, after the overheat condition is removed or the fire is extinguished.

4. Pressure-type Sensor Responder Fire Detection System

The continuous-loop fire detection system initiates a fire warning signal when any portion of the continuous loop reaches the temperature for which the loop element is designed. The pressure-type sensor responder system actuates when any portion of the element reaches the temperature that would signal a fire condition, or when a large portion of the element is exposed to a lower temperature, as could happen in an overheat condition that could cause structural damage or that could precede a fire.

The sensitive element of this system consists of a sealed gas-filled tube containing an element that absorbs gas at a low temperature and releases it as the temperature rises. This tube is connected to a pressure switch that will close when the gas pressure in the tube reaches a predetermined value.

Two slightly different types of this system may be found in use: the Lindberg system and the Systron-Donner system.

a. Lindberg System

The Lindberg fire detection system (figure 16-8) is a continuous-element type detector consisting of a stainless steel tube containing a discreet element. This element has been processed to absorb gas in proportion to the operating temperature set point. When the temperature rises (due to a fire or overheat condition) to the operating temperature set point, the heat generated causes the gas to be released from the element. Release of the gas causes the pressure in the stainless steel tube to increase. This pressure rise mechanically actuates the diaphragm switch in the responder unit, activating the warning lights and an alarm bell.

To test this system, low-voltage AC is sent through the outer sheath of the element. When this current heats the sheath to the required temperature, the element will release gas and the pressure on the diaphragm will close the contacts and initiate the fire warning. When the test switch is released, the detector element will cool off, the contacts will open, and the fire warning will stop.

b. Systron-Donner System

The sensing element of the Systron-Donner system contains a titanium center wire, which is the gas absorption material. This material contains

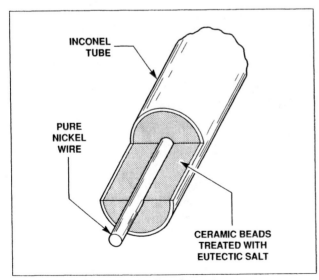

Figure 16-6. Fenwall sensing element.

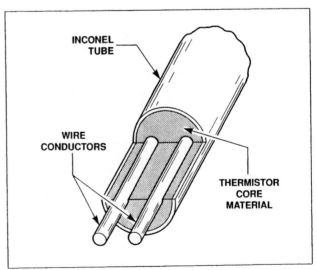

Figure 16-7. Kidde sensing element.

309

hydrogen gas. The center wire is wrapped with an inert metal tape for protection and stabilization. The tape is applied in a spiral fashion such that gaps between the turns of tape will allow release of the hydrogen gas from the wire when temperatures reach the established level. This wrapped wire is installed in a stainless steel tube and is surrounded with helium gas under pressure.

The helium gas provides the averaging or overheat function of the sensor. Because the pressure of the helium gas will increase as temperatures rise it will exert an increasing pressure on the pneumatic switch at the end of the sensor. At a preselected value, the switch will close and signal an overheat condition. If a fire exists, the localized high temperature will cause a large quantity of hydrogen gas to be released from the titanium wire. This will cause an increase in the total gas pressure in the tube, and will actuate the pneumatic switch. This action is known as the discrete function of the sensor.

When the fire is extinguished and the sensor begins to cool, the hydrogen gas will once again be absorbed by the titanium wire, gas pressures will reduce and the pneumatic switch will reopen. The system is again ready to indicate overheat or fire conditions. Test circuits, which include a pressure warning switch, will indicate the operational condition of the system. If helium gas pressure is lost, the test circuit warns the flightcrew that the system is not operational.

5. Fire Zones

Powerplant compartments are classified into fire zones based on the airflow through them.

Class A Zone. Zones having large quantities of air flowing past regular arrangements of similarly shaped obstructions. The power section of a reciprocating engine is usually of this type.

Class B Zone. Zones having large quantities of air flowing past aerodynamically clean obstructions. Heat exchanger ducts and exhaust manifold shrouds are usually of this type. Also, zones where the inside of the enclosing cowling or other closure is smooth, free of pockets, and adequately drained so that leaking flammables cannot puddle are of this type. Turbine engine compartments may be considered this class if engine surfaces are aerodynamically clean and all airframe structural formers are covered by a fireproof liner to produce an aerodynamically clean enclosure surface.

Class C Zone. Zones having relatively small air flow. An engine accessory compartment separated from the power section is an example of this type of zone.

Class D Zone. Zones having very little or no air flow. These include wing compartments and wheel wells where little ventilation is provided.

Class X Zone. Zones having large quantities of air flowing through them and are of unusual construction making uniform distribution of the extinguishing agent very difficult. Zones containing deeply recessed spaces and pockets between large structural formers are of this type. Tests indicate agent requirements to be double those for class A zones.

C. Smoke and Toxic Gas Detection System

A smoke detection system monitors the certain areas of the aircraft for the presence of smoke, which is

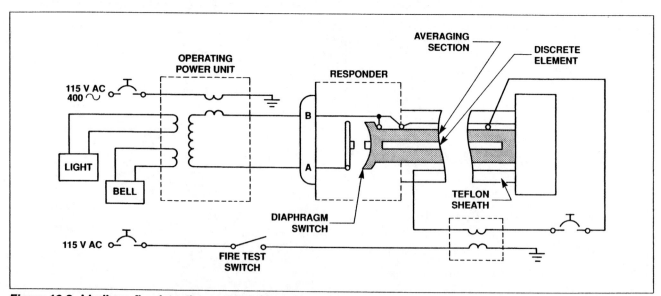

Figure 16-8. Lindberg fire detection system schematic.

indicative of a fire condition. These may include, but are not limited to, cargo and baggage compartments, and the lavatories of transport category aircraft. A smoke detection system is used where the type of fire anticipated is expected to generate a substantial amount of smoke before temperature changes are sufficient to actuate a heat detection system.

The presence of carbon monoxide gas (CO) or nitrous oxides are dangerous to flightcrews and passengers, and may indicate a fire condition. Detection of the presence of either or both of these gases could be the earliest warning of a dangerous situation.

1. Carbon Monoxide Detectors

The CO detectors which detect concentrations of carbon monoxide gas are generally used to detect the presence of deadly carbon monoxide gas in aircraft cabins or cockpits.

Carbon monoxide is a colorless, odorless, tasteless, non-irritating gas. It is the byproduct of incomplete combustion, and is found in varying degrees in all smoke and fumes from burning carbonaceous substances. Exceedingly small amounts of the gas are dangerous. A concentration of 0.02% (2 parts in 10,000) may produce headache, mental dullness, and physical fogginess within a few hours.

Probably the simplest and least expensive indicator may be worn as a badge, or installed on the instrument panel or cockpit wall. It is a button using a tablet which changes from a normal tan color to progressively darker shades of gray to black. The transition time required is relative to the concentration of CO. At a concentration of 50 PPM (0.005%), the indication will be apparent within 15 to 30 minutes. A concentration of 100 PPM (0.01%) will change the color of the tablet to gray in 2-5 minutes, from tan to dark gray in 15 to 20 minutes.

There are several types of portable testers (sniffers) in use. One type has a replaceable indicator tube which contains yellow silica gel, impregnated with a complex silico-molybdate compound and is catalyzed using palladium sulfate.

During operation, a sample of air is drawn through the detector tube. When the air sample contains carbon monoxide, the yellow silica gel turns to a shade of green. The intensity of the green color is proportional to the concentration of carbon monoxide in the air sample at the time and location of the tests.

2. Smoke Detectors

To be reliable, smoke detectors must be maintained so that smoke in a compartment will be indicated as soon as it begins to accumulate. Smoke detector louvers, vents, and ducts must not be obstructed. Smoke detection instruments are classified by method of detection.

a. Light Refraction Type

This type of detector consists of a photoelectric cell, a beacon lamp, and a light trap, all mounted on a labyrinth. Air samples are drawn through the detector unit. An accumulation of 10% smoke in the air causes the photoelectric cell to conduct electric current. Figure 16-9 shows the details of the smoke detector, and indicates how the smoke particles refract the light to the photoelectric cell. When activated by smoke, the detector supplies a signal to the smoke detector amplifier. The amplifier signal activates a warning light and bell.

A test switch (figure 16-10) permits checking the operation of the smoke detector. Closing the switch connects 28 volt DC to the test relay. When the test relay energizes, voltage is applied through the beacon lamp and test lamp in series to ground. A fire indication will be observed only if the beacon and test lamp, the photoelectric cell, the smoke detector amplifiers, and associated circuits are operable.

b. Ionization Type

Ionization type smoke detectors use a small amount of radioactive material to ionize some of the oxygen and nitrogen molecules in the air sample drawn into the detector cell. These ions permit a small current to flow through the detector chamber test circuit. This cell is illustrated in figure 16-11.

If smoke is present in the air sample being drawn through the detector, small particles of the smoke will attach themselves to the oxygen and nitrogen ions, reducing the electrical current flow in the test

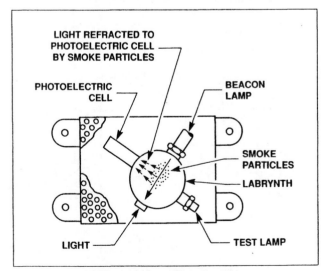

Figure 16-9. Photoelectric smoke detector.

circuit. If the current flow falls below a preset value, the alarm circuit will activate visual and aural cockpit alarms.

c. Solid-state Type

Solid-state smoke or toxic gas warning systems operate by comparing signals from two detecting elements. One will be located in the area being monitored, and the other is exposed to outside air.

The detecting elements consist of a heating coil encased in a coating of semiconductor material. Carbon monoxide or nitrous oxides, if present, will be absorbed into this coating and change the current-carrying ability of the detector. These sensors are connected into a type of bridge circuit so that when both elements are conducting evenly the bridge will be balanced, and no warning signal will be present. If the element in the area being monitored is subjected to CO gas or nitrous oxides, an unbalanced condition will be created across the bridge and the warning circuit will illuminate the cockpit warning lamp.

3. Flame Detectors

The presence of flames may be detected by placing a photoelectric cell in the area to be monitored. The change in light striking the cell, caused by a fire, will cause a change in the current flow through the photoelectric cell. This change will activate the amplifier circuit and produce an alarm indication in the cockpit.

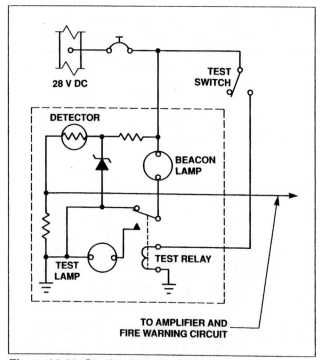

Figure 16-10. Smoke detector test circuit.

D. Extinguishing Agents — Portable Fire Extinguishers

Aircraft fire extinguishing agents have some common characteristics which make them compatible to aircraft fire extinguishing systems. All agents may be stored for long time periods without adversely affecting the system components or agent quality. Agents in current use will not freeze at normally expected atmospheric temperatures. The nature of the devices inside a powerplant compartment require agents that are not only useful against flammable fluid fires but also effective on electrically caused fires.

1. Halogenated Hydrocarbons

The most effective extinguishing agents are the compounds formed by replacement of one or more of the hydrogen atoms in the simple hydrocarbons methane and ethane by halogen atoms. The probable extinguishing mechanism of these agents is a "chemical interference" in the combustion process. This may be termed "chemical cooling" or "energy transfer blocking". This extinguishing mechanism is much more effective than oxygen dilution and cooling.

These agents are identified through a system of "halon numbers" which describe the chemical makeup of the agent. The first digit represents the number of carbon atoms in the compound molecule; the second digit, the number of fluorine atoms; the third digit, the number of chlorine atoms; the fourth digit, the number of bromine atoms; and the fifth digit, the number of iodine atoms, if any. If there is no iodine present, the fifth digit does not appear. For example, bromotrifluoromethane ($CBrF_3$) is referred to as Halon 1301 or sometimes by the trade name Freon 13.

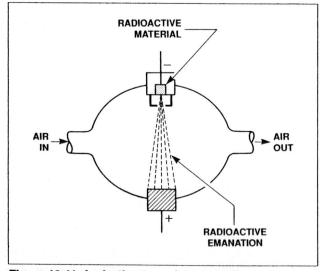

Figure 16-11. Ionization-type detector cell.

A number of these agents have been used in the past, and many are no longer in production. Some early halon extinguishing agents produced toxic gases when exposed to fire. For example, carbon tetrachloride was the first generally accepted agent of the halogenated family, and was very popular for electrical hazard. When exposed to heat the vapors of this compound may form deadly phosgene gas.

Because of changing regulations, and developing environmental impact data, the aviation technician should keep abreast of current developments pertaining to the use of halogenated hydrocarbons as fire extinguishing agents. Halogenated hydrocarbons may be used in both portable extinguishers and installed fire extinguishing systems on aircraft.

2. Inert Cold Gases

Both carbon dioxide (CO_2) and Nitrogen (N_2) are effective extinguishing agents. Both are readily available in gaseous and liquid forms; Their main difference is in the temperatures and pressures required to store them in their compact liquid forms.

Carbon dioxide has been used for many years to extinguish flammable fluid fires, and fires involving electrical equipment. It is noncombustible and does not react with most substances. It provides its own pressure for discharge from the storage vessel, except in extremely cold climates where a booster charge of nitrogen may be added to "winterize" the system. Normally, CO_2 is a gas, but it is easily liquified by compression and cooling. When discharged into the atmosphere, most of the liquid expands to gas. Heat absorbed by the gas during vaporization cools the remaining liquid to $-110°F$ and it becomes a fine white solid, dry ice "snow."

CO_2 is about 1½ times as heavy as air, which gives it the ability to replace the air above burning surfaces and maintain a smothering atmosphere. It is effective as an extinguishing agent because it dilutes the air and reduces the oxygen content so that the air will no longer support combustion. CO_2 is not effective on fires involving chemicals containing their own oxygen supply, such as cellulose nitrate (some aircraft paints). Also, fires involving magnesium and titanium cannot be extinguished by carbon dioxide.

Nitrogen is an even more effective extinguishing agent. Like carbon dioxide it is an inert gas of low toxicity. Nitrogen extinguishes a fire by oxygen dilution and smothering. More cooling is provided by N_2 and, pound for pound, nitrogen provides almost twice the volume of inert gas as CO_2 resulting in greater dilution of oxygen.

The main disadvantage of N_2 is that it must be stored as a cryogenic liquid, which requires special storage and handling equipment. This equipment represents a significant amount of weight and makes this system practical for only the largest aircraft as an onboard fire extinguishing system.

3. Dry Powder

Dry powder fire extinguishers are sealed containers of a powder similar to bicarbonate of soda, pressurized with an inert gas. When this powder is heated, it releases carbon dioxide and smothers the fire.

4. Water

Most class-A fires can be extinguished using water, delivered in any of a number of ways. Water is not suitable for other class fires, and may be dangerous if used. Water extinguishes a fire by its cooling action.

5. Class D Fires

Class-D Fires involve a burning metal, and the selection of an extinguishing agent is critical to successful fire suppression and safety of personnel. Specially formulated dry-powder extinguishers are available for this type of fire. Be sure to check the extinguisher for the proper symbol indicating that it is suitable for a class-D fire.

6. Cockpit and Cabin Interiors

All wool, cotton, and synthetic fabrics used in interior trim are treated to render them flame resistant. Tests conducted have shown foam and sponge rubber to be highly flammable. However, if they are covered with a flame-resistant fabric which will not support combustion, there is little danger from fire as a result of ignition produced by accidental contact with a lighted cigarette or burning paper.

Fire protection for the aircraft interior is usually provided by hand-held extinguishers. Four types of fire extinguishers are available for extinguishing interior fires: water, carbon dioxide, dry chemical, and halogenated hydrocarbons.

a. Extinguisher Types

Water extinguishers are for use primarily on nonelectrical fires such as smoldering fabric, cigarettes, or trash containers. For cabin fires, small containers of water fitted with a carbon dioxide cartridge are installed in racks where the flight attendants have ready access to them. In case of a fire, the attendant need only twist the handle 90° to the right to puncture the seal in the CO_2 cartridge. The water spray from the nozzle is controlled by a trigger on top of the handle. This type of extinguisher is illustrated in figure 16-12.

Carbon dioxide fire extinguishers are provided to extinguish electrical fires. A long, hinged, tube with a nonmetallic megaphone-shaped nozzle permits discharge of the CO_2 gas close to the fire source. The trigger-type release is normally protected from accidental discharge by lockwire, which can easily be broken by a pull on the trigger.

A dry chemical fire extinguisher can be used to extinguish any class A, B, or C fire. However, this type should not be used in the cockpit due to possible interference with visibility, and the collection of nonconductive powder on electrical equipment. The extinguisher is equipped with a fixed nozzle which is directed toward the fire source to smother the fire. The trigger is also lockwired but can be broken with a squeeze of the trigger. The state of charge of this type of extinguisher is usually indicated by a gauge near the trigger and nozzle assembly.

Halon 1301 is low on the toxicity scale and is a logical successor to CO_2 as a hand-held type fire extinguisher agent. It is effective on fires in lower concentrations. Halon 1301 can extinguish a fire with a concentration of 2% by volume. This compares with about 40% by volume concentration required for CO_2 to extinguish the same fire.

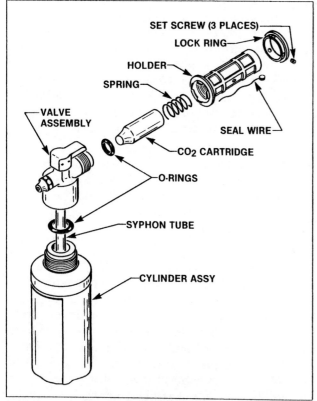

Figure 16-12. Pressurized water-type fire extinguisher for aircraft cabin fires.

This quality allows Halon 1301 to be used in occupied personnel compartments without depriving people of the oxygen they require. Another advantage is that no residue or deposits remains after use.

b. Extinguishers Unsuitable as Cabin or Cockpit Equipment

The common aerosol can-type extinguishers are definitely not acceptable as airborne hand type extinguishers. Aerosol cans are prone to explosion, even at temperatures which may be encountered on the ground, and should not be carried in the passenger or crew compartments. In addition to the danger from explosion, the size of this type of extinguisher is inadequate to combat even the smallest fire.

Dry chemical extinguishers may, by reason of materials used in their manufacture, or by careless location near heater vents, pose a serious danger of explosion.

Information relative to airborne hand fire extinguishers may be obtained from the local FAA District Office and from the National Fire Protection Association (Quincy, Massachusetts).

E. Installed Fire Extinguishing Systems

A complete fire protection system consists of a fire detection and a fire extinguishing system. In an aircraft, it is very important that any fire extinguisher available be of the proper type to fight the class of fire that is likely to occur. There are two basic categories into which installed extinguishing systems are placed: conventional systems and High-rate-of-discharge (HRD) systems. These systems may also be identified by the type of extinguishing agent used. Conventional systems are usually associated with the use of Carbon Dioxide and HRD systems by the use of Halogenated Hydrocarbons.

1. Carbon Dioxide

Conventional system is a term applied to those fire extinguishing installations first used in aircraft. Still used in some older aircraft, the systems are satisfactory for their intended use but are not as efficient as newer designs. The CO_2 system is one of the earliest types of fire extinguisher systems for transport category aircraft, and is still used on many older aircraft.

This fire extinguisher system is designed around a cylinder (figure 16-13) that stores the carbon dioxide under pressure, and a remote control valve assembly in the cockpit to distribute the extinguishing agent to the engines. The gas is distributed through tubing from the CO_2 cylinder valve to the control valve assembly in the cockpit, and then to the engines via tubing installed in the fuselage and wing tunnels. The tubing terminates in perforated loops which encircle the engines.

To operate this type of engine fire extinguisher system, the selector valve must be set for the engine which is on fire. An upward pull on the T-shaped control handle located adjacent to the engine selector valve actuates the release lever in the CO_2 cylinder valve. The compressed liquid in the CO_2 cylinder flows in one rapid burst to the outlets in the distribution line of the affected engine. Contact with the air converts the liquid into gas and "snow" which smothers the flame.

Other CO_2 type systems may use multiple bottles to enable the system to deliver the extinguishing agent twice to any of the engines. Each bank of CO_2 bottles is equipped with a red thermosafety-discharge indicator disk, set to rupture at or above a set pressure (about 2,650 PSI). If the ambient

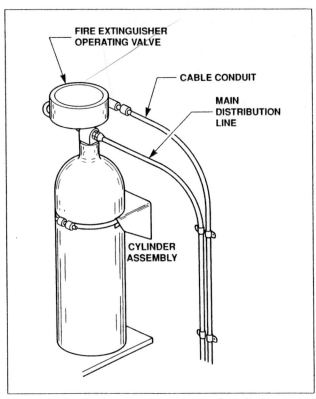

Figure 16-13. Carbon dioxide cylinder installation.

FIRE EXTINGUISHER
OPERATING VALVE

CABLE CONDUIT

MAIN
DISTRIBUTION
LINE

CYLINDER
ASSEMBLY

temperature raises the pressures of the bottles to this value, the disk will rupture, discharging the bottles overboard. Each bank of bottles is also equipped with a yellow system-discharge indicator disk. Mounted adjacent to the red disk, the yellow disk indicates which bank of bottles has been emptied by a normal discharge.

2. Halogenated Hydrocarbons

High-rate-of-discharge (HRD) is the term applied to the highly effective systems most currently in use. Such HRD systems provide high discharge rates through high pressurization, short feed lines, large discharge valves and outlets. The extinguishing agent is usually one of the halogenated hydrocarbons (Halon) sometimes boosted by high-pressure dry nitrogen. Because the agent and pressurizing gas are released into the zone in 1 sec. or less, the zone is temporarily pressurized, and interrupts the ventilating air flow. The few, large sized outlets are carefully located to produce high velocity swirl effects for best distribution.

Figure 16-14 illustrates the fire extinguishing system for a transport category jet aircraft. The system utilizes two high-rate-discharge bottles of fire extinguishing agent. These bottles are sealed with a metal seal. When the fire switch is pulled, the bottle discharge circuit is armed. As soon as the bottle discharge switch is pressed, a powder charge is ignited with an electric squib. The charge blows a knife into the seal and allows the contents of the bottle to flow into the fire manifold. Pulling the fire switch opens the engine selector valve and the extinguishing agent flows to the correct engine.

Each of the two agent bottles have a pressure gauge to show the pressure of the contents. An electrical pressure switch is mounted on each bottle to illuminate a bottle discharge light on the instrument panel when the pressure of the agent bottle is low.

A thermal fuse is installed in each bottle which will melt and release the contents if the bottle is subjected to high temperatures. If a bottle is emptied in this way, a red blowout disk on the side of the fuselage will indicate the thermal discharge. If the bottle is discharged by normal operation of the system, a yellow disk, similarly mounted, will be blown out.

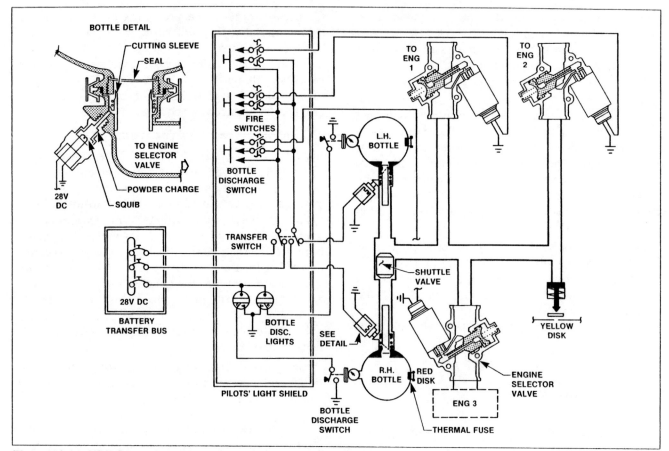

Figure 16-14. *HRD fire extinguisher system for a transport category airplane.*

Index

318